John B. Henderson

The Development
&
Decline of Chinese
Cosmology

Windstone Press
Taipei
Hong Kong

The Development & Decline of Chinese Cosmology
Originally Published by Columbia University Press (1984, 1989)
Neo-Confucian Studies Series

Copyright © 2011 by John B. Henderson
Published by Windstone Press, Ltd.
Taipei, Taiwan
www.windstonepress.com

Cover design: Chen Shih-i

Cover Art from "A Solitary Temple amid Clearing Peaks" by Li Cheng
(Song Dynasty)

Library of Congress Cataloging in Publication Data
Henderson, John B., 1948–
The development and decline of Chinese cosmology.
Bibligraphy
1.   Philosophy, Chinese—History.   2. Cosmology
B127.C68H46   2011   113'.0951   84-400
ISBN-13: 978-0-9823212-4-9
ISBN-10: 0-9823212-4-4

Version 1.0

Contents

Periods of Chinese History

Shang Dynasty	1766 — 1122 B.C. (traditional dates)
Zhou Dynasty	1122 — 256 B.C.
	Spring and Autumn era, 722 — 481 B.C.
	Warring States era, 403 — 221 B.C.
Qin Dynasty	221 — 206 B.C.
Han Dynasty	202 B.C. — 220 A.D.
	Former Han era, 202 B.C. — 9 A.D.
	Later Han era, 25 — 220 A.D.
Period of Disunion	220 — 589
Sui Dynasty	589 — 618
Tang Dynasty	618 — 906
Song Dynasty	960 — 1279
	Northern Song, 960 — 1126
	Southern Song, 1126 — 1279
Yuan Dynasty	1279 — 1368
Ming Dynasty	1368 — 1644
Qing Dynasty	1644 — 1911

Other chronological terms used in this book include "classical," which generally refers to the Spring and Autumn and Warring States eras, and "late classical," which covers the last three centuries B.C. and occasionally the Later Han as well. I use the term "medieval" to designate the era from the Later Han through the Yuan. "Late traditional" refers to the Ming and Qing periods, but especially to the sixteenth, seventeenth, and eighteenth centuries. My use of these terms is not intended to imply any theory of historical development.

Acknowledgments

A number of my teachers, friends, and colleagues have contributed to the development and improvement of this study. These include my mentors in Chinese history and the history of science at the University of California, Berkeley, John L. Heilbron, David N. Keightley, Tu Wei-ming, and particularly Frederic Wakeman, Jr. All of these gentlemen generously offered expert guidance and constructive criticisms on the early drafts. Several of my fellow students at Berkeley and at the Inter-University Center for Chinese Language Studies in Taiwan, especially Alison Black, Judith Whitbeck, and Ch'eng I-fan, provided me with insights on some of the major issues in the intellectual history of late-traditional China. I am especially grateful to Professor Nathan Sivin of the University of Pennsylvania for his extensive comments, corrections, and helpful suggestions on several earlier drafts of this book. Professor Sivin's support and encouragement have been invaluable to me, as to many other students of the history of Chinese science. One of my colleagues at Louisiana State University, Stephen Farmer, contributed much to the comparative dimensions of this study through frequent conversations on the world history of correlative cosmology. I also benefited from Steve's perceptive comments on an earlier draft, as well as from his bibliographical suggestions. Other colleagues, particularly Gary Crump, David Lindenfeld, and Karl Roider, generously responded to my requests for advice and comments on aspects of this study. Karen Mitchell of Columbia University Press deserves much credit for her thorough and sensitive editing of the manuscript.

Finally, I would like to thank the LSU Foundations for having provided a subvention to support publication of this book and the chairman at the Department of History at Louisiana State University, Professor John L. Loos, for having secured that subvention. Much of the research and writing of this work was accomplished while visiting with my grandmother, Mrs. Hugh Henderson, during summer vacation periods. So I wish to thank her as well as other members of my family for their support and encouragement. Naturally, I alone am responsible for all of the shortcomings that remain in this book. I would also like to thank Richard Goodman and Windstone Press for their hard work and good cheer throughout the editing process, as well as for their offer to reissue this book. I would like to dedicate this reissue to my wife, Nathalie, and our daughter, Ruby.

Introduction

The term "cosmos" is often used today as an antiquarian synonym for "universe." Moderns who employ the word seldom mean to imply that any particular type of order or pattern prevails in the world, though they might believe that such an order exists. The Greek root of "cosmos," however, is much more specific in its meaning, indicating the existence of a certain harmony and proportion in the world, even a "consonance between ourselves and the universe."[1]

Most ancient peoples whose records have been preserved, including the Chinese, formulated a view of the world that may be characterized as a "cosmos" in this stricter sense of the word. Some of these views resemble one another so closely that a number of prominent scholars have attempted to abstract a universal stage or mode of human thought from a comparative study of early cosmological ideas. Classic works in twentieth-century sociology, philosophy, psychology, and anthropology such as Emile Durkheim's *Primitive Classification*, volume 2 of Ernst Cassirer's *Philosophy of Symbolic Forms*, Carl Jung's studies of several oriental classics, and Claude Lévi-Strauss' *Savage Mind* are partly devoted to this aim, demonstrating that "primitive classification," "mythical thought," "synchronicity," or "savage thought" is a general stage of human intellectual development which was not superseded until the era of the scientific revolution. But while these studies have revealed close parallels in the cosmological views of primitive and premodern peoples, the pictures they present are generally static. Seldom do such works aim at describing how cosmological schemata develop or decline. Their principal concern, rather, is with the structure or operation of those modes of thought which informed the premodern intellectual world.

Historians, however, have understandably shown more interest in the question of how premodern views of cosmic order were formulated and superseded. Students of early Greek philosophy, for example, have attempted to explain the origins of classical Western cosmology through their studies of Presocratic thought. Moreover, historians of Western science have long been concerned with the demise of that cosmology and its medieval extension in the seventeenth century. But they focus on issues that are particularly relevant for the history of science, such as the critique of Ptolemaic astronomy and Aristotelian cosmology. More general accounts of the decline and rejection of the larger sense of cosmos that ramified into medieval and Renaissance philosophy, religion, politics, literature, art, and popular culture, as well as science, are relatively rare.

General studies of moments of cosmological transition, of the formulation and dissolution of world pictures, are also uncommon in sinological literature. However, historians of Chinese thought have long recognized the importance of cosmological ideas of harmony, proportion, and correspondence in early China. Such classic studies as Marcel Granet's *Chinese Thought* are devoted primarily to describing the articulations and ramifications of these notions in the Han (202 B.C.—A.D. 220) and later ages. More recently, several scholars have explored the origins and early development of particular aspects of Han cosmology, including the idea of cosmic resonance, the concept of the five phases, and the cosmography of the simple magic square.[2] But few studies have been devoted to explaining the development of early Chinese cosmology as a whole. Nor have many sinologists explored the possibility that the cosmological conceptions that dominated the intellectual world of the Han era ever came to be generally superseded before modern times.[3]

Not all major post-Han thinkers adhered to the cosmological schemata formulated in late classical times; but these conceptions exercised a pervasive influence throughout premodern Chinese thought and culture. Their impact is manifest in most of the arts and sciences, most conspicuously in medicine, alchemy, astrology, and the various divinatory sciences, but also in such impeccably orthodox branches of learning as official historiography, literary criticism, Neo-Confucian philosophy, and mathematical astronomy. So great was the significance and so wide the influence of what Joseph Needham has called "correlative thinking"—the heart of traditional Chinese cosmology—that it might well be regarded as a sort of perennial philosophy in the history of Chinese civilization. Hence, the development of this mode of thought from the late-classical era and its decline in the late-traditional period, culminating in the seventeenth century, are matters of considerable import in the history of Chinese culture.

The seventeenth century thus marked an epoch in the history of Chinese as well as European cosmological thought, for it saw the rejection of a sense of cosmos that was pervasive, in both high philosophy and popular culture, through almost two thousand years of Chinese history. The cosmological reformation of the early Qing era was not marked by the same drama that attended the overthrow of classical Greek and medieval cosmology in seventeenth-century Europe. Remnants of older views persisted longer and more vigorously in China than in the West. Nevertheless, this reformation transformed important aspects of Chinese culture, even though it did not proceed with such fanfare and dispatch as did its European analogue in the age of Galileo and Kepler.

Chapter One

Correlative Thought in Early China

Correlative thought is the most basic ingredient of Chinese cosmology. It is not, however, exclusively Chinese; it appears prominently in the intellectual history of most civilizations and has roots in what anthropologists call primitive cultures. Correlative thinking in general draws systematic correspondences among aspects of various orders of reality or realms of the cosmos, such as the human body, the body politic, and the heavenly bodies. It assumes that these related orders as a whole are homologous, that they correspond with one another in some basic respect, even in some cases that their identities are contained one within the other. Correlative thought thus differs from analogy, metaphor, and symbol, which seldom refer systematically to larger orders or domains. It may assume such diverse forms and expressions as totemism (in primitive cultures), allegory (in medieval cultures), and to some extent even scientific models (in modern cultures).[1]

The correspondences drawn by correlative thinkers vary widely in complexity and coherence, as well as in type. They may be rather simple, such as the homology between the structure of the human body and that of a political state. Numerological or symbolic systems of correspondence, such as those devised by Yang Xiong (53 B.C.–A.D. 18) and Shao Yong (A.D. 1011–1077), may be so elaborate as to try the patience and challenge the ingenuity of even the most enthusiastic students of Chinese cosmology. Some systems were truly cosmic in their dimensions in that they aimed to comprehend the key aspects of every major order of reality, encompassing heaven, earth, and man. In view of the great variety of correlative systems that appeared historically in China and elsewhere, it seems unlikely that they could have all developed from a single motive or origin. But before attempting to explain why various modes of correlative thought arose in early China, it is necessary to describe them, if only in a provisional way.

BASIC MODES OF CORRELATIVE THOUGHT

The most universal mode of correlative thought to appear in early China was that based on the correspondences between man and the cosmos, microcosm and macrocosm. Statements of this kind of correspondence may be found in texts from such diverse time and places as ancient India and Elizabethan England.[2] Even the mythologies of preliterate peoples contain numerous adumbrations of this mode of correlative thought, especially in the form of animist and anthropomorphic interpretations of natural phenomena.

There is little reason to doubt that inhabitants of China from Neolithic times similarly personified natural forces. However, detailed systematic accounts of correspondences between man and cosmos do not figure in Chinese sources dating from before the third century B.C. Early classical texts such as the *Songs Classic* (Shi Jing) and the Confucian *Analects* (Lunyu) do, to be sure, occasionally liken human figures to natural objects. One of the *Songs*, for example, compares a bride with a peach tree in bloom, and a passage in the *Analects* likens the virtuous ruler to the pole star.[3] But the composers of these texts apparently made no deliberate effort to proceed from poetic metaphor and didactic analogy to the construction of systems of correspondence. Early classical texts contain no definite acknowledgment, still less a detailed description, of the general commensurability of man and cosmos.

In such major Han-era compendia as the *Huainanzi* (c. 139 B.C.), the *Chunqiu Fanlu* (c. 130 B.C.), the *Huangdi Neijing Suwen* (Plain Questions of the Yellow Sovereign's Inner Classic), and the *Baihu Tongyi* (Comprehensive Discussions in White Tiger Hall) (A.D. 79), there appear detailed accounts of correspondences between man and aspects of the physical world. One such account, based on the idea of numerological concord, appears in the *Huainanzi:*

> Heaven has nine layers, and man likewise has nine orifices. Heaven has four seasons with which to regulate the twelve months. Man likewise has four limbs with which to employ the twelve larger joints. Heaven has twelve months with which to regulate the 360 days [of the year]. Man likewise has twelve minor limbs with which to employ the 360 lesser joints. Thus one who in taking up an affair does not accord with heaven is contravening his own existence.[4]

Another description of human-cosmic correspondences appears in chapter seven of the *Huainanzi:*

> Therefore the head's roundness resembles heaven and the feet's squareness resembles earth. Heaven has four seasons, five phases, nine sections, and 366 days. Man likewise has four limbs, five viscera, nine orifices, and 366 joints. Heaven has wind and rain, cold and heat. Man likewise has taking and giving, joy and anger. Thus the gall bladder is cloudy, the lungs are pneumatic, the liver is windy, the kidneys are rainy, and the spleen is thunderous. [These organs] correspond with heaven and earth, and yet the heart serves as the sovereign [of all]. Thus the eyes and ears are the sun and moon; and the blood and pneuma are the wind and rain.[5]

Even more elaborate accounts of correspondences between man and cosmos appear in Later Han texts, particularly the *Baihu Tongyi.*[6] Medical and alchemical works of later ages, such as the *Baiwen Pian* (Compendium of a Hundred Questions), developed such correlations so far as to make those recounted in the *Huainanzi* seem rudimentary.[7] Most later accounts of correspondences between microcosmic man and macrocosmic nature are of the same type as those which appear in the *Huainanzi.*

Another early source for this first basic mode of correlative thought, the *Chunqiu Fanlu* attributed to Dong Zhong-shu (c. 179–c. 104 B.C.) did, however, extend correspondences between man and cosmos into new dimensions. Dong remarked that human moods and emotions, as well as the parts of the body, are directly linked with particular cosmic units, especially the seasons of the year. "Thus to say that 'heaven has phases of delight, anger, grief, and joy [associated with man], and that man similarly has the pneumas of spring, fall, winter, and summer [associated with heaven]' is to refer to their correspondence." So close is this correspondence, and so organic is the relationship of heaven and man with each other, that "delight and anger are the alternate pneumas of cold and heat."[8]

In Dong's view, human physiological and psychological functions also correspond with particular cosmic or calendrical units, for "the alternating opening and closing of the eyes corresponds to day and night, the alternating of strength and weakness corresponds with winter and summer, the alternating of grief and joy corresponds to yin and yang. The mind has calculations and deliberations corresponding with degrees and measures [of space and time]. [Human] conduct has ethical standards corresponding to heaven and earth." Dong justifies the drawing of such diverse correspondences by explaining that "In what may be numbered, there is correspondence in number; in what may not be numbered, there is correspondence in kind. All are matched and similar, and thus correspond with heaven, [forming a] unity."[9] The existence of such close correspondence, numerological, anatomical, psychological, and moral, between man and the heavens is, moreover, an indication of man's superior position in the cosmos, a sign that "man is distinguished from other things and forms a triad with heaven and earth."[10]

Dong Zhong-shu was not the first major Chinese thinker to have expressed the general idea of the unity of heaven and man. Several important philosophical works dating from the third century B.C., particularly the *Zhongyong* (Doctrine of the Mean) and the *Lüshi Chunqiu* (Master Lü's Spring and Autumn Annals), also asserted the unity of man and cosmos, though principally as a way of characterizing the sage or of promoting moral and spiritual cultivation. The *Lüshi Chunqiu* states that "man is similar to heaven and earth . . . Thus the ancients in ordering themselves and the realm necessarily modeled themselves on heaven and earth." The *Zhongyong* compares the conduct of the sage to the comprehensiveness of heaven and earth, the succession of the four seasons, and the alternation of the sun and moon. The Confucian *Analects* comment that "It is heaven that is great; and it was [the sage king] Yao who patterned himself on it."[11]

Thus the detailed correspondence which Han cosmologists drew between the cosmos and man may find a philosophical sanction, if not necessarily their genetic origin, in statements by thinkers of the classical era. For later Han cosmologists generally devised correspondences not so much to promote moral cultivation or to exalt Confucian sagehood as to establish and consolidate social and intellectual order. The *Baihu Tongyi* of Ban Gu (A.D. 32–92), for example, legitimizes various human rules and institutions through identifying numerological correlates in the cosmos. The text explains that the ruler may take nine wives, one for each of the classical provinces in the realm. Similarly, since an intercalary month must be inserted once every three years, then a man must remain in mourning for three years following the death of a parent.[12]

A second basic mode of Chinese correlative thought, what Joseph Needham has called the "state analogy," is based on the correspondence of aspects of the cosmos, especially the heavens, with the dynastic state and the imperial bureaucracy. While correlations of this type are not so widely diffused as those based on man and cosmos, they were quite important politically in early imperial China. They gave the Han dynasty and its bureaucracy a sort of supernal aura that they might otherwise have lacked in view of the relative newness of the imperial state and the lack of a strong contemporary Chinese belief in divine kingship. Several of the major sources for this second mode of correlative thinking date from the second century B.C., the first century of Han rule. The *Huainanzi* pairs particular offices of the Han bureaucracy with the five directions of space. The *Chunqiu Fanlu* correlates units of bureaucracy with those of both the calendar and the human body, concluding that "the measures of heaven, the forms of man, and the institutions of officialdom correspond with one another." Perhaps the best-known Han source for state-analogy correlative thought is the "Treatise on the Celestial Offices" (Tianguan Shu) in the *Shi Ji* (Records of the Historian), which identifies the constellations of the heavens by the names of offices of the imperial administration.[13]

This particular type of correspondence naturally provided a basis for astrological prediction, as well as a means of legitimizing the newly established state. Han cosmologists, however, used state-cosmos correlations for other purposes as well, particularly for prescribing the ways in which the ruler and the imperial bureaucracy should function. Thus, according to the *Chunqiu Fanlu*, "punishment [without virtue] cannot be employed to perfect the world, just as yin [without yang] cannot be employed to complete the year."[14] The *Baihu Tongyi* proposes a cosmic model for the proper relationship between ruler and minister, pointing out that just as "the sun moves slowly and the moon moves quickly," so "the lord takes his ease while the vassal toils." Similarly, when one duke appoints three ministers, he is following the Way of heaven, which "is always completed in threes. For heaven has the three luminaries, the sun, moon, and stars. Earth has the three configurations, high, low, and level. Man has three honored positions, lord, father, and teacher."[15]

The cosmos or "heaven" with which the operation of the imperial state ideally corresponded was sometimes seen in supernatural terms. Antecedents of this form of state analogizing appeared as early as the Shang era (1766–1122 B.C.). For "the Shang afterworld," according to Sarah Allan, "was already patterned in a hierarchic and political manner which reflected that of the living."[16] And "the vocabularies of ancestor worship and administration overlapped significantly," as David Keightley has pointed out.[17] In later times, supernatural realms became increasingly bureaucratized. By the

Ming period (1368–1644), almost every city of any importance had its own city god whose place in the celestial bureaucracy exactly corresponded to that of the city's earthly magistrate in the terrestrial, even to the extent that both were subject to the orders of the provincial governor.[18] Even into the 20th century, as reported by Bredon and Mitrophanow, "The usual *zheng huang* [city god] temple in a big city is the exact counterpart of an official *yamen* with flagstaffs at the gate, and a hall containing a big figure of the god dressed in a long robe, a scholar's cap, and black satin boots with thick white soles."[19]

The two basic modes discussed thus far are probably the most comprehensible of the types of correlative thought developed in China. Even to contemporary Westerners, such correspondences may seem rather natural, though perhaps also quaint. Other modes of Chinese correlative thought, being generally more abstract and less universal, have less appeal to contemporary sympathy. Among these are the numerological systems of correspondence based upon such simple orders as the "five phases" (wu xing).

As this currently accepted translation implies, *wuxing* in its mature form was not just a means of classification. It was also the basis of a comprehensive theory for explaining change in the cosmos. In the pre-Han era, however, the *wuxing* was only one of several commonly used enumeration orders. Classical sources such as the *Zuo Chronicle* (Zuozhuan) and the *Documents Classic* (Shu Jing) also record numerologies based on three, four, six, eight, nine, ten, and twelve. Marcel Granet, noting the appearance of varied enumeration orders in pre-Han texts, went so far as to link some of them with particular social groups or classes, five with the peasants, six with the nobility, and three with the urban military class.[20] Granet's interpretation of divergences in pre-Han numerology is unsubstantiated, and in fact a good example of Durkheimian assumptions about the social basis of cosmology run amok. Nevertheless, it does raise the significant question of why five-based numerology eclipsed its rivals in the early Han era. One explanation might involve objective factors, for example the fact that five and only five planets are visible to the naked eye.[21]

Whatever the reason, *wuxing* did become one of the pivots of correlative cosmology in China. But the idea evolved considerably between the time of its first appearance in classical texts and its apotheosis in the works of Han cosmologists. In the "Great Plan" (Hongfan) chapter of the *Documents Classic*, wherein appears the earliest literary reference to *wuxing*,[22] the term apparently refers to material substances which are conceived in terms of their functional attributes: "Water is said to soak and descend; fire is said to blaze and ascend; wood is said to curve or be straight; metal is said to obey and change; earth is said to take seeds and give crops."[23] The "Great Plan" goes on to correlate each of these functionally defined substances with one of the five flavors: "That which soaks and descends produces saltiness; that which blazes and ascends produces bitterness; that which curves or is straight produces sourness; that which obeys and changes produces acridity; that which takes seeds and give crops produces sweetness."[24]

The *Hongfan* and *Gaoyaomo* (Counsels of Gao Yao) chapters of the *Documents* mark off other sets of things in fives, including the five conducts, five periods, five punishments, five rules, five degrees of garments, and five classes of emblems.[25] Han cosmologists extended this list of things grouped by five and associated with the *wuxing*, naming five planets, five seasons, five directions, five colors, five musical tones, five sagely emperors, five viscera, five orifices, five animals, five grains, five mountains, five reservoirs, and still others. The *Record of Rites* (Liji) mentions sixty-two different kinds of five, even the five turnings of the royal boat.[26]

While thus using the *wuxing* as a set of numerological classifiers, Han cosmologists more frequently employed it to explain the configuration of change on such various time scales as the cosmic, the historical, the seasonal, and the diurnal. Hence, the currently established translation, "five phases," while inappropriate for the early appearances of the term in the *Hong Fan* and *Guo Yu* (Conversations of the States), is a good rendering of the meaning of the word as it is used in such Han works as the *Baihu Tongyi* and *Chungqiu Fanlu*. In Chinese medical works as well, Manfred Porkert explains, the five phases "constitute stretches of time, temporal segments of exactly defined qualities that succeed each other in cyclical order at reference positions defined in space."[27]

Cosmologists of the late Zhou and Han eras arranged the five phases in particular sequences, aiming thereby to explain cosmic and historical evolution, as well as various seasonal, diurnal, and medical changes and rhythms. The *Lüshi Chunqiu* accounts for the rise of a number of the sagely rulers of high antiquity, including the Yellow Sovereign, Yu the Great, Tang, and Wen Wang, by the theory of succession of the five phases, the reign of the Yellow Sovereign corresponding with the earth phase, that of Yu corresponding with the wood phase, and so forth.[28] This sequence was later supplemented by the "mutual production" order of the five phases, by which each phase in the sequence "produced" its successor phase, or at least formed the substrate necessary for the rise of its successor. Thus wood produces fire, fire produces earth, earth produces metal, metal produces water, and water produces wood. Another sequence used to explain various types of change was the "mutual conquest" order by which wood is conquered by metal, metal reduced by fire, fire extinguished by water, water blocked up by earth, and earth manipulated by implements made of pure wood.[29]

The *Baihu Tongyi* used these and other standard five-phase sequences to legitimate particular political procedures and social relations. For example, in explaining why a mature son should remain with his parents while the daughter should leave home, the text makes use of the "mutual production" order: "The son not leaving his parents models himself on what? He models himself on fire which does not depart from wood. The daughter leaving her parents models herself on what? She models herself on water which by flowing departs from metal."[30]

The *Baihu Tongyi* even attempts to explain the physical configuration of each of the "five punishments" by reference to the steps in the "mutual conquest" order of the five phases: "The 'capital punishment' (dapi) models itself on water, which extinguishes fire. The 'punishment of castration' (gong) models itself on earth, which blocks up water."[31]

The use of five-phase orders and sequences to explain all sorts of cosmic, historical, and social changes led to many forced fits, as should be apparent from some of the examples above. Indeed, the degree of Han thinkers' commitment to five-phase cosmology is indicated by the lengths to which they often went to establish even the most unlikely correlations on the basis of five-phase ideas. In some cases, however, Han cosmologists were unable to agree on how to resolve particularly troublesome questions involving five-phase correlations. Two examples are especially celebrated.

One arose from the question of which of the five phases corresponded to the Han dynasty itself. As related in the "Treatise on the *Feng* and *Shan* Sacrifices" in the *Records of the Historian*, debates on the proper phase correlate of the dynasty raged at court during the first century of the Han era, the prime candidates being earth and water. Altogether, the Han switched the identity of its patron phase four times.[32] On at least two of these occasions, it was found necessary to adopt a new order of ritual paraphernalia, including court vestments of a different color and a calendar beginning in a different month, both of which had to correspond to the phase in question.

A second major conundrum involving five-phase correlations arose from the problem of how to mesh the five phases with the four seasons (and four quarters). The effort to coordinate these sets of five and four deeply concerned Han cosmologists, for whom the phases, seasons, and cardinal directions were the very warp and weft of the cosmos, the chief markers of cosmic space and time. To fail to match properly sets as basic as these would have been almost tantamount to admitting that numerological cosmology and systems of correspondence in general were inadequate means of revealing cosmic order.

The ingenuity of the solutions proposed by cosmologists of the late Zhou and Han times indicates how seriously they took the issue. One of the earliest extant solutions, related in the "You Guan" (Office of Youth) chapter in the *Guanzi*, appears to have been graphic or geometrical rather than numerological. W. Allyn Rickett, following Guo Mo-ruo, supposes that this chapter, which consists primarily of a sort of seasonal almanac, was originally arranged as a chart in which the text for each seasonal division was situated in its appropriate quarter (as spring in the east), with the four segments arrayed about a central square. Each of the four seasons and four directions was correlated with one of the five phases, wood with east and spring, metal with west and autumn, and so forth. The remaining phase, earth, "as the central element, was not correlated with any specific portion of the year, but was believed to operate throughout all four seasons of the year equally." Thus it was placed in the center of the chart. In this way, Rickett concludes, the chart maker intended "to show the relationship between the four seasons and the Five Elements [or phases]."[33]

Although most Han cosmologists meshed the five phases with the four seasons in a numerological manner they, like the designer of the "You Guan" calendrical chart, took the earth phase as the odd element in the system. This in itself suggested a solution to the problem, namely that earth be set apart from the other phases, and even invested with a physical primacy or moral superiority. Thus the *Baihu Tongyi*, arguing for the seminality of earth, points out that "wood without earth does not live, fire without earth does not blaze, metal without earth is not completed, and water without earth is not elevated. Earth supports the humble and aids the weak to orderly complete their courses."[34]

The earliest purely numerological solution, one that appears in the

Lüshi Chunqiu, the *Chunqiu Fanlu*, and the *Huainanzi*, simply divided the summer season in two to provide an extra season to be correlated with earth.[35] This arrangement, however, was not acceptable to most later systematizers inasmuch as it violated the requirements of symmetry. First, it did not locate the season associated with the pivotal earth phase in the center of the year. Second, it made the lengths of the seasons unequal by splitting the summer while leaving the other three seasons unchanged.[36] Hence, Ban Gu's *Baihu Tongyi* presented another numerological arrangement by which earth was phased in with the four seasons in a more symmetrical fashion. By this formula, an eighteen-day period was subtracted from the ends of each of the four seasons and allotted to earth, the cosmological rationale for this arrangement being that each of the other phases, wood, fire, metal, and water, requires earth to consummate its work.[37] Since $18 \times 4 = 72$, and $72 \times 5 = 360$, then the number of days of the year allotted to each of the five phases was equalized, even though this arrangement failed to account for approximately 5¼ days.

This numerological arrangement, broached in the *Baihu Tongyi* and developed by the great Tang-era scholastic Kong Ying-da (574–648), came to be regarded as the most satisfactory solution to the problem.[38] Thus whereas the older sections of the canonical medical text, the *Huangdi Neijing* (The Yellow Sovereign's Inner Classic), insert the earth phase in the last month of summer in the manner of the *Huainanzi*, chapters interpolated after the Han era allot to earth four eighteen-day segments falling at the ends of the seasons.[39] However, alternate arrangements continued to be devised in the post-Han era, as illustrated by the astronomical formula for meshing the four seasons with the five phases outlined in the "Treatise on Astronomy and Harmonics" of the *Wei History* (Weishu, Lülizhi).[40]

The four-season–five-phase numerological disjunction was not the only such problem faced by correlative thinkers in traditional China. As Bernhard Karlgren relates, a pre-Han writer in the *Zuozhuan* found it necessary, in pairing the "five elements" with "five gods," to attach "quite loosely . . . a 6th god, Tsi, who falls entirely outside that system of elements," but who could not be ignored.[41] The introduction of Indian cosmological ideas into China in post-Han times also juxtaposed divergent enumeration orders which had to be numerologically coordinated in order to maintain a coherent cosmology. For example, Sun Si-miao (581–682), a Tang era medical and alchemical writer, attempted to reconcile the four-element theory of Indian medicine with the five viscera of Chinese medicine by

allotting 81 ailments to each of the Chinese viscera (81 × 5=405) and 101 to
each of the Indian elements (101 × 4=404).⁴² The sums produced by this
arrangement were apparently deemed close enough to establish a degree of
cosmological concord between the two systems. Through such manipulations, Chinese cosmologists attempted to reconcile not only foreign with
Chinese cosmological sets but also various native enumeration orders and
classificatory schemata. Later commentators on the *Classic of Change* (Yijing), for example, correlated the five phases associated with the "Great
Plan" chapter of the *Documents Classic* with the eight trigrams of the
Change by simply pairing three of the phases with two trigrams each.⁴³

Through their facility in adjusting odd elements in correlative sets,
postclassical Chinese cosmologists were able to construct a unified
correlative numerology around only a few conceptions, such as yin-yang
and the five phases. But the numerological manipulation of diverse sets was
not peculiar to China. Many illustrations could be drawn from the works of
medieval and Renaissance thinkers in the West. A comparatively simple one
arose from the problem of pairing the nine muses with the eight celestial
spheres. Since some provision had to be made for Thalia, the extra muse,
"accordingly Thalia is assigned to Earth at the bottom (and in the center of
this universe)."⁴⁴ Another numerological manipulation appears in Giulio
Camillo's attempt to reduce the ten cabalistic Sephiroth to seven in order to
establish a correspondence with the seven planets and seven angels.
Camillo accomplished this by first reverently omitting the two highest
Sephiroth, Keller and Hokmah, to which not even Moses had ascended, and
then inexplicably assigning two Sephiroth to the planet Venus.⁴⁵

The basic modes of Chinese correlative thought related thus far all
have analogues in the intellectual history of other civilizations. A fourth
developed in China, that based on the figures of the *Classic of Change* and
its canonical appendices, the "Ten Wings," is more peculiarly Chinese.
Indeed, the *Change* itself apparently has no analogue in the classical
literature of any other culture. Yet many of the more studied and elaborate
correlative systems constructed by Chinese cosmologists were based on the
figures associated with the *Change*.

The "classic" itself, as distinguished from the appendices it acquired by
the end of the second century B.C., might not appear to offer very promising material for the construction of systems of correspondence. As Nathan
Sivin has noted, "there is by now a consensus that the *I Ching* (Yijing) is a
jumble of straightforward divination judgments ('Profitable if to the

southwest, unprofitable if to the northeast') and rhymed but often trun-cated proverbs or sayings."[46] These judgments are, however, matched with a set of sixty-four hexagrams each consisting of a set of six parallel lines which may be either broken or unbroken, representing all possible combi-nation of two signs in six places.[47] For example, the first of the sixty-four hexagrams, *qian*, is a set of six unbroken horizontally parallel lines.

Whatever these hexagrams were originally designed to represent, the later canonical appendices to the classic, especially the "Great Commentary" (Dazhuan) attributed to Confucius, do invest the work with a metaphysical dimension, and contain the germs of some of the correlative systems constructed by Han cosmologists. Rudimentary systems of correspondence may be found in some of these appendices, especially in the *Shuogua* (Discussion of the Trigrams), in which each of the eight trigrams (half of a hexagram) is correlated with particular signifiers and attributes. The *Shuogua* pairs the *qian* trigram, for example, with "father," "heaven," "roundness," "the lord," "jade," "metal," and so forth.[48]

More important for later correlative thinkers, the appendices estab-lished the *Classic of Change* as the simulacrum or doppelgänger of cosmic patterns. Thus "the broadness and greatness [of the *Change*] match that of heaven and earth and its flux and continuities match those of the four seasons."[49] According to Willard Peterson, even the forms of the hexagrams "duplicate relationships and processes at work in the realm of heaven-and-earth."[50] "[Just as] the low-lying and the high-standing are spread out on [the surface of the earth], [the relative places of] high and low [lines in the hexagrams] are positioned."[51] The *Change*, moreover, simulates patterns which should ideally prevail in human society. Later Chinese commentators frequently approached the *Change* as if it were a master key to both the cosmos and culture, and used the figures of the *Change* as a basis for the construction of systems of correspondence among the various realms.

To trace the evolution of all the correlative systems developed from the figures associated with the *Change* would itself require a major study. The eight trigrams alone seem to have been correlated, at one time or another, with almost as many different sets of things as the five phases.[52] This discussion will focus on three of the more influential systems of corre-spondence devised by Han students of the *Change*, the *guaqi*, the *najia*, and the schema presented by Yang Xiong in his *Tai Xuan Jing* (Classic of the Great Mystery).

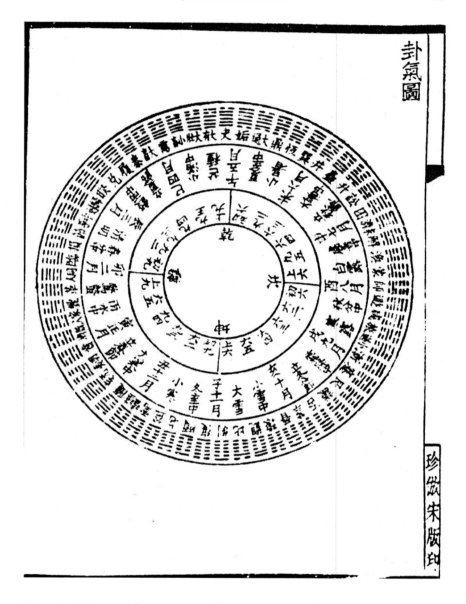

Figure 1: A diagram of one version of the *guaqi* system. The items correlated in this chart, reading from the innermost circle outward, are four of the sixty-four hexagrams, the twelve "earthly branches" or chronograms, the twelve months plus the twenty-four solar periods, and the other sixty of the sixty four hexagrams. Source: *Songyuan Xue'an* (SBBY ed.) 10.9b.

The *guaqi* and *najia* systems, having been variously developed by postclassical commentators on the *Change*, are not easily defined. However, the basic structure and evolution of each may be briefly told. The *guaqi* schema, said to have been first devised by Meng Xi and later developed by Jing Fang (79-39 B.C.), was based on the idea of numerological correspondence between the figures of the *Classic of Change*, particularly the hexagrams, and the calendrical periods. Early forms of the *guaqi* correlated the sixty-four hexagrams with the twelve months, the twenty-four solar periods, and even the 365¼ days of the year.[53] Wei Bo-yang, in the later Han era, applied *guaqi* correlations to alchemical practice, creating yet another level of correspondence.

As with a few of the five-phase correlations discussed above, the number of some of the units in paired *guaqi* sets could not easily be coordinated. One such difficulty was the incommensurability of the 365¼ days of the year and the 384 lines of the 64 hexagrams (64 × 6=384). Han cosmologists proposed several different solutions to the problem. One was to subtract four hexagrams from the sixty-four, correlating these with the two solstices and two equinoxes or alternatively with the four seasons or the four directions. Since each hexagram contains six lines, this deducts twenty-four lines (4 × 6=24) from the total of 384, yielding the figure of 360, the "round" number of days in the year. Another solution, proposed by Jiao Yan-shou in the *Jiaoshi Yilin* (Mr. Jiao's Forest of [Symbols Associated with] the *Change*) (c. 40 B.C.), was again to correlate the 360 lines of 60 of the hexagrams with the first 360 days of the year, and to correlate each of the four remaining hexagrams with one day each.[54] This solution, however, left a rather untidy reminder of 1¼ days.

The *najia* schema, though also correlating calendrical units with the figures associated with the *Change*, was developed by later commentators into a more complex system. Originally the term *najia* referred only to the pairing of the eight trigrams of the *Change* with the ten heavenly stems (tiangan), an enumerative order used as early as the Shang era for counting days.[55] The numerological disjunction between eight and ten was adjusted by pairing the first two trigrams, *qian* and *kun*, with two "stems" each. However, Jing Fang, the purported codifier of the *najia* schema, inserted other enumerative sets, including the twelve earthly branches (dizhi) and the five phases, into the system. Later commentators, notably Zheng Xuan (A.D. 127–200) and Wei Bo-yang, further developed the *najia*. Cheng paired the twelve lines in the *qian* and *kun* hexagrams with the twelve

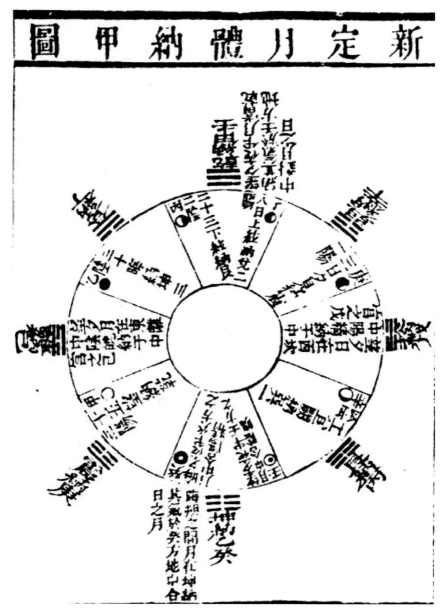

Figure 2. A diagram of a simple form of the *najia* system, correlating the eight trigrams of the *Change* with the phases of the moon and the days of the lunar month. Source: Hu Wei, *Yitu Mingbian* (Taipei: Guangwen reprint, 1971) 3.178.

months of the year, the twenty-four solar periods, and the twenty-eight lunar lodges, as well as the twelve pitchpipes. Wei Bo-yang extended the *najia* in an astronomical direction, even conceiving the eight trigrams as images of the phases of the moon. He identified the *tui* trigram, for example, with its two *yang* (unbroken) lines on the bottom and one yin (broken) line on top (☱), as a simulacrum of the half moon on the eighth day of the lunar month.[56] Since the *yang* power was said to emerge from the bottom of the trigram and gradually work its way upward, the *tui* trigram represented the process of the moon's waxing in the period from the new moon to the full moon, as well as the physical appearance of the moon on the eighth day of the lunar month.

However far such astronomical developments of the *najia* system departed from the original purport of the *Classic of Change* upon which they were supposedly based, postclassical commentators often attempted to rationalize such schemata by reference to that text and its appendices. Such claims were not entirely without foundation. There was some support in the "Great Commentary" even for Wei Bo-yang's matching of the trigrams with the phrases of the moon.[57] Moreover, such Han cosmological commentators as Jing Fang and Yu Fan regarded the figures associated with the *Change*, especially the eight trigrams, as having been conceived in the first place on astronomical models.[58] According to Dong Ba, a fourth-century commentator, the mythical sage king Fu Xi invented the eight trigrams of three lines each in order to simulate the twenty-four solar periods.[59] Even the form of the graph for "change," Yu Fan contended, was an indication of the astronomical origins of the *Change*, since this character combined the characters for "sun" and "moon." The Tang era commentator Li Ding-zhuo took this to mean that "the images of the eight trigrams are the same as the images that are in the heavens. For sages devised the diagrams [of the *Change*] to simulate the heavens."[60]

The idea of correspondence between the figures of the *Change* and the figures of the heavens furnished a cosmological basis for the science of mathematical astronomy in the Han period. Han cosmologists deduced from the manipulation of the figures in that classic not only such standard constants as the number of months and days in the year, but even the lengths of various astronomical concordance cycles. To take a simple example, cosmologists in the Han and later "derived" the number of years in a simple intercalation cycle (19) by combining the final yin and yang numbers (10 + 9) given in the "Great Commentary" to the *Change*.[61]

A desire to harmonize the astronomical and calendrical units with the type of figurative numerology developed from the *Change* may well have been the major motive inspiring the composition of Yang Xiong's *Tai Xuan Jing*. Apparently dissatisfied with the awkwardness of some of the numerological adjustments employed by the inventors of the *guaqi* and *najia* systems, Yang Xiong devised a "classic," modeled loosely on the *Change*, which was yet deliberately tailored to fit the units of the astronomical and harmonic systems in that use. Thus for the sixty-four hexagrams and 384 lines of the *Change*, Yang substituted eighty-one tetragrams (shou) with a total of 729 lines (zan).[62] Since nine and its multiples figured prominently in the calculations of mathematical astronomers and mathematical harmonists of the day, Yang Xiong's numerological system did, in fact, accord more closely than did those built on the *Change* figures with the "exact" sciences of that era.[63]

Yang did occasionally find it necessary to resort to forced fits in order to reconcile his schema with calendrical or astronomical constants. The most notable such instance is his attempted correlation of the 729 *zan* in his system ($81 \times 9 = 729$) with the total number of days and nights in a year of 365¼ days. Since $729 \div 2 = 364.5$, Yang found it necessary to create two extra *zan* in order to make up for the ¾-day difference. However, this solution overshoots the mark by ¼ of a day, yielding 365½ days rather than 365¼, the approximate number of days in the year as calculated by Han astronomers.[64]

The correlative system outlined in Yang Xiong's *Tai Xuan Jing* attracted a few later imitators, notably the great Song-era scholar Sima Guang (1019–1086). But the *Change* and its appendices remained the major classical basis for the construction of numerological and figurative systems of correspondence. For the *Change*, in part by dint of its canonical status, set the basic terms of cosmological discourse that later commentators were obliged to follow in designing their more coherent schemata.

The four basic modes of correlative thought are by no means mutually exclusive. Chinese cosmologists sometimes correlated man and cosmos and state and cosmos through five-phase correspondences. They occasionally incorporated five-phase conceptions into some of the correlative systems based on the figures of the *Change*. Thus this classification of the basic modes of correlative thought in early China is by no means the only possible one, nor is it exhaustive. Many examples of correlative thought cannot reasonably be included in any of the four categories outlined above.

This should not be surprising, in view of the universal scholastic propensity for correlating all sorts of odd things, seraphim with cherubim, for example. Han commentators applied a form of correlative thought in their philosophical studies, frequently explaining the meaning of obscure characters by sound analogy on the assumption that a phonetic correspondence indicated a semantic relation.[65] However, commentators rarely developed linguistic puns into larger systems of correspondence between two general orders of reality.

But there was at least one additional form of correlative cosmology, really a sort of composite of the first three basic modes, which was quite highly developed and influential in Chinese intellectual history. This was the elaborate system, outlined in the *Yueling* (Monthly Ordnances) chapter of the *Li Ji* (Record of Rites) and other contemporary sources, for correlating the ritual acts and attitudes of the ruler with the cycle of the seasons. In Hsü Dau-lin's words, this schema served as "a kind of almanac for Emperors" in which "for each month activities and rituals are prescribed which the emperor should perform and prohibitions are stated which he should avoid."[66] Though this *Yueling* schema might be linked with the "state analogy" mode of correlative thought, there is some reason to treat it separately. First, this arrangement was the object of extensive commentary and analysis by scholiasts from the Han to the Qing, not least because variations of it were to be found in at least three important texts dating from the third and second centuries B.C., the *Lüshi Chunqiu*, the *Huainanzi*, and the *Liji*, the last of which was one of the five Confucian classics. Second, the *Yueling* schema presents more elaborately than perhaps any other classical system the idea of "cosmic resonance" (ganying). According to this theory, things of the same category but different cosmic realms were supposed to affect one another by virtue of a mutual sympathy, to resonate like properly attuned pitchpipes. Some modern commentators have argued that resonance was an essential ingredient in correlative thought.

Although the classical version of the system may be found in the *Yueling*, it first appeared in the *Shiji* (Monthly Record), the opening sections of each of the first twelve chapters of the *Lüshi Chunqiu*. The extant later versions of the system, those that appear in the *Yueling* and in the *Shize Xun* (Introductions on Rules for the Seasons) chapter of the *Huainanzi*, are only slightly modified versions of the "Monthly Record."[67] It is unlikely, however, that such an elaborate system as is presented in that source was unprecedented, especially since the *Lüshi Chunqiu* was a deliberately synthetic work. A possible antecedent may be found in the *Xia Xiaozheng* (Little Calendar of the Xia), probably a fifth- or fourth- century B.C. text, which Derk Bodde characterizes as a "kind of farmer's almanac, describing the animals, plants, and climatic conditions of each month, and instructing the peasant what he should then be doing in the fields."[68]

However, the *Lüshi Chunqiu* and later versions of this particular type of correlative system are, as Allyn Rickett has noted, "less concretely natural and more abstractly cosmological, less agricultural and more political in content" than is the *Xia Xiaozheng* schema.[69] Each of the first twelve chapters of the *Lüshi Chunqiu* lists the god, ruler, number, sound, taste, smell, creature, pitchpipe, sacrifice, type of apparel, and imperial obser- vances and prohibitions associated with the corresponding month of the year. For example, the text says of the first month of spring that "its divine ruler is Tai Hao, its god Gou Mang, its creatures are scaly, its musical note *jue*, its pitchpipe *tai cou*, its number eight. Its taste is sour, its smell goatish, its sacrifice is at the inner door for which one first offers the spleen [of the victim]."[70] The text gives the following account of the proper rituals to be observed during this month:

> The son of Heaven shall live in the apartment to the left of the Green Bright Hall. He shall ride in a belled chariot driven by dark green dragon [horses], and bearing green flags. He shall wear green clothes with green jade [pendants]. He shall eat wheat and mutton. His vessels shall be open [in order to represent a] coming forth . . .[71]

The text proceeds to describe and list the various procedures, ordinances, and prohibitions appropriate to this first month of spring. It concludes by warning that if activities corresponding to seasons other than spring are performed at this time, natural disaster will ensue. For example, "If in the first month of spring, [the ruler] carries out the summer ordinances, then wind and rain will not come in season, trees and grass will soon dry up, and the country will thus be in fear."[72]

The various rituals and prescriptions described in the *Lüshi Chunqiu* were, as Bodde remarks, probably only abstract theorizing at the time of that text's compilation (240 B.C.). But later they "directly inspired the Han ritualists in their work of creating analogous ceremonies for their own dynasty."[73] In the later Han era (A.D. 25–220), some of the seasonal activities prescribed in this text, especially "welcoming the seasons" and the "proclamations of broad clemency," came to be incorporated into imperial ritual, though they gradually fell into disuse in later ages.[74] In view of its classical sanction and political application in imperial China, it is not surprising that some later commentators regarded the *Yueling* schema as the system of correspondence par excellence and the idea of cosmic resonance which pervades the work as basic to correlative thought.

COSMOLOGICAL RESONANCE

Modern historians of Chinese thought have sometimes written as if almost any two items that could be correlated in Chinese cosmology could also be made to interact at a distance, to affect one another by virtue of a mutual sympathy, if not by any specific mechanism, then at least by virtue of the allegedly "organic" structure of the traditional Chinese cosmos. But a consideration of the last section should suggest that correlative sets which do not resonate can exist. Is there any sense, for example, in which the matching sets in the *guaqi* or *najia* schema interact or intercommunicate in the sense implied by the meaning of the term *ganying*?

The idea of resonance thus does not seem to have been intrinsic to correlative thinking. But it did play a major role in some systems of correspondence, especially those developed by such politically oriented Han cosmologists as Dong Zhong-shu and the contributors to the *Huainanzi*. Moreover, the conception of *ganying* was important in the operation of two of the basic modes of correlative thought in the sketch above, man-cosmos and state-cosmos correspondence. It also played a key role in the *Yueling* system.

Perhaps the most obvious traditional application of *ganying* conceptions was in the field of music. As Charles Le Blanc has pointed out, accounts of the resonance of properly attuned lute strings appear in such diverse Warring States (403–221 B.C.) and Han texts as the *Zhuangzi*, the *Chu Ci* (Songs of Chu), the *Lüshi Chunqiu*, and the *Huainanzi*.[75] Han cosmologists frequently cited instances of musical resonance to illustrate the existence of resonant phenomena on other levels.[76] They also extended the conception of acoustical resonance into statecraft, arguing that musical tones, especially those emitted by the twelve standard pitchpipes, resonate with the current political situation. According to the "Treatise on Astronomy and Harmonics" of the *Han History* (Hanshu, Lülizhi), the pitchpipes will automatically be properly tuned in a well-ordered age.[77] Conversely, no degree of technical expertise in the crafting or tuning of the pitchpipes or in the science of mathematical harmonics could ever succeed in tuning the pipes properly in an age of misgovernment. Thus testing the notes emitted by the pipes, like observing unusual phenomena in the heavens, was developed into a political science, though one not so securely institutionalized as portent astrology.

Han cosmologists applied the concept of musical resonance not only to divining the character of states and rulers, but also to affecting the course of events in the natural world. They maintained that by performing the music or sounding the pitchpipe appropriate to a particular season, one facilitated the normal waxing and waning of yin and yang powers through the course of the year. This idea was broached in the "Monthly Record" of the *Lüshi Chunqiu* and the "Monthly Ordinances" chapter of the *Liji.* But it was actually institutionalized in the Later Han era, when "Eight Skilled Gentlemen" were employed to play cosmic music, which, in Derk Bodde's words, is "music intended to facilitate the passage from *yin* to *yang* or vice versa at the solstices."[78] More mundanely, one of the functions of the Director of Music (Dazi Yue) in the canonical *Zhouli* (Rites of Zhou) was to call or excite certain species of animals by playing the musical mode to which the species in question responded.[79]

It is not difficult to imagine how Han cosmologists might have constructed correlative systems on the basis of the musical theories outlined above. Their understanding of resonance might, for example, have inspired them to correlate musical tones with the months of the year, since the pitchpipes, like the months, numbered twelve. That correlative systems were actually founded on conceptions of harmonic resonance is indicated by the account of the therapeutic value of music given in the *Taiping Jing* (Classic of Great Peace) as interpreted by Max Kaltenmark. In this text, according to Kaltenmark, each of the five notes of the Chinese pentatonic scale "is in tune with a spatial direction and each of them acts on one of the five internal organs. Thus the note *jue* . . . delights the genies of the east and assures the good health of the liver."[80] But even in this case, one might well argue that the correlative numerology, the matching of the five notes of the scale with the five cardinal directions and five internal organs, preceded the conception that there was a resonant relation among the various sets, and that the latter idea was formulated by Han cosmologists in an effort to rationalize the quinary cosmology that they had inherited from classical sources. Illustrations of quinary numerology appear in such texts as the *Documents Classic,* which predates the *Taiping Jing* by several hundred years.

The primary field of application of resonance theory in post-classical China was in political cosmology. Modern commentators have given it a special name, "phenomenalism," or "the theory of natural catastrophe as the result of misgovernment."[81] But in their efforts to limit imperial power in the Han and later ages, Confucian officials and commentators frequently tended, as a practical matter, to dwell on calamities rather than on auspicious signs.

As with the basic modes of correlative thought, the chief sources for the doctrine of resonance between polity and cosmos are the great compendia of Han cosmological thought, particularly the *Chunqiu Fanlu*, the *Huainanzi*, and the *Baihu Tongyi*, as well as the five phases and astrological treatises in the *Records of the Historian* and *Han History*. Dong Zhong-shu, who is sometimes credited with having formalized this doctrine or with giving it its classical expression, focused particularly on the actions of the ruler as the ultimate source of cosmic fortune and misfortune. Dong remarked that "If the king is correct, then the primal pneuma will be harmonious and compliant, winds and rains will be timely, auspicious stars will appear, and the yellow dragon will descend. If the king is not correct, then above a [strangely] transformed heaven and [below] rebellious airs will appear at the same time."[82]

The contributors to the *Huananzi* sometimes identified the polity as a whole, not just the ruler, as the resonant earthly counterpart of heaven:

> The feelings of men and rulers rise up to penetrate heaven. Thus executions and cruelties give rise to many whirlwinds. Oppressive laws and ordinances give rise to many insect plagues. If the innocent are put to death, then the countryside will redden with drought. If ordinances are not accepted, then there will be many disastrous floods.[83]

Cosmologists of the former Han era thus appear to have given the doctrine its definitive expression; but intimations of the idea that political actions might affect the course of natural phenomena appear in the Confucian classics. The *Spring and Autumn Annals* (Chunqiu), supposedly composed by Confucius in order to admonish the rulers of his time, is often taken as the ultimate classical source for theories of cosmological resonance.[84] But as Qing commentators pointed out, the *Annals*, while *listing* political events alongside natural disasters and portents, does not link the two systematically, or even explicitly. Readers are left to draw their own conclusions regarding cause and effect. A much clearer classical statement of the idea appears in the "Great Plan" (Hongfan) chapter of the *Documents Classic*, where the essayist writes of "the various verifications." Of these, "(Some) are called the lucky verifications. Gravity—seasonable rain responds to it; orderliness—seasonable sunshine responds to it; wisdom—seasonable heat responds to it; sageness—seasonable wind responds to it. (Some) are called unlucky verifications. Wildness—constant rain responds to it; incorrectness—constant sunshine responds to it. . ."[85]

It is unlikely that the general idea that human actions might affect meteorological and astronomical phenomena was the invention of any particular classical writers, so widespread is the conception among premodern peoples throughout the world. The studies of Jean Piaget have established that even children, or at least children in modern European culture, pass through a stage of intellectual development in which they believe that human will or actions cause clouds and heavenly bodies to move. One mode of causality in children's thought as described by Piaget, namely "participation," is reminiscent of the theory of resonance in Chinese cosmology. "Its principle," Piaget remarks, "is the following: two things between which there subsist relations either of resemblance or of general affinity, are conceived as having something in common which enables them to act upon one another at a distance."[86]

Contemporary children generally abandon the notion of "participation" before they acquire the wherewithal to codify the idea. In contrast, early correlative cosmologists, such as the authors of the *Lüshi Chunqiu* and the *Huainanzi*, began to synthesize and develop popular beliefs concerning the resonant interaction of polity and cosmos. But even the schemata outlined in the *Lüshi Chunqiu* and the *Huainanzi*, which consist principally of lists of natural portents that were supposed to appear in resonance with particular political actions, are seldom presented in a very systematic manner. The *Huainanzi* does not explain why executions and cruelties should give rise to whirlwinds, or oppressive laws cause plagues of insects. There is, in other words, little apparent logic behind many of these associations.

As cosmological thought developed in the Han, however, resonant associations between polity and cosmos, or man and nature, were rationalized in at least two important ways. First, Dong Zhong-shu and his contemporaries developed the conception of a physical medium, a subtle and pervasive pneuma (qi),[87] through which human events and natural processes were supposed to interact. Dong thus accounted naturalistically for effects that had earlier been explained in magical or animistic terms, if at all. For contrary to what may be implied in some modern presentations of traditional Chinese cosmology, the idea of a resonant *qi*, like the *spiritus mundi* in Neoplatonic cosmology in the West, appears to have been a later scholastic rationalization of resonant effects.[88] There is no indication in the *Spring and Autumn Annals* that the relationship between political acts and cosmic events chronicled therein is mediated by the *qi*, or for that matter by any other medium.[89] Likewise, children of around four or five years, while believing that physical events may be caused by related objects acting upon one another at a distance, yet evince "a remarkable absence of interest as to 'how' phenomena occur."[90] Not until the transitional phase to the next stage in the development of ideas of causality does the child explain apparent action at a distance "by reaction of the surrounding medium." Hence, in child logic, as well as in the historical development of cosmology in China, it seems that general ideas of "resonance" or "participation" preceded attempts to explain resonant effects.

The earliest Chinese attempts to account physically for the resonant interaction between polity and cosmos did not invoke the theory of the mediatory *qi*, which does not seem to have become established until the second century B.C. Classical texts occasionally invoked what might be regarded as more primitive or anthropomorphic intermediaries through which state and cosmos, or humanity and divinity, communicated with one another. Thus the *Lü Xing* (Punishments of Lü) chapter of the *Documents Classic* records that "God surveyed the people; there was no fragrant virtue, the smell sent out by the punishments was rank."[91] Only later, it seems, were such smells subsumed into the colorless, odorless, and tasteless *qi* of the Han cosmologists. In the same way such anthropomorphized devices as speech by which Yahweh communicated with the prophets of the Old Testament were metaphysically transmuted by such Neoplatonic thinkers as the Pseudo-Dionysius. For the latter, it was "Love" or "Yearning" which "holds together things of the same order by a mutual connection, and moves the highest to take thought for those below and fixes the inferior in a state which seeks the higher."[92] "Yearning," like the resonant *qi*, was not, moreover, just a physical mediator but also a special quality that inhered in both cosmos and polity, God and man.

The second way in which Han cosmologists rationalized and systematized the idea of cosmic resonance was to explain particular instances in which a condition in one domain of experience affected those in another by reference to standard cosmological categories, such as yin-yang and the five phases. For example, Han cosmologists posited that the sexual licentiousness or political domination of the court by women might lead to serious floods.[93] For an excess of the yin power (associated with women) in the political domain sympathetically stimulated an overflow of the yin force (associated with water) in the realm of nature. With respect to the *wuxing*, Han commentators argued that a ruler who placed too much stock in the power of metal by pressing military expeditions and criminal executions to an abnormal degree was responsible for an out-of-season appearance of the processes of decay associated with autumn, the phase of the year in which metal was dominant.

The Chinese term for "resonance," *ganying*, has still broader applications. As L.S. Yang has pointed out, the general idea of *ganying* was widely applied even in social relations. Such notable Han thinkers as Dong Zhong-shu and Liu Xiang (77–6 B.C.), for example, justified the cardinal Confucian social virtues, loyalty and filial piety, as the proper resonant responses to the benefits received from one's ruler or parents.[94] The Confucian belief in the efficacy of exemplary action, insofar as it posits that things of the same nature though at different levels may affect one another by a mutual sympathy, might also be conceived as a form of resonance theory, for "When the gentleman feels profound affection for his parents, the common people will be stirred to benevolence. When he does not forget friends of long standing, the common people will not shirk their obligations to other people."[95] But for all its versatility, the idea of *ganying* is hardly the essential basis for the formulation of correlative systems.

ORIGINS OF CORRELATIVE THOUGHT IN CHINA

There is no consensus on when and why correlative cosmology emerged in China or elsewhere. Scholars even disagree on the question of whether systems of correspondence have an explicable historical origin at all. In the view of some authorities, including historians of Chinese thought, anthropologists, and philosophers, correlative thinking seems so natural and universal in both primitive cultures and early civilizations that it is vain to search extant texts for specific origins. For several of these authorities, the Han compendia quoted above merely record, or at most codify, a type of thought that was truly perennial in Chinese civilization, and perhaps even in premodern cultures in general.

The partisans of the universality of correlative thought include some of the most eminent figures in twentieth-century intellectual history. Emile Durkheim and Marcel Mauss, for example, characterize the Chinese "classifications of regions, seasons, things, and animal species" by a set of numerological schemata as but one particular manifestation of "primitive classification." Explicitly comparing historical Chinese systems of correspondence with those found among the Australian aborigines and the North American Indians, they remark that the Chinese "classification of things under eight headings, the eight powers . . . is comparable, save for the fact that the notion of clan is absent, to the Australian classifications."[96] Chinese classificatory schemata were thus peculiar only in that they apparently lacked the all-important (to Durkheim) social correlate of the other numerological sets.

Ernst Cassirer also compared Chinese systems of classification to those of primitives and premoderns in general, characterizing all these as forms of "mystical thought." He argued, for example, that the idea, expressed by Chinese cosmologists, that all "qualitative distinctions and oppositions," such as colors, elements, seasons, and human emotions, "possess some sort of spatial 'correspondence' " is typical of the premodern stage of intellectual development.[97] Cassirer did acknowledge, however, that Chinese cosmologists, as compared with thinkers in other traditional societies, developed this idea with the "greatest subtlety and precision." He credited Chinese cosmologists with having attained the higher reaches of "mythical thought," though not with having accomplished the breakthrough to "scientific thought."

Finally, several eminent Western sinologists, including such diverse figures as Marcel Granet, Jospeph Needham, Wolfram Eberhard, and Paul Wheatley, also seem to support the idea that correlative cosmology was perennial in Chinese civilization, if not universal throughout the premodern world. For example, Wheatley, following René Berthelot, proposes that the correlation of celestial and terrestrial rhythms, or "astrobiology," was "characteristic of that phase of social and intellectual development intervening between the stages of pre-urban folk society" and "modern industrial society."[98] Logically, this mode of thought would have arisen at the dawn of Chinese civilization, if not before. In that case, its formation would be undocumented and hence practically inaccessible to conventional historians.

My own view on this question is that correlative systems in China were devised in a fully historical epoch, particularly the third and second

centuries B.C., for largely historical reasons. Apart from implicitly contra-
dicting the conclusions of such past masters as Durkheim and Cassirer, this
hypothesis also appears to contravene the findings of later students of
symbolic systems in primitive cultures, especially structuralist anthropologists. For even a cursory examination of, for example, Lévi-Strauss' *The Raw
and the Cooked* will reveal evidence that primitive peoples devised simple
systems of correspondence generically similar to those more highly
developed ones presented in the Han cosmological compendia. However,
the tables or charts of correspondence that appear in the works of some
structuralists are, if their critics are to be believed, largely products of the
authors' own efforts to systematize relations that are far more flexible in the
cultures under investigation. In other words, the investigator, operating on
the assumption that there must be a fixed, coherent, symmetrical structure
to the cosmological views of primitive people, often proceeds to construct
one from data that are quite scattered. Once the anthropologist has
succumbed to the temptation to present his reconstruction in the form of a
table, chart, or list, he often becomes preoccupied with filling in the blank
spaces, thus imitating the Han cosmologists in his willingness to resort to
forced fits to complete the system.[99] Such anthropological systematizers
would do well heed the warning of Clifford Geertz that "Only short flights
of ratiocination tend to be effective in anthropology; longer ones tend to
drift off into logical dreams, academic bemusements, with formal symmetry."[100]

The comparative perspective does not require that we view the systems
of correspondence that appear in Han texts as simply written versions of
schemata deeply rooted in the folk cultures of preliterate China. If the
contemporary British social anthropologist Jack Goody is to be believed, it
requires that we draw the opposite conclusion. For by committing a
primitive or folk classification to writing, Goody argues, one inexorably
"sharpens the outlines of the categories." The literary systematizer has "to
make a decision as to whether rain or dew is of the heavens or of the earth."
On the other hand, "in oral discourse it is perfectly possible to treat 'dew' as
a thing of the earth in one context and a thing of the sky in another." But
when the classification is being set down in writing, "a series of forced
choices, binary choices" has to be made, the result of which is the formation
of a system with its own internal logic and momentum.[101]

Goody further argues that the commitment of a primitive or folk
classification to writing, apart from fixing the relationships of the various

categories with respect to one another, "also permitted the construction of more elaborate schemas as well as the greater manipulation of letters, words, and numbers." With the invention of charts and tables, moreover, such letters, words, and numbers "could be drawn into new and esoteric relationships by means of elaborate tables of correspondence."[102]

In sum, Goody contends, as against Lévi-Strauss and his school, that the construction of correlative systems is not a primordial activity in which the "savage mind" invariably engages because correlative thoughts are "good to think," satisfying the primal intellectual need and exhibiting a primordial mental structure. While *some* kind of classification is "an obvious condition of language and of knowing," the kind of formal, decontextualized systems of correspondence formulated by Han cosmologists were in part products of the absorption, synthesis, and development of preliterate classifications by literate culture.

Goody's discussion, taken by itself, hardly proves that systems of correspondence did not appear in China until the late Zhou and Han eras. It simply renders more plausible the idea that correlative schemata crystallized in a mature historical period long after the development of Chinese writing. But is there documentary evidence sufficient to establish that correlative cosmology did not fully emerge in China until the late classical period?

There does seem to be such evidence, though it is mostly negative. For few intimations of the systems of correspondence outlined earlier in this chapter appear in texts dating from before the third century B.C. The *Lüshi Chunqiu* (c. 240 B.C.) seems to be the earliest extant text in which relatively studied, complex correlative systems appear. Sections of earlier texts, such as the *Zuo Chronicle* and the *Documents Classic* do contain references to several of the categories used later in systems of correspondence. But they are seldom used as bases for the construction of systems correlating various realms of the cosmos.

However, the point that earlier texts rarely outline complex systems of correspondence might be countered in various ways. One might argue that the bibliocatastrophes of the last years of the third century B.C. could have destroyed earlier sources of correlative thought. But the quantity of Zhou literature that has survived is not negligible. It includes major historical chronicles as well as the chief works of several philosophical schools, most of which the Qin Dynasty (221–206 B.C.) sought to extirpate. Yet none of these works describes a correlative schema that approaches in comprehensiveness to those presented in the chief Han cosmological compendia. As both H.G. Creel and Benjamin Schwartz have argued, early and mid-Zhou writing in general manifests a "naïve realism" quite foreign to the type of cosmology that emerged in China in the Warring States and Former Han eras.[103]

A second possible argument for dating correlative cosmology from a more remote epoch is the hypothesis that Han cosmological compendia simply recorded popular classificatory systems that had been transmitted orally over a period of some centuries and generally ignored by the more aristocratically oriented writers of the Zhou. Indeed, it seems quite likely that relatively simple, anthropomorphic correspondences arose from a folk tradition. To correlate the eyes with the sun and moon, for example, would hardly have required the cogitations of a literate systematizer. But it is hard to imagine more abstract systems of correspondences such as those developed from the canonical appendices to the *Classic of Change* having been devised by a "savage thinker" in a preliterate culture. Some of the very categories in the more complex systems, such as the twenty-four solar period or the five notes of the pentatonic scale, do not seem to have been formulated until rather late in the classical period. Even such a simple man-cosmos correspondence as that drawn between the 365 days of the year and the 365 smaller joints of the body, based as it was upon systematic measurements of the lengths of gnomon shadows, would probably not have occurred to a Neolithic correlative thinker. In sum, what Bernhard Karlgren has remarked of the mythology in Han sources–that it has a distinctly scholastic, synthetic air despite its having incorporated some primitive folk elements–might well be applied to Han systems of correspondence; for many of the categories in Han correlative systems could not have had much meaning outside the world of court and capital in early imperial China.

Assuming that Han systems of correspondence were neither taken en bloc from now lost Zhou texts nor extracted from a hoary folk tradition, let us now consider why correlative cosmology crystallized in the late classical period, particularly in the third and second centuries B.C. This being a question that has created a considerable literature and to which, moreover, no simple answer can be given, I will begin by discussing some of the interpretations proposed by traditional commentators and modern scholars. Not all these interpretations focus on correlative thought as I have defined it. Some are concerned with such general issues as the origins of "systematization" in early Chinese thought, and others more particularly with the formulation of such important ideas as yin-yang and the five phases.

Several scholars, both traditional and modern, have traced the origin, especially of the yin-yang and five-phase ideas to a particular school of classical philosophy, the *yinyang jia* or "Naturalists" (Needham's term), and more specifically to the principal theorist of this school, Zou Yan (305–240 B.C.?).[104] Unfortunately, or perhaps fortunately for those who profess this rather neat solution to the problem, no complete work by any member of this school is extant, if indeed such a school ever existed.[105] Zou, in fact, is the only Naturalist thinker whose basic ideas were recorded in the earliest standard histories of China, particularly the *Records of the Historian* of Sima Qian (145–90 B.C.?). This work credits Zou with having propounded the theories of the alternation of the yin and yang and the succession of the five phases, the latter idea apparently having been used by Zou to explain the rise and fall of dynasties in early Chinese history.[106] Han commentators also credited Zou with having devised simple numerologies for classifying notable geographical features, particularly with having invented the standard cosmography in which geographical units were enumerated by nines.[107]

Modern historians of early Chinese thought, such as Fung Yu-lan and Lo Kuang, have continued to trace to Zou and his "school" the origin, or at least the cosmological integration, of yin-yang and five-phase ideas.[108] However, these modern commentators, developing a suggestion first made by Sima Qian, have associated Zou not so much with the school of Naturalists as with the learning of his native state of Qi. They posit, in other words, not so much a scholastic as a regional origin for early Chinese cosmology.[109] More recently, John Major has taken this idea a step further, proposing that the cosmology of Zou and his school, derived from the belief system of the peoples of the classical states of Qi and Chu, may have originated ultimately in a pan-Eurasian Grand Origin Myth "transmitted to them by the proto-Indo-European inhabitants of the south Siberian steppe."[110] Major thus raises the possibility that the "cosmological mythology of ancient China" was introduced from abroad, not invented independently by the early Chinese.

Inasmuch as the Han-era descriptions of the thought of Zou Yan and his school are rather brief and suspect, it is difficult to evaluate interpretations of the Naturalist influence on the rise of Han cosmology. While there is little evidence that Zou made a crucial contribution to the general evolution of correlative thought, he might well have developed a few of the key terms and ideas used by Han thinkers. For example, Zou might have helped to transform the meaning of *wuxing* from the functional "five substances" of the "Great Plan" to the cyclical "five phases" of the major Han cosmologists. One might also plausibly credit him with the articulation and dissemination of the nonary cosmography that later came to dominate Han cosmography. But there is little documentary evidence that Zou or other members of his shadowy school invented any of the basic modes of correlative thought.

Thus perhaps the most significant question regarding Zou Yan is historiographical rather than historical. That is, why have both traditional commentators and modern historians, building on such a slender documentary base, credited (or blamed) him with so much, even with creating Chinese cosmology, at least that of the yin-yang and *wuxing* variety? One possible reason, which may be especially relevant for modern rationalist historians, is that by consigning numerological speculations and occult ideas to a particular classical school, all taint of such ideas could be removed from classical Confucianism and Daoism. One could thus attribute the embarrassing appearance of questionable cosmological conceptions in the postclassical Confucian and Daoist traditions to an extrinsic source.

This raises the possibility that developments in other schools of classical philosophy may indeed have facilitated the crystallization of correlative thought in China in the third and second centuries B.C. While mature systems of correspondence do not appear in late-Zhou philosophical classics such as *Mencius*, the *Laozi*, or even the canonical appendices to the *Change*, perhaps these works helped to lay the groundwork for the correlative cosmology that emerged in the Han period.

That a correlative cosmology might develop from a prior philosophical metaphysics could be illustrated by the history of Platonism and Neoplatonism in the ancient, medieval, and Renaissance West. By positing a realm of Ideas, of unchanging forms beyond the material world, Platonism invited the systematic correlation of these forms with mundane objects. Indeed, not just with Platonism, but "in any cosmology that places ultimate reality at some level above sense perception, the objects of physical nature become counters that correspond to the unchanging essences in the absolute world."[111] One might expect some form of correlative thought to have arisen in almost any civilization whose intellectual life was informed by an idealist metaphysics.

That such a metaphysics was ever propounded by any classical Chinese philosopher is very doubtful. But the classical Daoists, especially Laozi, in proposing that man pattern himself after heaven and earth,[112] did establish an ideal model for human conduct. This idea did not lead directly to the systematic pairing of human and cosmic units, but it did help to create an epistemological space in which correlative thought could develop. Later and lesser minds could interpret the classical Daoist calls for the harmonization of man and nature in a literalist fashion, devising anatomical, numerological, and psychological correspondences.

Among other late-Zhou philosophical works, the "Great Commentary" to the *Change* also may have helped to establish the intellectual basis for this mode of correlative thought. For that text posits that the ancient sage kings created important instruments of human culture through the abstraction of certain patterns from natural objects and processes. They modeled such inventions as boats, fishnets, ploughs, and markets on the forms of the eight trigrams, which they in turn abstracted from their observations of heaven and earth.[113] Hence, inasmuch as the sages first patterned the chief institutions of human culture on models taken ultimately from the natural world, the correspondences that could be established between the two realms were truly natural. By discovering such correlations, one in a sense recapitulated the creative process by which the sages brought civilization into being.

The examples cited above from the *Laozi* and the "Great Commentary" to the *Change* hardly exhaust the list of possible philosophical antecedents of correlative thought. A thorough discussion of this topic would include an examination of the philosophical use of metaphor and analogy that appear prominently in the Confucian classics.[114] Perhaps one or two such metaphors, such as the likening of the virtuous ruler to the pole star in the *Analects*,[115] helped to inspire the idea of correspondence between state and cosmos.

The two explanations outlined thus far for the rise of correlative thought in late-classical China both emphasize trends dating from the Warring States era. A third explanation, which emphasizes not so much the emergence as the institutionalization of correlative cosmology, attributes its florescence in the Former Han to the more immediate ideological demands of the newly formed dynasty. So urgent were these demands that the Han, from the outset, sought to legitimate its rule by identifying itself with the correct correlates in five-phase cosmology. Through the invocation of the "mutual conquest" sequence of the five phases, by which earth (Han) conquers water (Qin), the Han was able to justify its overthrow of the Qin rule and its assumption of power. Once the dynasty was established, imperial ideologists also found it useful to invoke the hierarchical relation of yang to yin and heaven to earth as a way of legitimating various authoritarian political and social relations, such as that of ruler over subject and husband over wife.[116] They paired units of the Han bureaucracy with such cosmic counterparts as astronomical constellations and calendrical periods, as I have noted.

Han cosmologists also used state-cosmos correspondences as checks on Han imperial despotism. Dong Zhong-shu admonished the Son of Heaven to follow the way of virtue (de) as opposed to "punishments" (xing) by correlating the former with yang, summer, life, and growth, and the latter with yin, winter, emptiness, and uselessness.[117] In addition, Han officials invoked the theory of resonance between polity and cosmos to reprove rulers who failed to measure up to Confucian standards. They interpreted such untoward celestial phenomena as comets and eclipses as cosmic simulacra of a ruler's misdeeds.

In sum, both imperial ideology and political criticism in the Han era rested on a world view shaped by correlative cosmology. This facilitated the wide dissemination of correlative modes of thinking among members of the politically engaged Han elite.

The three possible reasons discussed thus far for the rise of correlative thought in China help account for the development of systems of man-cosmos and state-cosmos correspondence, but they do not satisfactorily explain the emergence of more artificial modes based on such numerological orders as the five phases or the figures of the *Change*. It may be that Zou Yan helped to develop the five-phase conception, and that Han imperial ideologists applied it politically. But there is little evidence that either Zou or the major Han imperial ideologists are responsible for the invention of numerological orders in general, or for the formation of systems of correspondence associated with the *Change*. To account for the development of correlative systems *not* based principally on the idea of correspondence between macrocosm and microcosm, another explanation is required. Such an explanation is suggested, though not stated explicitly, in Bernhard Karlgren's classic article, "Legends and Cults in Ancient China."

Karlgren's point of departure is an initially rather rigid distinction between "free pre-Han texts" and the "systematizing texts" of the Han and later eras. The former, as William Boltz remarks, "are wholly independent of other textual records as far as constructing a 'systematic whole' out of the various data," while the latter "are works like the *Shiji* (Records of the Grand Historian) that purport to lay down a consistent and systematic overview based on the data or earlier documents."[118] According to Karlgren, the myths and legends which appear in the "free" texts were recorded by the nobleman writers of the Zhou era in order to buttress the positions of the noble houses supposedly descended from the heroes whose exploits are recounted therein. This explains why the majority of the myths recounted in the free texts are hero legends, or else nature myths that were "hooked on to the hero cults in the grandee families."[119]

But after the demise of many of the old noble families in the conflicts of the third century B.C. and the loss of many of the old free texts during the Qin era, the myths and legends ceased to be part of a living tradition; they were no longer actually celebrated by cult masters attached to the retinues of noble families. To the extent that they survived at all, they were preserved and reconstituted by Han systematizers, who were confronted with the task of piecing together the fragments and "distorted remnants" of the ancient myths and legends. The aim of these systematizers, in any case, "was not simply and faithfully to recount the traditions living in the minds of the cult-masters and nobleman-writers of the Zhou era, but to *work up* the materials, picked out from various texts anterior to their own time—therefore they had to resort to all kinds of amputations, alterations, and additions."[120]

Karlgren seems to have originally adduced this distinction between free and systematizing texts principally as a means of establishing the unreliability of Han documents as sources for the study of Zhou myths. He thus speaks of Zheng Xuan's having "misunderstood and distorted the data handed down from pre-Han times," and of the systematizers' work as a whole as having "nothing to do with the history of early China but only with the history of scholarship in medieval China."[121]

The key point to be considered here, however, is the *manner* in which Han scholastics sought to "work up" the material they gleaned from Zhou texts. Inasmuch as the aim of many of these systematizers was syncretic, to "make a consistent whole of the ancient traditions and ritual ideas," or in Sima Qian's words to "bring fully in accord the differing traditions of the Six Classics and put in order the various sayings of the hundred schools,"[122] their "systematizing" often involved the matching of related items and ideas from diverse classical sources. On the strictly numerological level, for example, Han commentators found it possible to create chains of correspondence based on the number five by simply gleaning different sets of five from various classical sources. Thus they paired the five substances of the "Great Plan" chapter of the *Documents* with the five grains of *Mencius* (bk. 3, pt. 1, chap. 4), the five gods of the *Zuozhuan* (Zhao 29), and the five colors, five tastes, and five musical notes from chapter 12 of the *Laozi*, adding a few quinary sets of their own invention to round out the list.[123] Some of the Han correlative systems based on the figures of the *Change* and its appendices also seem to have been formed in this fashion. For example, the creators of the *najia* system evidently correlated enumerative sets of quite diverse origins, including the eight trigrams from the *Change*, the ten heavenly stems and twelve earthly branches (two sets of chronograms in use from early times), the five phases from the "Great Plan," and the phases of the moon. Later articulators of the system, especially Zheng Xuan and Wei Bo-yang, added numerological sets from such diverse fields as astronomy and alchemy. So serious were Han systematizers in their efforts to thus "work up" the heterogeneous material that survived from the Zhou in order to create a "consistent whole" that they quite frequently resorted to numerological manipulation in order to assimilate odd elements.

Han systematizers also meshed established cosmological ideas drawn from diverse sources. For example, though the terms "yin-yang" and *wuxing* are not matched with one another in any surviving Zhou text (though they were supposed to have been related by Zou Yan), Han syncretists endeavored to integrate them into a system for describing the various phases of cosmic change.[124] In some cases, they accomplished this in a rather mechanical way, as illustrated in the *Baihu Tongyi*'s pairing fire with greater yang, water with greater yin, wood with lesser yang, metal with lesser yin, and earth with the phase in which yin and yang were balanced.[125] The Neo-Confucian cosmologist Zhang Zai (A.D. 1020–1077) proceeded to describe each of the five phases in terms of the various physical states of yin and yang. He characterized water, for example, as "yin congealed yet yang not yet overcome" and fire as "yang resplendent yet yin not yet exhausted."[126] Through such manipulations of lesser systems, in this case those based on yin-yang and the five phases, could be synthesized into more comprehensive schemata.

Han cosmologists were not the only ones to build systems of correspondence to reconcile diverse ideas, texts, and traditions. Buddhist writers of the Six Dynasties era (A.D. 316–589), seeking to facilitate Chinese acceptance of this foreign religion as well as to construct a unified cosmology, devised correlative constructions to accomplish their aims. For example, they paired the Chinese five phases with the Buddhist *mahābhū-tas* (four elements), and the "five constant virtues" (wuchang) of Confucianism with the "five precepts for the behavior of Buddhist lay adherents."[127] Later attempts to integrate Chinese and Indian Buddhist cosmology produced more complex systems of correspondence. An astrological diagram kept in the treasurehouse of the Tōji in Japan, based ultimately on a Tang Buddhist model, juxtaposes such Chinese and Indian astrological series as the twenty-eight lunar lodges, the twelve Indian zodiacal signs, the nine planets of Indian astronomy, and the seven star deities of the Northern Dipper, five of which are associated with the Chinese five phases.[128]

Apart from Han and Buddhist cosmologists, other syncretists in Chinese intellectual history also constructed systems of correspondence in order to reconcile heterogeneous material inherited from diverse traditions. Among the most notable of these are the figures associated with the "Unity of the Three Teachings" (sanjiao heyi) movement in Ming times (1368–1644), as illustrated in Judith Berling's study of Lin Chao-en (1517–1598). As Berling points out, the establishment of correspondences among aspects of the three teachings, Confucianism, Daoism, and Buddhism, was, for Lin, "a pedagogical rather than an analytic device."[129] On the other hand, Han cosmologists, according to Karlgren, really did try to "make a consistent whole of ancient traditions and ritual ideas."[130] They were syncretists by intention as well as by strategy.

The tendency of syncretists to construct systems of correspondence is also evident in the history of Western thought, particularly that of late antiquity and the Renaissance. In their efforts to reconcile, to find a common truth behind, various antique schools of philosophy, Hellenistic thinkers correlated key philosophical terms associated with diverse schools. For example, they paired the Platonic "receptacle" with the Aristotelian "hyle" and the Stoic "substance," and the Platonic Demiurge with the Aristotelian Prime Mover and the Stoic Soul of the Universe.[131] The Hellenistic Jewish historian Josephus went so far as to correlate Jewish religious sects with Greek philosophical schools, the Sadducees with the Epicureans, the Pharisees with the Stoics, and the Essenes with the Pythagoreans.[132] But Renaissance thinkers, including Pico della Mirandola (1463–1494), Robert Fludd (1574–1637), and Athansius Kircher (1602–1680), were far more deliberate in their correlations of supposedly parallel terms, texts, and traditions. Pico, for example, "studiously conflated the cabalistic cosmogony with that of Platonism and Christianity. Thereafter the cabala, the *Timaeus* [of Plato], and the Bible were seen as equal authorities, usually as parallel texts professing the same eternal verities even if in different terms."[133] Although Pico generally presented such correspondences in literary rather than diagrammatic form, other Renaissance syncretists devised charts to illustrate the correlations among terms and ideas drawn from distinct philosophical traditions. Kircher, for example, constructed such a chart for his *Arithmologia* in which three parallel columns illustrate the parallel hierarchies in three distinct realms: the cabala, Christianity, and cosmology.[134]

In sum, Renaissance philosophers, as well as Han cosmologists, devised systems of correspondence as a way of coordinating heterogeneous material. However, the materials thus systematized by Han thinkers consisted generally not of whole philosophical traditions but rather of various numerological orders, mythological fragments, and cosmological terms and ideas found in Zhou literature. The aims of Han commentators also appear to have been more modest than those of the Renaissance syncretists. Whereas Pico sought to accomplish "the intellectual fusion of all knowledge in an abstract scheme of the divine mind,"[135] most major Han commentators appear to have been inspired by the less ambitious design of weaving diverse strands of the classical literary legacy into a consistent whole.

There were a few major Han thinkers who did deliberately attempt to reconcile the teachings of two or more schools of classical philosophy, especially Confucianism and Daoism. But these thinkers did not generally employ systems of correspondence toward this end. They resorted to other strategies, such as simply redefining key philosophical terms from the Confucian and Daoist classics in order to bring the two in accord. For example, Yang Xiong reinterpreted the *Dao* of the classical Daoists in such a way as to harmonize it with the Confucian virtue of *ren* or "humanity."[136]

Thus the construction of correlative systems was only one of several ways in which syncretization and systemization proceeded in the Han and later epochs. Berling's study of Lin Chao-en enumerates five different "syncretizing strategies" used by her subject, "correspondences" being only one among five.[137] Inasmuch as syncretism is one of the chief marks of traditional thought in general,[138] it is hardly surprising that Chinese as well as other premodern thinkers employed such a considerable number of devices to reconcile diverse traditions. On the other hand, Han cosmologists constructed systems of correspondence for purposes other than coordinating related material. Correlative thought cannot be treated as simply one aspect of the problem of syncretism; it was a mode of thinking quite general and pervasive in both Chinese and Western civilizations from late antiquity to nearly the modern age. Hence, it is appropriate to proceed to other possible sources of correlative thought in China. Karlgren reviews one of the earliest of these in his article, "Some Sacrifices in Chou [Zhou] China."

Karlgren, as mentioned before, initially drew quite a rigid distinction between the pre-Han "free texts" and the "systematizing texts" of the Han and later eras. But he later admitted the existence of "early systemization" in Zhou times, concluding that "we can discern that some ideas of this kind may have already existed in the last centuries before the Han."[139] Although Karlgren is vague on what he means by "early systemization," the examples he cites suggest that he is referring to correspondences, albeit primitive ones. He refers, for example, to the *Zuozhuan*'s pairing of the states of China with primeval rulers and astronomical constellations, and to the same text's connecting the "three primeval potentates" with the "five nature-gods."[140] Thus he identifies a few rudimentary correlative designs in pre-Han "free texts." Having done so, Karlgren offers an explanation, which is that these connections were made "in the interest of the religious prestige of some powerful clans." In fact, "the powerful families vied with each other in appropriating the popular gods and attaching them to their ancestral cults," which may help to account for the lack of uniformity in the correlations they devised.[141]

Thus some of the correlative schemata developed by Han cosmologists may have originated from Zhou cult-masters' having paired popular deities, especially nature gods, with their own clan heroes in an effort to increase the prestige of the latter. Such pairings may have been totemic in nature. In any case, Han systematizers who built on their work were apparently unaware of their forbears' motives. They may have even thought their predecessors' primary inspiration was not social or religious, but scholastic or cosmological. In that respect, Han cosmologists would have anticipated structuralist anthropology by some two thousand years.

At least one further dimension of correlative thought remains to be explored—the aesthetic. The aesthetic import of some of the systems of correspondence outlined above, especially the more symmetrical ones, should be obvious. But might some such systems have been created in the first place from aesthetic motives, from a desire to impose (or reveal) a certain symmetry in things?

A possible example of such a system, of which Karlgren has given a classic description, appears in the first few lines of the *Yaodian* (Canon of Yao) chapter of the *Documents Classic.* Here one reads of a "Xi He," a legendary semidivine hero who, so other Zhou texts inform us, was anciently the mother or alternatively the chariot driver of the sun. A later editor of the text evidently split Xi He in two, and gave each resulting pair two younger brothers, thus producing a total of six personages. He then in effect correlated the four younger "Xi"s and "He"s with the four quarters and the primary Xi and He with the time-reckoning principles (and according to later commentators with heaven and earth).[142] In doing this, the editor, as Derk Bodde has observed, "was no doubt motivated by the desire to provide enough brothers to take care of all celestial operations in all quarters of the sky."[143] In other words, the editor's sense of symmetry, his idea that there should be one-to-one correspondence between the divisions of the cosmos and its human (or semidivine) regulators, apparently led him to create this simple correlative schema by multiplying the original Xi He into six. In this case, a prior sense of symmetry seems to have inspired the formulation of a rudimentary system of correspondence, albeit one that is not clearly presented as such in the text in question.

Other instances of correlative schemata being inspired by a sense that there should be a parallel to a given series may be cited. But ideas of symmetry seem to have been more instrumental in rounding out existing correlative sets, as illustrated in Han scholastics' studied efforts to match the five phases with the four seasons. Later savants occasionally based philosophical conclusions on the argument that there must be a certain category of things to round out an otherwise symmetrical pattern. A good example is found in Han Yu's (A.D. 768–824) response to the question of whether ghosts exist:

> There are things that have form but no sound, namely earth and stone. There are things that have sound but no form, namely wind and thunder. There are things that have both form and sound, namely men and beasts. There are things that have neither sound nor form, namely ghosts and spirits.[144]

That is, unless ghosts and spirits exist, the symmetry of the schema would be violated. Since symmetry undergirds the cosmos, such beings must exist.

This quotation manifests a certain linguistic symmetry. The four sentences in the argument (in the original Chinese) are parallel with one another in almost every way. In this and other cases, it seems that the linguistic parallelism of the argument itself constitutes an implicit proof of the proposition. For inasmuch as the basic structure of the cosmos is symmetrical, any cosmological proposition which can be stated in a symmetrical or parallel fashion has a strong claim to truth insofar as the structure of language corresponds with the structure of reality.

The balanced parallelistic style of writing illustrated above seems to have emerged in the same era as correlative cosmology, the late Zhou and Han. For while even the language of the Shang oracle bones manifests a rigid antithetical symmetry, not until the Warring States period is linguistic parallelism in Chinese literature fully elaborated. According to Burton Watson, even a comparison of the language of the *Mencius* with that of the *Xunzi*, composed less than a hundred years later, reveals that in the latter "the sentences are more often cast in balanced, symmetrical forms." In the *Guoyu*, a late-Zhou historical text, a passion for parallelism is sometimes carried to the point where even "two speeches of advice and their wording are made to match and balance each other in a wholly artificial manner."[145]

In ancient Greece as well, a passion for linguistic parallelism seems to have emerged in late classical era. For while the perennial Greek love of symmetry is manifest in so many areas of Greek culture as to have become almost proverbial, the "antithetical style" in prose did not arise until the latter years of the fifth century B.C. According to John Finley, the advent of this style, reflected most dramatically in the debates of Euripides' plays, "marks a generation that saw things by paired opposites, in speeches, paragraphs, sentences, clauses."[146] In sum, the origins of correlative thought can hardly be traced to a single source, the ingenious cogitations of theoretical anthropologists on this subject notwithstanding.

Even the invention and dissemination of writing did not so much inspire the creation of systems of correspondence as it provided a means by which such schemata might be developed and elaborated. On the other hand, none of the sources of correlative cosmology is unique to late-classical China. The syncretic motive evidently inspired complex systems of correspondence in the Hellenistic and Renaissance West. Indeed, at least one or two important motives for the development of correlative systems appear to have arisen in most traditional civilizations, whence the apparent universality of correlative modes of thought. Some of these motives, moreover, such as the allegorical euhemerization of myth in Hellenistic antiquity and the development of the scholastic art of memory in the medieval and Renaissance West, have no readily identifiable Chinese counterpart.

However, the convergence, in Han China, of at least a half-dozen sources of correlative cosmology practically insured that forms of correlative thought would dominate the intellectual history of the era and, perhaps to a lesser degree, that of later epochs as well. Correlative cosmology in China was not just an artifact of Han culture, or merely an aspect of the Han world view. Unlike TLV mirrors, new-text scholarship, and imperial Confucian rites, it did not fade from the intellectual scene with the fall of the Han dynasty, nor did the assimilation of Buddhism or the rise of new forms of Daoism in the post-Han era challenge correlative thought. On the contrary, these developments seem to have spurred its elaboration. In view of the persistence and pervasiveness of correlative thought in medieval Chinese history and culture, it is appropriate to consider a few of its ramifications in the arts, sciences, and popular culture of post-Han China.

LATER RAMIFICATIONS OF CORRELATIVE THOUGHT

It is difficult to think of a major branch of learning in traditional China on which correlative cosmology did not leave a significant imprint. But its most profound influence was on the sciences and pseudosciences, including medicine, alchemy, astronomy, astrology, geomancy, and the divinatory arts in general. So extensive are the ramifications of correlative thought into most of these fields that to thoroughly explore its influence on any one of them would probably require a major study, like Manfred Porkert's work on systems of correspondence in traditional medicine. Here, I confine myself to offering a few examples involving medical, alchemical, and geomantic theory.

In classical Chinese medicine, especially as related in commentaries on the Han medical classic the *Huangdi Neijing* (The Yellow Sovereign's Inner Classic), one of the chief bases of good health was the maintenance of harmony between the pneumas of the body and those of the cosmos as a whole.[147] By contravening cosmic processes, particularly the cycle of the seasons, one risked disease. For example, in order to avoid illness in the yang seasons of spring and summer, one might eat food or engage in activities correlated with the yang. The determination of correspondences in Chinese medicine was, for the adept, much more than an intellectual exercise; it could conceivably be the difference between life and death.

When sickness did arise, a cure might still be effected through medicine intended to remedy the particular excess or deficiency in one's bodily functions that had caused the disease. Here, too, theories of correspondence came into play; according to later Chinese medical theory, the fundamental properties of the medicine prescribed generally had to accord with the bodily pneuma or phase that had to be strengthened, or else to counteract that which was in excess. Thus the proper classification of medicine into a certain number of basic cosmological categories, such as yin and yang, the five phases, and the five flavors, was, theoretically, a necessary preliminary to the cure of any disease. Here again, the proper construction of systems of correspondence was an urgent task, though there was considerable room for disagreement regarding the correct cosmological classification of medical remedies.

Other explanations of health and disease also frequently invoked theories of correspondence. The *Yunqi Lun* (A Discussion of the Revolutions of the Pneumas), for example, posits that seasonal irregularities in the circulation of the cosmic pneumas give rise to corresponding irregularities (=diseases) in human beings. If, for example, the wood pneuma waxes too strongly, then disease will arise in corresponding parts of the body, including the liver and the spleen. In such a case, one would presumably take medicine to counteract changes in the environment rather than to harmonize oneself with them.[148]

In alchemy, as in classical medicine, correlative systems were generally based on the idea of correspondence between macrocosm and microcosm. However, cosmologically oriented alchemists regarded not only the human body but also their materials, equipment, and even procedures, including the chemicals, the furnace, the reaction vessel, and the control of time and temperature as in some sense microcosmic. An eighth-century illustration of an alchemical furnace described by Nathan Sivin depicts "three tiers, which correspond to sky and earth and man centered between them. The central tier has twelve doors, which correspond to the hours in the day and months in the year." In such ways did alchemists seek to "be sure that what went on within their reaction vessels was identical with the work of nature."[149]

In "inner alchemy," in which the human body served as the reaction vessel, the correspondences between macrocosm and microcosm were drawn out even more meticulously. As Judith Berling explains, the body "was a small-scale model of the universe in which all forces of nature were present, homologous to the cosmic laboratory."[150] In one mode of inner alchemy described by Henri Maspero, the interior gods who reside in the body simultaneously presided over heavenly administration. Moreover, "for the identity to be perfect, the gods who preside over the various parts of the one preside at the same time over the corresponding parts of the other."[151] The entire celestial administration, in other words, was duplicated in the body of the adept.

So thoroughly imbued was alchemy with the correlative mode of thought that it was the correlative science par excellence in traditional China as well as in medieval Islam and Renaissance Europe—as indeed it should have been in view of its highly syncretic character.[152] Even the language of alchemy, its technical terminology, was correlative in that it was intended to describe events on a number of different levels at once. For example, a given alchemical text might be read as a description of labora- tory operations, of cosmological processes, of sexual or yogic disciplines, of spiritual cultivation or religious redemption. As Sivin notes, "The alche- mists' world of meaning, unlike that of the modern chemist, united every aspect of experience—empirical, sensual, symbolic, esthetic—in a single whole."[153] Aside from allowing the writer to pack multiple levels of signifi- cance into a composition, correlative use of language also made it possible for him to render his art more respectable by interpreting the great philosophers as secret alchemists. Alchemical writers frequently used key terms drawn from classical philosophy, such as "Great Ultimate" (taiji) and "Great Void" (taixu), in their own technical vocabulary.

Of the various divinatory sciences in which correlative cosmology figured prominently, geomancy, the art of determining auspicious sites for buildings and burials, was among the most widely practiced in late-traditional China. Indeed, this art may well have served as one of the principal conduits through which correlative thought was channeled from high Chinese culture to folk culture, though generally only the wealthy could afford to hire professional geomancers. Geomantic theory was, as Steven Bennett has remarked, quite fluid and diverse, but most geomantic conceptions were based ultimately upon some form of correlative thought. Correspondence between man and landscape, for example, is the subject of a key passage form the *Yellow Sovereign's Site Classic* (Huangdi Zhai Jing) translated by Steven Bennett as follows: "The forms and configurations are considered to be the body; water and underground springs are the blood and veins; the earth is the skin; foliage is the hair; dwellings are the clothes; door and gate are the hat and belt."[154]

Other levels of correspondence also figured in geomantic theory. Geomancers, in evaluating a site, sometimes based their judgments on the idea that the land forms enveloping a good location should resemble celestial patterns, such as constellations. Celestial-terrestrial correspondence was also expressed in the pairing of specific topographical forms with particular planets in the heavens. Finally, the shapes of mountains, an especially important factor in geomantic reckoning, were sometimes correlated with the five phases.[155]

In fact, most major modes of correlative cosmology influenced geomantic theory. The geomancer's compass, which incorporated as many as thirty-eight circles of symbol sets, including the trigrams and hexagrams of the *Change*, the ten heavenly stems and the twelve earthly branches, the five phases, yin and yang, the twenty-eight lunar lodges, the twenty-four solar periods, and the four seasons and directions,[156] is a good emblem of the cosmological comprehensiveness of geomancy in traditional China. Whatever its empirical origins may have been, geomancy later became in essence cosmology applied to the study of land forms and to the art of siting buildings and burials.[157]

Correlative cosmology in some form furnished the theoretical foundations of most of the sciences and pseudosciences. However, correlative thought also influenced almost every field of learning cultivated in premodern China. Even unimpeachably orthodox studies that were generally monopolized by the Confucian elite, such as historiography, literary criticism, moral philosophy, and law, were informed by correlative modes of thinking.

The influence of correlative thought on literary criticism in China may be traced at least as far back as the classic work on the subject by Liu Xie (c. A.D. 465–523), *The Literary Mind and the Carving of Dragons* (Wenxin Diaolong). In several chapters of this treatise, Liu emphasizes that inner and outer realities, mind and cosmos, and language and reality must correspond in order for literary creation to take place. He observes that in literature "What is manifest and what is within always tally with each other. Is this not the enduring property of nature and the general principle of talent and spirit?"[158] From this and other such passages, Pauline Yu concludes that "the notion of correspondences pervades Liu Xie's entire work, whose 'anatomy' of literature posits a number of organic relationships among universe, writer, language, and literary work, and within the work as well."[159]

Correlative thought also influenced poetry, especially poetic metaphor. Of course, metaphor in general correlates two or more entities in some significant way, facilitating "the transfer of meaning from one level to another."[160] In modern poetry, however, such correspondences tend to be creations of the individual poet's imagination. Only rarely are they ciphers of a unified world view. Indeed, it is difficult to think of a major English poet after the seventeenth century whose metaphors were expressions of a *shared* sense of the cosmos, though such Romantic poets as Wordsworth attempted to recreate such a unity.

In ancient poetry as well, the use of simile and metaphor rarely reflects any system of cosmological correspondence. The *Song Classic*, to be sure, does adduce metaphorical comparisons between human and natural figures, for example likening a new bride to a peach tree in bloom. And Homer's long similes likewise compare varied human and natural objects—troops and bees, and words and snowflakes. But there is little evidence that his similes were originally intended to be understood in the context of a general theory of correspondence between macrocosm and microcosm.[161]

Postclassical poets, however, frequently did employ metaphors based upon such a theory. Some even composed entire poems which are almost wholly concerned with systematically relating macrocosm and microcosm. Thus a Spanish poem by Antonio Mira de Mecusa (d. 1644) depicts "a beautiful landscape as a replica or reflection of Heaven"; and a number of poems by a popular Vietnamese poetess of the eighteenth century, Ho Xuan Huong, describing landscapes and favorite scenic places, are apparently intended to be read as depictions of "male and female anatomy, and intercourse between men and women."[162]

Even where postclassical poets did not devote whole compositions to systematically evoking correspondences, the metaphors they used were often based on the cosmologically commonplace. Thus Sir Edward Dyer (1550?–1607) wrote, in the opening lines of a famous poem, that "My mind to me a kingdom is." And Han Yu linked man and cosmos by recalling that "When I was young my spirit truly wild, / Purposely competing with spring."[163] Such comparisons as mind/kingdom and youth/spring might quite easily appear in modern poetry as well, but with Dyer and Han Yu, such metaphors evidently were not simply poetic fictions. Inasmuch as they were grounded in medieval systems of correspondence, they were intended to be cosmologically descriptive. Even such a hackneyed metaphor as that linking youth with spring might well, for the medieval reader, have called to mind an entire system matching the ages of man with the seasons of the year,[164] and might have led him to reflect on the general correspondence between man and cosmos.

The modern reader, lacking the "double sight" of the Elizabethans[165] or Tang Chinese, is much less apt to regard such a metaphor in the context of a larger cosmology. The modern, moreover, is inclined to view metaphor in general as a product of the imagination. Hence, the modern must have images that are "original," "striking," or "imaginative." Were our minds, like that of Sir Edward Dyer, truly like kingdoms, then we could enrich almost any metaphor, no matter how commonplace, by simply relating it to the order to which it belonged.

Other orthodox Confucian intellectual pursuits in traditional China which were influenced by correlative thought include historiography, law, and even political economy. The tables in the standard histories of China frequently classify men or events under a number of fixed categories on the assumption that every subject must correspond to one of the headings. The best-known example of this type of generic classification in the standard histories is probably the "Table of Ancient and Modern Men" (Gujinren Biao) in the twentieth chapter of the *Han Shu* (Han History). In this table, Derk Bodde notes, 1,955 personages in early Chinese history are "classified under nine different categories, according to the compiler's opinion of their moral and intellectual worth."[166] While this table might well be regarded as an example of categorical rather than correlative thinking, it still appears to be based on a metaphysical belief in the essential correspondence of microcosm and macrocosm, in this case of individual men and the moral qualities believed to inhere in the cosmos. Like the hexagrams of the *Classic of Change*, the various categories heading the table, under which the individuals are classified, were supposed to be quite exhaustive, including all possibilities.

The influence of correlative cosmology on law, especially in the application of the principle of requital and the seasonal scheduling of punishments, is generally recognized.[167] It is not so widely known, however, that five-phase and celestial-terrestrial correspondences informed even the economic theory of such a hard-headed "realist" as Sang Hong-yang (152-80 B.C.). According to Sang, since the products of each of the four quarters (and center) are dominated by their corresponding elements (e.g., wood in the east and metal in the west), then raw materials of the earth as a whole are unevenly distributed. Earth, in this respect, is unlike heaven, which is undifferentiated and universal. The role of the merchant is to distribute more evenly the wealth of the earth, which is differentiated, can be made to correspond with heaven, which is truly universal.[168]

The ramifications of correlative thought into the popular culture of traditional China cannot be so easily documented as its influence on orthodox Confucian studies. Still, it is likely that even illiterate Chinese were acquainted with the rudiments of correlative cosmology through such media as the more popular divinatory arts, including geomancy, chronomancy, glyphomancy, physiognomy, and horoscopic astrology. As C.K. Yang has pointed out, the most widely sold books in late-traditional China were the ubiquitous almanacs (lishu),[169] chronomantic handbooks which correlated specific activities such as weddings and funerals with the times in which they should be performed. Popular medical beliefs and practices, as well as the arts of divination, were frequently based on forms of correlative thought, though seldom on the meticulously drawn systems of correspondence that appear in high-classical medical theory.[170] Correlative cosmology even influenced the ways in which food was prepared and consumed at all social levels.[171] For ideas of proper nutrition and good taste in traditional Chinese cuisine were generally based on the conception that particular foods corresponded with certain cosmological categories, such as yin and yang and the five flavors. Unless the foods correlated with the categories were set off or blended properly, the fare might be unhealthful, unpalatable, or both.

While correlative cosmology thus influences such common activities as preparing food and medicine, divining the future, contracting a marriage, appealing to gods, ghosts, and ancestors, and siting a grave, it is unlikely that the complicated systems formulated by Han and Song cosmologists permeated popular culture. First, these elaborate correlative schemata could hardly have been comprehended by those unable to interpret lists, charts, and tables. Second, cosmologists of the Han and later epochs apparently went beyond codifying widely accepted correlative relationships. Their general world view permeated nearly every level of culture, elite and popular. But like the illiterate astrologers and diviners of Madagascan tribes examined by anthropologists, Chinese cosmologists sometimes went "out of their way to complicate their maneuvers in order to increase the possibilities of associations, while retaining a certain uniformity of principles and method." [172] Post-Han cosmologists, particularly those figures of the Song-era (960–1279) like Shao Yong, were especially adept at elaborating commonly accepted correspondences in such odd and complex ways as might well have mystified even literate temple diviners, to say nothing of literate peasants. [173]

CORRELATIVE THOUGHT
IN TRADITIONAL WESTERN CIVILIZATIONS

The general influence of correlative cosmology on various aspects of Chinese culture was so profound and pervasive that some observers have interpreted it as a peculiarly Chinese phenomenon. Indeed, correlative modes of thought seem to have dominated intellectual life in traditional China more than in most civilizations. Yet systems of cosmological correspondence were at least as highly developed, though perhaps not so universally applied, in ancient, medieval, and Renaissance Europe, as well as in medieval Islamic culture. [174]

Antecedents of correlative thought appear in the oldest extant works of European literature, the *Iliad* and the *Odyssey*, chiefly in the thoroughly anthropomorphic picture that these poems present of the divine world. Of course, anthropomorphic representations of divine beings and natural phenomena are quite common in primitive religion and mythology. But in the poems of Homer as Moses Finley has noted, "The whole of heroic society was reproduced on Olympus in its complexities and its shadings." [175] In this respect, the *Iliad* and the *Odyssey* might be very roughly compared to the Shang oracle bones which depict a supernatural world modeled closely on the structure of the Shang administration.

The Homeric poems do not, however, outline cosmological correspondences between any two orders of reality. The first traces of these in Greek literature appear in surviving fragments of the Presocratics. In Empedocles (c. 492–432 B.C.), there is "a hint of the theory of humors and of the doctrine of correspondence between the elements of physical nature and those of the human body." [176] Although such systems of correspondence seem to have first become established in Greek medicine, Plato proceeded to apply correlative schemata in his political and moral philosophy, albeit without making these the major point of his discourse. In the *Republic*, for example, Plato recounts "the division of the soul enters into three parts, corresponding to the three orders in the state. Each part seems . . . to have its own form of pleasure and its peculiar desire; and any one of the three may govern the soul." Where the appetitive soul, for example, is supreme, then the lovers of gain will predominate and the form of the state will be despotic. Such correspondences, Plato argues, must hold true, since "Constitutions cannot come out of stocks and stones; they must result from the preponderance of certain characters in their wake. So if there are five forms of government, there must be five kind of mental constitution among individuals."[177]

The philosophers of fifth- and fourth-century Greece thus outlined rudimentary correlative schemes based on a belief in the essential congruence of two or more orders of reality. But cosmological systems of correspondence were not fully elaborated or widely applied and did not become the center of intellectual attention, until the Hellenistic Age, a period very roughly contemporaneous with the Former Han era in China. Stoics and Neoplatonists, in particular, developed such systems both to establish a theory of correspondence between macrocosm and microcosm and to syncretize various antique schools of philosophy. Hellenistic commentators also proceeded to reinterpret works of classical literature in allegorical terms based ultimately on correlative cosmology. The Stoic philosopher Crates of Mallos characterized the shield of Agamemnon as an "imitation of the cosmos," and further interpreted the ten parts of the shield of Achilles (*Illiad*, bk. 18) as emblems of the ten circles of the sky.[178] The third-century Neoplanonist Porphyry read the Homeric Cave of Nymphs (*Odyssey*, bk. 13) as an allegory of the mixture of the four elements.[179] Finally, Hellenistic scientists applied correlative cosmology in a much more systematic manner than did their classical predecessors. Galen (A.D. 129–199?) grounded his physiology on correspondences, matching the four elements with the four humors, and the three main faculties of the soul (rational, spiritual, and appetitive) with the three major organs of the body (brain, heart, and liver).[180]

Medieval Islamic thinkers further developed systems of correspondence, especially numerological ones. For example, Islamic-medical cosmologists correlated the seven cervical and twelve dorsal vertebrae of the human body with the seven planets and twelve zodiacal signs of the heavens, as well as with the seven days of the week and twelve months of the year, thus meshing the measures of the human body with those of astronomical space and calendrical time. They also paired the twenty-eight discs thought to be in the vertebrae with the twenty-eight letters of the

Arabic alphabet and the twenty-eight stations of the moon.[181]

It was in the Renaissance, however, the syncretic age par excellence in the history of Western civilizations, that correlative cosmology was developed most imaginatively and to its highest degree of complexity. To list the items in the complicated systems of correspondence constructed by Renaissance cosmologists would be quite tedious. Indeed, S.K. Heninger remarks that Robert Fludd's depiction of the human body as a microcosm of atmospheric phenomena "is so full of information that a prose transcription of the data extends to several pages. And even then it is doubtful that the verbal paraphrase achieves either the intensity or the fullness of the visual image."[182]

The last point raises an important feature of Renaissance systems of correspondence, that they were frequently depicted in pictorial form. Moreover, the Western cosmographical imagination in general seems to have been much more picturesque than the Chinese. There do exist figurative representations of Chinese correlative systems, such as the diagrams attached to many later commentaries on the *Classic of Change*. But these figures, whatever philosophical profundity may be read into them, pale beside the artistry, complexity, and sheer picturesqueness of Renaissance cosmological diagrams.

One possible reason is that Renaissance cosmological schemata were often devised as memory systems. The images in such systems, the corporeal similitudes," were supposed to engrave on the memory impressions of the higher spiritual intentions to which they corresponded. But in order for such imprinting to work, the memory images had to be striking. It was best the "they should have ridiculous movements, amazing gestures, or be filled with overpowering sadness or severity.[183]

A second peculiarity of Renaissance European correlative systems is that they were more varied numerologically than were their Chinese counterparts. Even individual Renaissance cosmologists were often eclectic in their numerological preferences. Cornelius Agrippa (1486–1535), for example, based most of the schemata presented in his *Three Books of Occult Philosophy* on the number four, but he also occasionally used twelve, "an unusually adaptable number in cosmic speculation—as Agrippa says, 'that whereby the Celestials are measured.'"[184] Numerological systems based on three, seven, and nine, among others, were also quite common in the Renaissance. In postclassical China, individual cosmologists rarely used more than one base number in their schemata. Yang Xiong built his system on three and its multiples, Shao Yong based his on four, and Sima Guang opted for ten. Generally speaking, however, systems of correspondence based on the five phases predominated in China from the Han era, much more so than did those based on the four elements in the West. This postclassical Chinese tendency to enumerate things in fives seems to have inclined some scholars to think that the chief object of investigation in studies of traditional Chinese cosmology should be yin-yang and *wuxing*, rather than correlative thought or systems of correspondence.

A final peculiarity of Renaissance European correlative systems, considered from the perspective of traditional Chinese cosmology, is that various planes of correspondence were frequently arranged hierarchically. Inasmuch as the different orders of reality, such as the mineral, the vegetable, the animal, the human, and the angelic, or again the terrestrial, the celestial, and the supercelestial, were ordered in a graded series, the matching entities on each plane were as links in a chain which connected the lower realms of existence with the higher. This idea is perhaps best explained by a passage from the "Second Proem" of Pico della Mirandola's *Heptaplus*:

> Truly, whatever is in the lower world is also in the higher ones, but of better stamp; likewise, whatever is in the higher ones is also seen in the lowest, but adulterated. In our world there is the elemental quality of heat, in the heavens there is a heating power, and in angelic minds there is the idea of heat. I shall speak more precisely: among us there is the fire which is an element; the sun is fire in the sky; in the ultramundane region fire is the seraphic intellect. But see how they differ. The elemental fire burns, the celestial fire gives life, and the supercelestial loves.[185]

Few Chinese cosmologists arranged correlative sets in such an explicitly hierarchal fashion. For most of them, mundane fire was not necessarily any less elevated or real than was its simulacrum in the heavens, the planet Mars. Chinese schemata, from a Western viewpoint, might seem to be arranged in a random way. For why, a Western cosmologist might well have asked, draw correspondences in the first place if one did not order them hierarchically, so as to lead the mind from earth to heaven, from the shadowy to the real? As Saint Bonaventure (1221–1274) declared, the "creatures of this sensible world" are but "shadows, echoes, and pictures, the traces, simulacra, and reflections of that First Principle, most powerful, wisest, and best."[186]

So strong was the influence of Neoplatonic metaphysics and Christian redemptorism on Western correlative thought that the notion of an ordered hierarchy, a chain of being, seems inextricable from the systems of correspondence drawn by medieval and Renaissance cosmologists. A study of Chinese or even early Western cosmology, however, should demonstrate that the various orders linked by systems of correspondence need not be conceived as graded in a hierarchical fashion. The notion of hierarchy seems to be absent even in some Western medieval and Renaissance systems. Further, forms of correlative thought survived in Western culture long after the weak links in the chain of being were snapped in the seventeenth century. I shall return to this in later chapters. First, however, I will outline, in the next chapter, the early history of another major aspect of traditional Chinese cosmology, geometrical cosmography.

Chapter Two

Geometric Cosmography
in Early China

Unlike correlative thought, geometric cosmography in China was concerned mainly with the division of space, celestial and terrestrial, civic and agrarian, and ceremonial and secular, into regular rectilinear units. But the idea of systematic correspondences between two or more orders of reality, an essential of correlative cosmology, also figured in most modes of schematic cosmography, most conspicuously in the *fenye* or "field allocation" astrological system and in the structure of the imperial cosmological temple called the Ming Tang or "Luminous Hall." Correlative thinkers and geometrical cosmographers of the late Zhou and Han periods shared other general orientations and concerns. Both maintained that the basic structure of the cosmos was marked by a general regularity, symmetry, and congruence among its various parts. They also shared an animus against any anomaly, any odd element that might unbalance cosmic symmetry. Correlative thought and geometrical cosmography may be regarded as expression of a single world view that assumed its classical form in China in the late Zhou and former Han eras.

ORIGINS OF GEOMETRICAL AND NONARY COSMOGRAPHY

The remote origins of geometric cosmography, the ordering of various types of space on the model of forms that are both geometrically regular and cosmologically significant, may be traced to the highest antiquity in both Chinese and Western civilizations. As archeologists have discovered, the city plans and temple and palace complexes of some of the most ancient civilizations manifest a pronounced symmetry. Egyptian architects, for example, constructed temple complexes on the model of regular polygons inscribed within circles.[1] And Shang Chinese "domiciles, palaces, temples, and tombs," according to K.C. Chang, "were invariably square or oblong, governed in orientation by the four cardinal directions and dominated in design by a persistent attempt at symmetry."[2] However, the cosmological explanation for such structures was not developed, or recorded, until centuries later. This fact has led some scholars to argue that practical concerns, and not cosmographical ideas, initially shaped some of the models.[3]

In both Chinese and Western civilizations, the earliest notable theoretical expositions of geometrical cosmography appeared nearly contemporaneously with correlative thought, though somewhat earlier in Greece than in China. But in Greece, the most popular cosmographical pattern was not rectilinear but circular. The Platonic and Aristotelian dicta on the ideality of circular motion, especially in astronomy, are perhaps the best-known expressions of this preference. Plato's *Timaeus* describes the universe as "a circle moving in a circle"; and Aristotle's *De Caelo* proceeds from the assumption that "circular motion is necessarily primary. For the perfect is naturally prior to the imperfect, and the circle is a perfect thing."[4] Partly on account of these dicta, the central problem of Greek astronomy was the assimilation of the apparent irregularities of planetary motion to uniform circular motion.[5] Plato, moreover, favored circular forms not only in his cosmography but also in the more mundane field of city planning.[6] The Presocratic philosopher Empedocles went so far as to characterize God as "a rounded Sphere enjoying a circular solitude."[7]

In medieval astronomy, cosmography, theology, and art, the circle continue to be regarded as the ideal form, as is illustrated by such variegated sources as the rose windows of cathedrals, the depiction of Jerusalem on medieval maps, medieval diagrams of the planetary system, and the cosmography of Dante's *Divine Comedy*. In the Renaissance as well, leading thinkers declared that the circle informed the basic structure of various levels of reality. Pico della Mirandola wrote that "Heaven is a circle, and the soul is also a circle . . . Heaven moves in an orbit; a rational soul, going from causes to effects and returning again from effects to causes, revolves through an orbit of reasoning."[8] Not until the sixteenth and seventeenth centuries did artists, cosmographers, and astronomers in the European West begin to favor less regular forms, especially ellipsoids.

The circle, so pivotal in the history of Western cosmography from classical Greece to the Renaissance, appears occasionally in East Asian cosmographical designs as well, particularly Buddhist mandalas, Han-era

TLV mirrors, and some of the diagrams associated with the *Classic of Change.* But the dominant geometrical forms in the history of Chinese cosmography were rectilinear. Even the designs on some of the Neolithic pots unearthed at Banpo are rectilinear, "consisting of parallel bands or lozenges containing concentric squares, crosses, or diamonds."[9] The people of the Shang, the earliest Chinese civilization, evidently embraced rectilinear symmetry in political cosmography as well as in architecture.[10] Shang hieratic art also inclines toward rectilinear symmetry, marked as it is by "the imposition of abstract, balanced, geometrical patterns over entire surfaces."[11]

Thus the broad outlines of later cosmographical ideas may be traced back to the beginnings of Chinese history. In particular, the well-known statement in the *Huainanzi* and other Han sources that the earth is square[12] seems to reflect a conception already intimated in the divination records of a thousand years earlier. But by the second century B.C., the square was so firmly anchored in Chinese cosmography that it came to be regarded not only as the form in which the world was cast but as constitutive of space in general. In the words of Marcel Granet, Han cosmologists believed that "every surface . . . is in itself square." According to Granet's interpretation of a passage from the *Shanhai Jing* (Classic of Mountains and Seas), even the area illuminated by a torch was measured as a square.[13]

Cosmologists in late classical China customarily divided the cosmographical squares used for the arrangement of various types of space into nine equal squares, thus producing grids of 3 × 3. Scholars have proposed various theories to explain the rise of this nonary form in Chinese cosmographical thought. One of these theories attributes the invention of nonary cosmography in China to Zou Yan (305–240 B.C.?). Another explanation, not necessarily incompatible with the first, suggests that the various geographical models constructed of blocks of nine units, including the nine parcels of the well field, "all seem to have been conceived in a determined effort to apply to the greater world the plan of the simple magic square of three."[14] The economy of this theory, as stated by Schuyler Camman, is attractive, particularly in view of the wide diffusion of the magic square of three in many old world civilizations. But its advocates must face the difficulty that while this form is first described in the *Dadai Liji* (The Elder Dai's Record of Rites), a text compiled in the first century B.C., traces of nonary cosmography appear in the texts dating from no later than the fourth century B.C. In the "Yu Gong" (Tribute of Yu) chapter of the

Documents Classic, for example, the realm is divided into nine provinces, though that text does not depict these units as squares. The *Mencius* indicates that the ideal agrarian regime supposedly formulated by the sage rulers of high antiquity, the well-field system, was also divided into nine units.[15]

Further, quite a wide range of Zhou and early Han texts enumerate various items, particularly geographical features, by nines. The "Yu Gong" refers to the nine rivers, nine marshes, nine mountains, and the nine branches of the Yellow River, as well as to the nine provinces of the realm. The *Lüshi Chunqiu* and the *Huainanzi* identify nine mountains, nine marshes, nine strategic points of the mountains, and nine fields of the heavens.[16] The *Zhouli* (Rites of Zhou) applies a nonary schema to the construction of the ideal capital city, furnishing it with nine latitudinal and nine meridional avenues, and measuring it by nine *li* on each side. That text proceeds to measure out the units of the Zhou bureaucracy by nines, declaring it to be divided into nine sections, each headed by a minister of state.[17] The Han medical classic the *Huangdi Neijing Suwen* (Plain Questions of the Yellow Sovereign's Inner Classic) extended nonary numerology into the range of human anatomy, mentioning the nine orifices, the nine viscera, and the nine divisions of the human body.[18] Perhaps the most comprehensive single list of items enumerated by nines, thirty to be exact, is the one which appears in the *Hongfan Huangji* (Supreme Ultimate of the Great Plan) by the Song era cosmologist Cai Chen.[19] Thus nine became, next to five, the most important number in Chinese cosmological theory and numerological speculations.

The number nine was especially important in cosmography. Most of the major traditional cosmograms, including the "well field" (jingtian), the "field allocation"(fenyeh) astrological system, the imperial cosmological temple know as the "Ming Tang" (Luminous Hall), the enigmatic Luoshu "Luo River Writing" (Luoshu), and even some Buddhist mandalas were checkered, ideally, into nine cells. As stated previously, this special use of nine could, perhaps, be satisfactorily explained through the magic square hypothesis or though the influence of Zou Yan were it not for the fact that the beginnings of nonary cosmography in China predate the appearance of either Zhou Yan or the magic square. On the other hand, it is possible that Zou Yan's schematic cosmography promoted the extension of nonary divisions in Han geographical thought, and that the invention of the magic square of three inspired the reinterpretation of such figures as the Ming

Tang and the Luoshu along the 3 × 3 grid. Finally, the nonary division of the square was especially attractive to centripetalist ideologists; it produced one central unit to which superior cosmological qualities could be attached. Late-Zhou and Han writers endowed the central square of almost all the nonary cosmograms mentioned above with some special status. This and other aspects of the late-classical transformation of numerology into geometrical cosmography might, however, be better understood through an examination of the specific figures so transformed, beginning with the earliest and most famous, the well field.

THE WELL-FIELD SYSTEM

Inasmuch as the well-field schema is the simplest and most widely recognized of all classical cosmograms, its early development may be very briefly recounted,. The name "well field" refers to the fact that the ideal shape of the boundaries for dividing agricultural land in this schema resembles the Chinese character for "well" (jing), a rough approximation of the 3 × 3 grid. In its classical form, the system involved measuring land into square blocks one *li* to a side and marking off each of these blocks into nine equal lots which were also squares. But if several modern commentators on the early history of the well field are correct, the arrangement originally had no particular geometrical form. Wu Ch'i-ch'iang, for example, concluded from his study of the schema that its units "were lacking definite boundaries and units of calculation for land."[20] According to Hsü Cho-yun, the well-field arrangement at first was not a mensural scheme at all, but "something like a manorial system, under which the peasant was merely a manorial dependent."[21] Wolfram Eberhard also pictures the original system in socioeconomic terms. He speculates that the nine units that appear in the classical version of the system were in ancient times only scattered clearings made by the inhabitants of fortress communities at the beginning of spring when they ventured out of their winter retreats. Eight out of every nine of these clearings, according to Eberhard, were supposed to be cultivated by individual families, and the ninth cultivated in common for the sustenance of those left behind in the fortress community.[22]

Whatever the primeval character of the well-field arrangement may have been, the earliest notices of the system, those that appear in the classical *Zhouli* and *Mencius*, depict the fields as regularly shaped and spaced.[23] Paul Wheatley suggests that this geometrical reformation of the well field, the earliest stages of which are reflected in the classics, was

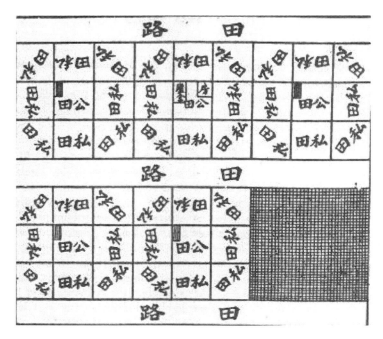

Figure 3. A diagram of the ideal geometrical form of the well-field arrangement, showing five such blocks of nine fields each. In the center of each block is the "public field," each of which is ringed by eight "private fields." Source: Yen Yuan, *Cunzhi Bian*, in Yen's *Ssu-ts'u pien* (Taipei: Shijie Shuju, 1966), p. 113.

completed by "systematizing editors" seeking to satisfy the demands of regularity.[24] If the generally accepted dates for the *Mencius* and the *Zhouli* are correct, this geometrical schematization probably began in the Warring States epoch in a period roughly contemporaneous with the rise of correlative thought. It would then have been consummated in the Han period in such works as the *Gongyang Zhuan* (Gongyang Chronicle) and the *Guliang Zhuan* (Guliang Chronicle), both commentaries on the *Spring and Autumn Annals*.

This hypostatization having been accomplished, classical commentators and political reformers of later ages repeatedly proposed actually measuring and allocating the land of the realm according to the geometrical version of the well-field arrangement. Following the *Mencius*, the more utopian among them generally argued that the central square of each nonary set, the "public field" (gongtian), be cultivated in common for the benefit of the state. However, as Xu Zhong-shu points out, "those in Chinese history who advocated the application of the allotment principle, such as Wang Mang (9–24 A.D.), the Northern Wei dynasty (386–535), and the Taiping regime (1850–1864) either failed in the attempt or did not actually apply it, or did it only for temporary and specific purposes."[25]

THE NINE PROVINCES

A second nonary geographical schema, also apparently geometricized by commentators of the late-classical era, was the pattern of the "nine provinces" (jiuzhou) in the "Yu Gong" chapter of the *Documents*. It reveals the boundaries of the original provinces of China, said to have been surveyed by Yu the Great, as very uneven, marked by such natural physical features as mountains and rivers. A later interpretation of the *zhou* as "the habitable places [or islands] in the midst of the waters" that were supposed to have once flooded China[26] also implies that its boundaries (or shores) were not staked out according to any cosmographical model. There is in fact no indication, in any extant pre-Han source, of the *jiuzhou* having been conceived along geometrical lines.

The late-Zhou philosopher Zou Yan, however, according to Han historians, did build a numerological cosmography on the basis of the classical *jiuzhou*. Zou held that these nine regions which comprised China, the Middle Country, occupied only one-ninth of the Red Continent which in turn constituted one-ninth of total land area in the world.[27] Although no Han source suggests that Zou conceived any of these units on geometrical lines, a modern scholar, Schuyler Cammann, has speculated that Zou may have known of the magic square of eighty-one cells (the "Giant Luoshu") "and was inspired thereby to suggest his eighty-one divisions of the world."[28]

Several Han cosmologists and commentators, while not necessarily picturing the *jiuzhou* in the form of the 3 × 3 grid, did proceed to geometrize its outer boundaries. Both the *Huainanzi* and the "Wang Zhi" (Royal Institutions) chapter of the *Liji* indicate that the nine provinces as a whole formed a square.[29] The *Zhouli* depicts the units of a related schema, the "nine domains" (jiufu), as concentric squares centered on the capital of the royal realm rather than as arrayed in the 3 × 3 grid.[30] By conflating these "nine domains" with the classical nine provinces in his commentary, on this particular passage in the *Zhouli*, the great Han scholiast Zheng Xuan (A.D. 127–200) facilitated the geometrization of the *jiuzhou*.

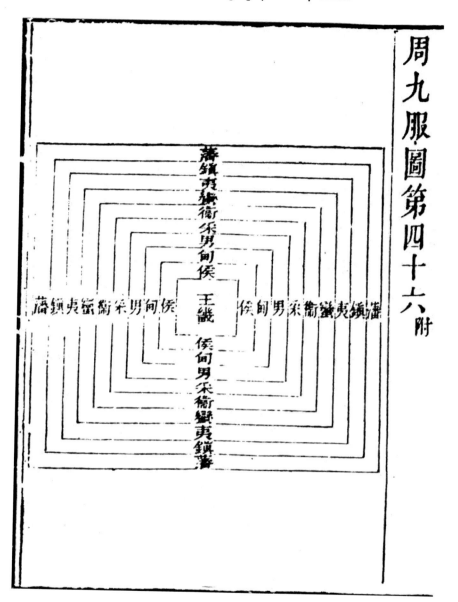

Figure 4. A diagram of the "nine domains of the Zhou," all of which are centered on the "area of the royal capital" which occupies the center square. According to this arrangement, the degree of barbarism icreases with the square of the distance from the center. Source: Hu Wi, *Yugong Zhuizhi* (Taipei: Guangxue reprint, 1975) B. 136.

However fanciful the geometrized versions of the *jiuzhou* and *jiufu* might appear to be, reformers in Chinese and Japanese history occasionally proposed reconstituting the boundaries of administrative districts, as well as of agricultural plots, along regular geometrical lines. Even as late as 1871 in Japan, "an effort was made to actualize local administration by dividing the entire country into large squares of uniform size called *ku*."[31] Almost three decades later, the prominent Confucian reformer Kang Yu-wei (1858–1927) proposed the eventual establishment of a similar administrative scheme in China, the boundaries of his proposed districts being: "fixed arbitrarily on the basis of square degrees of longitude and latitude."[32] Although the Japanese experiment was quickly abandoned and Kang's suggestion never implemented, the appearance of such proposals as late as the nineteenth century indicates the degree to which the political geometry formulated in late-classical China continued to be regarded as a source of solutions to administrative problems. By contrast, analogous ideas proposed by philosophers in Western antiquity, such as Plato's dictum that 5,040 constituted the ideal number of citizens per unit in the just society,[33] were rarely, if ever, taken seriously by those in power, much less implemented.

THE FIELD-ALLOCATION SYSTEM

The nine-province schema, though not necessarily the geometrical version, served as a cornerstone for a third classical cosmographical order, the "field-allocation system" (fenye). The *fenye* was not inextricably tied to the nine provinces. In its mature form it was based on the idea of a general astrological correspondence between sectors of the heavens and territories of the earth. Although the nature of the celestial and terrestrial units thus paired varied considerably, the idea of "field allocation" was implicit in any schema which linked significant movements in a given "field" of the heavens with noteworthy events in a corresponding (or "allocated") earthly region. A simple example of *fenye* verification, drawn from the "Treatise on the Five Phases" (Wuxing Zhi) of the *Han History* (Han Shu) is as follows:

> In the fifth month of the first year of the Yuan-feng period [110 B.C.], there was a comet in the Eastern Well asterism, and also a comet in the Triple Terrace asterism. Afterwards, Jiang Chong rebelled, and the capital was in chaos. This illustrates that the Eastern Well and Triple Terrace asterisms are the [celestial] counterparts of the territory of Qin.[34]

This idea of resonance between heavenly and earthly territories was by no means uniquely Chinese. The ancient Babylonians devised a similar system, though one not nearly so highly developed or finely articulated as the Chinese. Even Ptolemy linked the divisions of the inhabited world with signs of the zodiac, though his system is for divining the fates of rulers and states.[35] But the Chinese "field allocation" system seems to have developed independently of its Western counterparts, though early Babylonian influences cannot be ruled out entirely.

Although scattered prognostications based on the general idea of "field allocation" appear in such late-Zhou sources as the *Guoyu* (Conversations of the States) and *Zuozhuan* (Zuo Chronicle), the remote origins of *fenye* in China are obscure. Hashimoto Masukichi speculates that it was originally conceived not as an astrological schema but as a device for mapping the annual progress of the sun, moon, and planets, especially Jupiter, the "Year Star," through the heavens.[36] In this early version of *fenye*, each individual "field" constituted only a segment of the paths of the planets, not a division of celestial space in general. The boundaries of these fields, moreover, were apparently not determined with much precision so that this early antecedent of *fenye* was useful only for general astronomical orientation.

Late-classical systematizers managed to assimilate *fenye* to the emerging nonary cosmography. The *Lüshi Chunqiu* and the *Zhouli* paired the nine classic provinces of China with nine celestial fields or asterisms.[37] They also measured the limits of the celestial and terrestrial units more precisely, sufficiently so to make them vehicles of astrological prognostication. The third-century astronomer Chen Zhuo even went so far as to calculate by number the degrees the span of the heavenly sectors that correspond to the earthly regions.[38]

While the nonary version of the *fenye* came to be regarded as the classic formulation of the system, it was not the only one invented by Han cosmographers or used by political astrologers. An alternate arrangement correlated the twenty-eight lunar lodges with corresponding earthly regions, and still another paired the twelve Jupiter stations with twelve terrestrial provinces. Han cosmologists developed *fenye* into quite a complex prognosticatory device, linking the earthly regions not only with heavenly fields and lunar lodges but also with the ten heavenly stems, the twelve earthly branches, the eight trigrams, the five phases, and so forth.

Following its institutionalization in the Han era, *fenye* remained the staple of official astrology throughout most of imperial China's history.

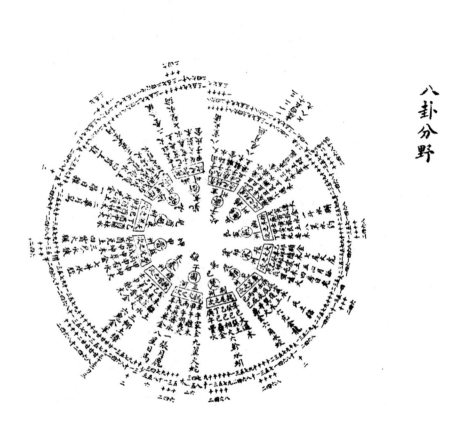

Figure 5. A diagram illustrating the relationship of the "eight trigrams and the
fenye." The units correlated in this complex version of *fenye* include the 8 trigrams,
the 12 "earthly branches" or chronograms, 12 of the political states of predynastic
China, the 12 provinces (zhou) into which the realm was supposedly divided in
high antiquity, the 12 stellar lodges or Jupiter stations, the 60 days of the sexagenary
cycle, the 5 phases, the 28 lunar lodges with their corresponding animals, and the
days of the year. While this diagram does not depict the spatial relationships of
celestial and terrestrial "fields," it does illustrate the complexities of the *fenye* in its
more highly developed form. Source: Lai Qu-tang, *Zhouyi Caitu*, p. 26b, in Lai's
Yijing Tujie (Taipei: Guangtian reprint, 1975).

Ho Peng-yoke notes that as late as the Ming era (1368–1644), "The Chief Astronomer (Ling Tailang) noticed the positions of the sun, the moon, and the planets in various celestial regions to which terrestrial regions correspond (fenye) in order to make prognostications regarding celestial abnormalities."[39] However, unlike most of the other schemata devised in late-classical China, the *fenye* system was modified significantly in the post-Han era, especially in the Tang period (618–906).[40] Alterations in political borders in post-Han times led the Tang cosmographer Li Chun-feng (602–670) to attempt to adjust the boundaries of the earthly regions in the *fenye* along the lines of Tang administrative districts.[41] A near contemporary of Li's, the great Tang astronomer Yi Xing, even proposed reforming the boundaries of the terrestrial *fenye* regions to fit physiographical features. Ouyang Xiu (1007–1070) commented that such reforms in the *fenye* were necessitated by historical changes in political boundaries.[42] This aspect of the schematic cosmography devised in the late Zhou and Han was thus already in the process of realignment by Tang times.

THE CLASSICAL CITY PLAN

Cosmographers in late-classical China devised geometrical models for the disposition of microcosmic space as well as macrocosmic, for city plans and architectural structures as well as for the heavens and the earth as a whole. They applied variations of the nonary schema outlined above to the description of both the ideal capital city and the Ming Tang (Luminous Hall), the cosmological temple which furnished the architectural setting for imperial rites. Adaptations of the nine-celled grid thus came to be applied to the ordering of several diverse types of space.

The classic plan of the ideal city is briefly described in a section of the *Rites of Zhou*, the *Kaogong Ji* (The Artificer's Record), which evidently dates from the first century B.C.[43] But antecedents of the pattern described in that early text may be traced back to the Shang era. There is some evidence that Anyang, the last Shang capital, had a roughly squared perimeter and that it was oriented along a north-south axis.[44] On the other hand, most pre-Han cities, including capitals, seem to have been asymmetrical in form. Even early Han Chang'an, according to Arthur Wright, had walls that were "highly irregular, bulging out to accommodate pre-existing settlements."[45] The deliberately geometrical construction of later imperial cities seems to have been inspired more by the design outlined by Han

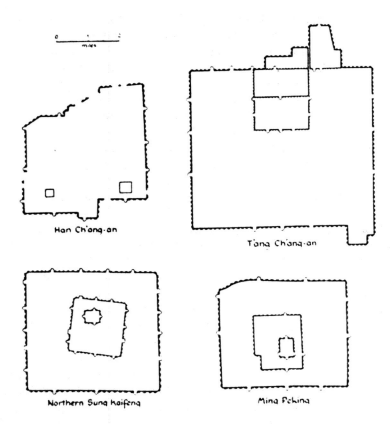

Han Ch'ang-an

T'ang Ch'ang-an

Northern Sung Kaifeng

Ming Peking

Figure 6. A chart depicting the sizes and shapes of four major imperial capitals in Chinese history. Note that the central unit, the inner or imperial city, in both Northern Song Kaifeng and Ming Peking approximates the size and position of the center square in the perennial nonary schema. Source: Arthur F. Wright, "The Cosmology of the Chinese City," in G. William Skinner, ed., *The City in Late Imperial China* (Stanford: Stanford University Press, 1977; © 1977 by the Board of Trustees of the Leland Stanford Junior University), p. 72, reprinted by permission of the publisher.

cosmographers than by the actual forms of early Chinese capital cities.

The classical literary descriptions of the ideal capital city include several cosmologically significant requirements, particularly orientation to the four points of the compass, cardinal axiality, and geometrical layout. The first two requirements were means of ensuring that the plan of the capital reflected, microcosmically, the structure of the heavens, with the north-south axis of the capital, for example, paralleling the celestial meridian.[46] However, the third, the layout of the ideal city, is of greater relevance to the subject of this chapter, the formation of geometrical cosmography.

According to the *Kaogong Ji* account, the interior of the capital city, of which the perimeter formed a square, was divided into smaller squares by nine meridional and nine latitudinal avenues.[47] Paul Wheatley has suggested that the nine "avenues" in the extant texts were originally meant to indicate nine squares or units. In that case, "the ideal-type city should have originally comprised a regular nonary layout of eight sectors, pivoted about a central unit consisting of one-ninth of the total area."[48] Wheatley thus raises the possibility that the 3 × 3 grid may have been the classic form of the ideal city plan, as well as that of the ideal agrarian order.

Unlike the well field, however, the ideal city plan presented in the *Kaogong Ji* actually assumed concrete form in some aspects of the patterns of imperial capitals, though no historical capital followed this plan precisely.[49] Luoyang in Northern Wei times (A.D. 386–535) was built around a central vertical axis, and included a separate palace unit.[50] Tang Chang'an, sometimes taken as the exemplar of imperial cities, was also patterned broadly according to the classical requirements of cardinal axiality, orientation, and rectilinear form. The Song capitals, particularly Southern Song Hangzhou, conformed less perfectly than did Tang Chang'an to the classical model. But even in Hangzhou, where the terrain and surroundings were most unfavorable to construction on such a plan, "ever effort was made to maintain the roughly rectangular form and approximate cardinal orientation."[51] Finally, the plan of Ming Peking accorded more closely with canonical prescriptions than did any previous imperial capital. There were even some traces of nonary symbolism, if not of the 3 × 3 grid, in the structure of that city and its buildings.[52]

The great imperial capitals of post-Han China, culminating in Ming Peking, furnish the most spectacular examples of the applications of the classical city plan. But smaller cities, including provincial and county seats, were frequently laid out with a square perimeter, cardinal axiality, and cardinal orientation.[53]

Except in some of its finer details, however, this classical urban model was by no means uniquely Chinese. The conception of capital or sacred cities as symbolic microcosms was widely diffused in Eurasian civilizations, and the urban geometry of ideal cities in some civilizations is reminiscent of the *Kaogong Ji* plan. Classical Indian sources, according to Jeffrey Meyer, favor "a square or rectangular form for the royal city, with twelve gates and three roads running east-west, three north-south." Medieval depictions of Jerusalem, while endowing it with rounded city walls, also show "a perfect orientation to the four directions, and two axial avenues crossing in the center."[54] However, such designs were rarely, if ever, actualized in the construction of whole cities in either Indian or European civilizations.

THE MING TANG (LUMINOUS HALL)

In China, as in the West, geometrical cosmography found its most perfect concrete realization in architecture. For unlike the types of space ordered by the well-field, nine-province, and field-allocation schemata, architectural space may be molded almost wholly by human artifice. Moreover, architectural constructions, being set on a smaller scale than city plans and not being bound by the complex human geography of urban centers, may more easily be made to conform to flights of the cosmographical imagination.

The prototype of Chinese architectural microcosms, and the one which has attracted the most commentary, is the Ming Tang. Not only was the form of this structure, as described by Han cosmologists, a numerological and geometrical microcosm, but at least one version of it was patterned on the familiar 3 × 3 grid. Yet the earliest references in classical literature to the Ming Tang, those that appear in the *Zuozhuan* and the *Mencius*, are brief and cryptic, giving no indication of its form and little of its significance.[55] There is, in fact, no firm foundation in all of Zhou literature for the reconstruction of the Ming Tang that appear in such Han compendia as the *Liji*, the *Zhouli*, the *Dadai Liji*, (The Elder Dai's Record of Rites), and the *Baihu Tongyi* (Comprehensive Discussion in the White Tiger Hall). Even the several references to the Ming Tang in the *Lüshi Chunqiu* are apparently based on cosmological speculation rather than historical memory, and in any case, do not closely conform to Han interpretations of the structure.[56]

The dearth of early descriptions of the Ming Tang has left a clear field for scholars to speculate imaginatively on the question of its early form and function. One such speculation, which appears to have been derived from a suggestion made originally by the Han commentator Cai Yong (A.D. 133–192), is that it anciently served as the ruler's ancestral temple.[57] A second common interpretation is that the antique Ming Tang was a multifunctional political and religious structure used for such varied purposes as imperial audiences, the worship of heaven and of the royal ancestors, the sustenance of the elderly, and the honoring of the virtuous.[58] Theories proposed by Western sinologists include Henri Maspero's idea that the Ming Tang was not originally a building at all, but rather a sort of sacred royal retreat within the confines of the palace and Alexander Soper's suggestion that it may have been a "royal vestibule attachable to any state building."[59] Finally, modern anthropologists have interpreted the Ming Tang as the ancient Chinese equivalent of the "assembly houses" constructed by the aboriginal peoples of Taiwan, Southeast Asia, and the Pacific Islands.[60]

The various traditional and modern views of the Ming Tang are distinguished by their having generally attributed high antiquity and great significance to the structure. But how, it might be asked, can scholars make so much of an establishment to which there are only a few offhand references in all of Zhou literature and none earlier than the fourth century B.C.? As if to anticipate this objection, both Han cosmologists and modern scholars have argued that the Ming Tang was called by different names in successive epochs of pre-Han history, enabling them to trace the structure to an early age.[61] Han commentators also incorporated various archeological references gleaned from early classical texts, such as the "magic tower" (lingtai) and the "moated mound" (biyong) of the *Songs Classic*, into the nomenclature of their reformed Ming Tang.[62] Through coalescing early classical references to architectural structures around the figure of the Ming Tang, post-Zhou systematizers broadened the foundations on which their own omnibus reconstructions rested. They also established a basis for interpreting the Ming Tang as a sort of cosmological temple in which the ruler performed all sorts of ceremonies proper to his role.

However intriguing the enigma of the original function of the Ming Tang, our main concern here is with its later assimilation into "geometrical cosmography" and transformation into a numerologically proportioned architectural microcosm. This transformation, which was expedited by the extreme brevity of classical references to the structure, occurred roughly contemporaneously with the rise of correlative thought. Having begun in the late Warring States period with the *Lüshi Chunqiu* (c. 240 B.C.), it culminated in the Later Han era (A.D. 25–220). The major systematizing texts which are the principal repositories of correlative thought and geometrical cosmography in late-classical China, the *Lüshi Chunqiu*, the *Liji*, the *Zhouli*, the *Dadai Liji*, and the *Baihu Tongyi*, are also the main sources for the cosmographical metamorphosis of the Ming Tang.

These sources do not, however, present a unified picture of the Ming Tang, though nearly all of them interpret it as an architectural microcosm replete with geometrical and numerological symbolism. The different Han views of the structure and symbolism of the Ming Tang obviously reflect different numerological preferences current at that time, and not divergent traditions handed down from classical times. Thus the major Han literary reconstructions of the Ming Tang are based essentially on the three most popular numerological orders of the day, those founded on five, nine, and twelve.[63] Of these, the quinary and the nonary seem to have been the most widely diffused.[64]

According to Henri Maspero, the quinary version, as described in the *Kaogong Ji* chapter of the *Zhouli*, is not purely a product of the cosmographical imagination, as a number of the measurements and proportions mentioned in that source are common in traditional Chinese architecture and, moreover, have no apparent symbolic significance.[65] But the later elaborations of the quinary model in such sources as Zheng Xuan's commentary on the *Zhouli*[66] are cosmographical fantasies. The structures these later texts describe are architectural monstrosities, and even, perhaps, architectural impossibilities.

The geometrical plan of the quinary model was an array of five squares formed in the shape of a Greek cross, with one central square bounded on each side by one of the other squares. Naturally, this pattern facilitated the integration of the Ming Tang into the elaborate system of correspondence which Han cosmologists built on the five phases. Moreover, by dividing each of the four peripheral squares into three rooms each, producing a total of twelve rooms, Han commentators linked the quinary pattern of the Ming Tang with the monthly imperial rituals described in the *Yueling* (Monthly Ordinances) and in the first twelve chapters of the *Lüshi Chunqiu*.[67] They even structured the complex correlative system related in these texts around the figure of the Ming Tang, thus synthesizing a geometrical cosmogram, the Ming Tang, with one of the major systems of correspondence described in the last chapter. So successful was this particular Han fusion of correlative thought and geometrical cosmography that the modern historian Luo Guang has characterized the Ming Tang as "the most concrete expression of five-phases thought."[68]

The nonary version of the Ming Tang, the *locus classicus* of which is the *Shengde* (Abundant Virtue) chapter of the *Dadai Liji*, is numerologically more complex, though its floor plan was based on the simple 3 × 3 grid. Indeed, Cai Yong, a later expositor of this version, weighed down the structure with such a numerological burden as to make its architectural realization practically impossible:

> The numerical measures of this institution all have a [cosmological] basis. The [base of the] hall is square [measuring] 144 feet [on each side], the number of the trigram *kun* [=earth]. The roof is round with a diameter of 216 feet, the number of the trigram *qian* [=heaven]. The Great Ancestral Temple of the Luminous Hall is square, measuring sixty feet [on each side], and the Chamber for Communicating with the heavens is ninety feet in diameter, [symbolizing] the changes of the yin and yang and nine and six [the numbers corresponding to the broken and unbroken lines in the hexagrams of the *Classic of Change*]. The round roof and square base [symbolize] the Way of six and nine. [The structure has] eight inner passages symbolizing the eight trigrams [of the *Classic of Change*]. It has nine rooms symbolizing the nine provinces. It has twelve palaces, thereby resonating with the twelve hours of the day. It has thirty-six doors and seventy-two windows, the number [produced by] multiplying the four doors and eight windows [of each] of the nine rooms [by nine]. The doors all open to the outside and are not shut, to illustrate that throughout the realm nothing is concealed. The Chamber for Communicating with the Heavens is eighty-one feet high, the product of the nine nines of the *huangzhong* [the tonic of the twelve pitchpipes]. [The structure's] twenty-eight pillars are evenly arrayed on the four sides, [the ones on each side] symbolizing seven of the [twenty-eight] lunar lodges. The [terrace of the] Hall is three *zhang* high, thus resonating with the three calendrical cycles [used by the Xia, Shang, and Zhou dynasties]. The five colors of its four faces symbolize [the five] phases. Its outer width is 240 feet, resonating with the twenty-four solar periods. It is surrounded on four sides by water, symbolizing the four seas.[69]

Cai Yong's numerological description of the Ming Tang is both historically and architecturally unfounded. Yet its cosmological and numerological comprehensiveness as well as its basic nonary floor plan made it the preferred model among scholars of the Later Han era.

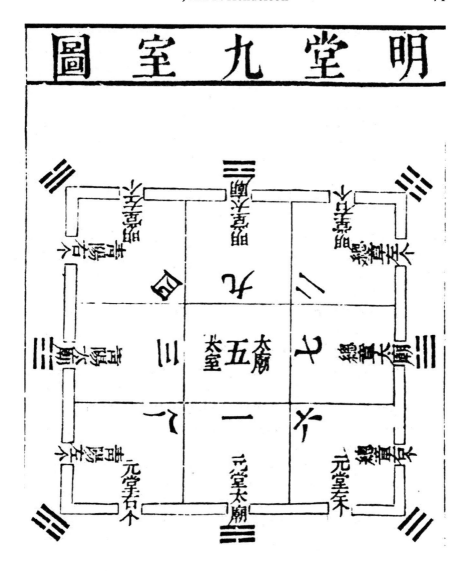

Figure 7. This diagram, a "chart of the nine chambers of the Luminous Hall," depicts a simplified nonary version of the Ming Tang. Each of the outer chambers is correlated with one of the eight trigrams and with a number. The numbers, when read through the figure in any direction, vertically, horizontally, or diagonally, add up to fifteen. Source: Hu Wei, *Yitu Mingbian* (Taipei: Guangwen reprint, 1971) 2.106.

Nevertheless, Han and later commentators did not reach any general agreement concerning the structural plan or dimensions of the Ming Tang. Indeed, prominent scholars continued to debate the relative merits of the quinary and nonary versions up to modern times. While Zhu Xi (1130–1200) declared that the Ming Tang "ought to have nine rooms, on the model of the well field," Kang Yu-wei (1858–1927) argued that the structure originally had five rooms, not nine.[70]

Yet unlike medieval and Renaissance European debates regarding the proportions and symbolism of Solomon's Temple or of the Holy City of Saint John the Divine, Chinese controversies on the form of the Ming Tang were not solely the business of scholars, but interested political figures as well. Some of the most famous rulers in Chinese history, including Emperor Wu of the Han Dynasty (r. 140–87 B.C.) and Empress Wu of the Tang (r. A.D. 684–704), had a hand in the controversies, sometimes inspiring them. The reasons for imperial sovereigns' concern with the Ming Tang were more practical than antiquarian. Several rulers in Chinese history actually constructed their own Ming Tangs to furnish a proper setting for performing cosmologically oriented imperial rites. Such rites served an important function in imperial political ideology. For inasmuch as the Ming Tang was truly microcosmic, its nine rooms representing the nine provinces of China and its twelve palaces corresponding to the months of the year, the Son of Heaven could sympathetically order space and time by proceeding through the structure in the proper sequence.[71]

Appropriately, the first imperial sovereign in Chinese history known to have constructed a Ming Tang was Emperor Wu of the Han, the patron of Dong Zhong-shu (c. 179–c. 104 B.C.) and other codifiers of correlative cosmology. Sima Qian's brief description of the structure, built at the foot of Mount Tai, does not associate any cosmological or numerological symbolism with the building.[72] Detailed accounts are also lacking of the plan of the Ming Tang built by the usurper Wang Mang in A.D. 4. But a notice of a rite performed there in A.D. 5 suggests that it was quite complex, perhaps based in part on the Ming Tang architectural numerology given in the "Abundant Virtue" chapter of the roughly contemporaneous *Dadai Liji*.[73] If the elaborate building recently uncovered just south of Han Chang'an is the ruin of Wang Mang's Ming Tang, then the plan of the edifice really did accord with the literary model in several respects. The excavated building evidently had a square base, structures symmetrically disposed in the shape of a Greek cross, nine divisions, and a circular watercourse surrounding the complex.[74] Although Wang Mang's Ming Tang was burned in A.D. 23 when his short-lived Xin dynasty fell, the Later Han emperor Guang Wu (r. A.D.

25–57) reconstructed one like it. If the accounts of that structure given in Later Han literary sources may be trusted, it was modeled as closely as was architecturally feasible on the numerological plan given in the *Dadai Liji*.[75]

Following the collapse of the Han, some of the dynasties of the Period of Disunion (A.D. 220–589), especially of the Northern Wei, continued to maintain scaled-down versions of the Later Han Ming Tang.[76] The Sui, following its reunification of the country in A.D. 589, intended to reconstruct the edifice on a larger scale, but gave up the idea when the literati could not agree on the proper plan for the project.[77] The Empress Wu actually completed such a structure in the year 688, one "as big as any predecessor and more extraordinary."[78] Though apparently not modeled very closely on any of the classical Han accounts, the dimensions and parts of this impressive three-storied reconstruction of the Ming Tang were replete with numerological symbolism. The institution of the Ming Tang was also revived in the middle of the eleventh century, under the Song, though not on nearly so grand a scale. But not until 1117, eight years before the fall of the Northern Song, did the Ming Tang have a special building. Before that time and during the Southern Song as well, whenever the rites appropriate to the Ming Tang were celebrated, one of the audience halls in the palace was used for the occasion.[79]

With the possible exception of a brief revival in the middle of the sixteenth century, the Ming Tang as such was never reconstructed after the Song. Yet, as Jeffrey Meyer has pointed out, the "Great Worship Hall" (da sitian) first established by the Yongluo Emperor (r. 1403–1424) and used thereafter for imperial rites, was structurally and functionally a sort of Ming Tang. It incorporated the same types of cosmographical and numerological symbolism as the Han originals, with four pillars representing the four seasons, twelve inner pillars representing the twelve months of the year, twelve outer pillars representing the signs of the solar zodiac, a round roof symbolizing the heavens, and a square base symbolizing the earth.[80]

In the Qing era (1644–1911), the quest for symbolic legitimacy and a taste for the archaic inspired the Manchu emperors to adhere more closely than most of their predecessors to Ming Tang cosmology and numerology. For example, when the imperial Altar of Heaven was extensively remodeled in the Qianlong era (1736–1795), the emperor "charged the planners 'to preserve the numbers five and nine' in the structure."[81] Whatever doubts Ming and Qing scholars expressed regarding the authenticity and orthodoxy of cosmological versions of the Ming Tang, the Qing sovereigns continued to endorse cosmological views reminiscent of their Han predecessors. While it is doubtful that Qing sovereigns shared Wang Mang's

belief that the realm, and space and time in general, could really be sympathetically ordered through the correct performance of rites in a structure
like the Ming Tang, they were at least aware of the political uses of traditional cosmology. Thus they maintained the façade of cosmological
orthodoxy even while Qing scholars exposed Han cosmology's extraca-
nonical roots.

THE LUOSHU (LUO RIVER WRITING) DIAGRAM

A final nonary cosmogram formulated in late antiquity from creative
interpretations of enigmatic references in diverse pre-Han texts was the
Luoshu or "Luo River Writing." Unlike the other figures discussed thus far,
neither the Luoshu nor its companion, the Hetu or "Yellow River Chart,"
served as a model for ordering any type of physical space. But the Luoshu is
particularly important in that postclassical commentators came to regard it
as the ultimate source of nonary cosmography in general. They viewed the
Luoshu figure as the prototype of such nonary schemata as the nine
provinces of China, the nine units of the well field, the nine halls of the
Ming Tang, and even the nine divisions of Daoist hell.[82]

Han and especially Song metaphysicians identified the Luoshu and its
complement the Hetu as primary sources of order in the world. These
diagrams, they believed, both embodied the underlying patterns of the
cosmos and served as models for aspects of civilization devised by the sage
kings of antiquity. So eternal are these patterns, Cai Yuan-ding (1135–1198)
believed, that the Hetu and Luoshu would take the same forms as of old
were they to reappear in a later age.[83]

That the Hetu and Luoshu would be so important in postclassical
Chinese thought could hardly have been guessed from a survey of the
accounts given of these figures in the classics. The references to the Hetu
and Luoshu in pre-Han texts, of which Karlgren lists six, are almost as brief
and cryptic as those to the Ming Tang. Karlgren gives the gist of most of
them in remarking that they "often speak of some *tu* 'drawing' or 'map' and
shu 'document' which came out of some sacred rivers and were good
auspices."[84] Pre-Han texts reveal little about the form of either figure,
though the *Zhuangzi* does associate the number nine with "Luo."[85]

Thus having only the vaguest clues to the original form of the Hetu and
Luoshu, Han systematizers were able to give free rein to their imaginations
in reconstructing them, leading to considerable confusion. However, the
majority of the major Han commentators on this subject, including Kong
An-guo (c. 156–c. 74 B.C.), Liu Xin (c. 46 B.C. –A.D. 23), and Ma Rong

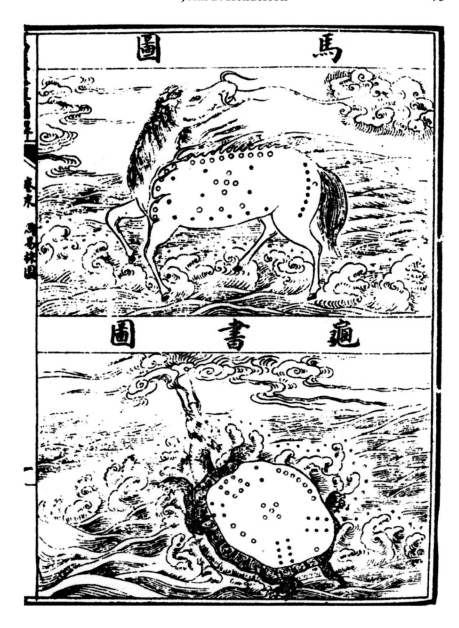

Figure 8. The forms of the Hetu and Luoshu, the former imprinted on the side of a horse wading in the Yellow River and the latter on the shell of a tortoise emerging from the Luo River. Source: Lai Qu-tang, *Zhouyi Caitu*, p. 1a, in Lai's *Yijing Tujie* (Taipei: Guangtian reprint, 1975).

(A.D. 79–166), identified the Hetu with the "nine sections" or "nine catego-
ries" of the "Great Plan" chapter of the *Documents*.[86] The "Treatise on the
Five Phases" of the *Han History*, for example, notes that "Liu Xin held that
Fu Xi continued [the work of] heaven as king, and thus received the Yellow
River Chart; when he patterned and drew it, the eight trigrams [were
produced]. Yu regulated the flood waters, and thus was favored with the
Luo River Writing: when he modeled and arranged it, the 'Great Plan' [was
produced]."[87] In thus identifying the Hetu with the trigrams of the *Change*
and the Luoshu with the "nine sections" of the "Great Plan," Han commentators traced the symbolic keys to two of the most revered of the Confucian
classics to the Hetu and Luoshu. Moreover, they described these figures as
having appeared to two of the most esteemed legendary sage kings, Fu Xi
and Yu the Great.

However, neither the *Han History* nor the other Han sources noted
above specifically identified the Luoshu with the 3 × 3 grid, the "nine
palace" (jiugong) formation, only with the "nine sections" of the "Great
Plan." The association of the Luoshu with the nonary grid form may
perhaps be traced to one of the later apocrypha on the *Change*, namely the
Yiwei Qianzuodu and, more remotely and tenuously, to the description of
the Ming Tang in the *Dadai Liji*.[88] Yet extant diagrams of the Luoshu, none
of which date from earlier than the Song era, seldom depict it strictly in the
form of the conventional magic square of three. Instead, these diagrams
generally both dispense with the square grid and represent each of the
Luoshu numbers by figures which resemble knotted cords rather than by
numerals. Schuyler Cammann, however, argues that pre-Song cosmology
commonly represented the Luoshu by the figure of the simple magic square.
Even a few later classicists occasionally depicted the Luoshu in the form of
the 3 × 3 grid.[89]

In sum, at least one historical form of the Luoshu was geometrically as
well as numerologically in accord with nonary cosmography. But there is no
particular reason for assigning historical or cosmological priority to the
identification of the Luoshu with the magic square of three. No pre-Han
source supports this association and even Han cosmologists devised other
interpretations of the Luoshu. Not until the rise of Neo-Confucian cosmology in the eleventh century did a variation of the nine-squared form of
the Luoshu become common intellectual currency.

Thus the 3 × 3 grid form by no means monopolized the Chinese
cosmographical imagination in the postclassical era. For some of the
cosmographical schemata outlined above, including the *fenye* and the Ming
Tang, as well as the Luoshu, were sometimes represented by figures that

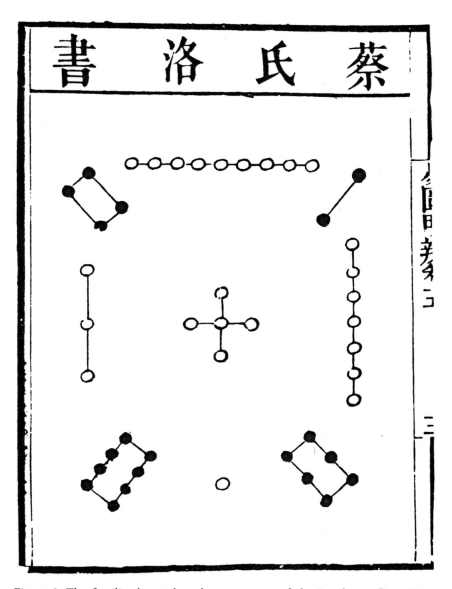

Figure 9. The familiar knotted-cord arrangement of the Luoshu or "Luo River Writing" popularized by Song cosmologists, here associated with Cai Yuan-ding. Source: Hu Wei, *Yitu Mingbian* (Taipei: Guangwen reprint, 1971) 5.300.

were neither nonary nor even square. Moreover, there were other areas of traditional cosmography, broadly defined, where the "nine palaces" form hardly figured at all, including such topics as celestial cartography and geographical mythology, and such artifacts as TLV mirrors and divining boards.

But the nonary cosmograms surveyed above are distinctive inasmuch as they were quite closely related to forms of correlative cosmology. Indeed, Han commentators built complex systems of correspondence around some cosmograms, particularly the *fenye*, the Ming Tang, and the Luoshu. But unlike most of the correlative systems described in the first chapter, geometrical cosmography neither developed nor devolved very far in the post-Han era, at least not before the Song.

Chapter Three

Medieval Criticisms and Extensions
Of Correlative Cosmology

The influence of correlative thinking on the culture of post-Han China was both profound and pervasive. Nevertheless, cosmological skepticism was not unknown in medieval China. Criticisms of certain aspects of correlative cosmology arose as early as the Han and occasionally reappeared in later epochs. Most students of Chinese civilization should be able to identify at least one or two post-Han intellectual phenomena, such as Chan Buddhism and Song empiricist historiography, that contravened important facets of the Han world view. Most are also aware of some of the more direct attacks on established cosmological notions posed by such celebrated skeptics as Wang Chong (A.D. 27–100?) and Ouyang Xiu (1007–1070). In light of the criticism, both implicit and explicit, that seems to have been directed against correlative cosmology from the Later Han on, one might legitimately ask why I have dated the "cosmological reformation" to the seventeenth century.

A satisfactory answer to this question must depend on the evidence to be presented subsequently. Nevertheless, one point may be stated at the outset. Cosmological criticism and skepticism in the era from the Han to the Ming was not so radical nor so extensive as some historians seem to have assumed. Even some of those who have been identified as chief critics of traditional cosmological conceptions, such as Wang Chong, were much more cosmologically conservative than is generally admitted. The critics that did appear were usually rather isolated both chronologically and intellectually, having little effect on either the climate of opinion in their own day or on the general development of Chinese cosmological thought. Not until the seventeenth century did a broad group of well-known scholars subject the fundamental assumptions of correlative thought and geometrical cosmography to direct, deliberate criticism.

On the other hand, some of the arguments posed by major Qing critics such as Wang Fu-zhi (1619–1692) appear to have been anticipated by earlier figures. Thus a brief survey of notable groups of alleged cosmological skeptics in medieval China is a necessary preliminary to gauging the originality of the Qing cosmological commentators.

SOURCES OF COSMOLOGICAL CRITICISM: TWO ABSTRACT POSSIBILITIES

From what sources might criticism of correlative cosmology have arisen in postclassical China? From an abstract point of view, two obvious possibilities are: (1) changes in the outer world, particularly in the natural and social environments; (2) the inner developmental logic of some mode of correlative thought. This might seem to exhaust the logical possibilities, covering both "external impact" and "internal dialectic" modes of explanation. It hardly does that, and in fact does not even account for most specific criticisms historically posed by cosmological commentators.

On the other hand, the reasons that a particular writer adduces for rejecting a cosmological schema (that it is unclassical for instance), may not be the only ones that moved him to challenge it. There may be unstated and perhaps even unconscious reasons. The two abstract possibilities mentioned above may be included among these. For both changes in the natural and social environments and changes in the inner logic of a mode of thought can proceed so slowly as to pass virtually unnoticed. Indeed, who but Hegel's owl of Minerva could fathom the internal dialectic of mode of thought?

Changes in the outer world, especially in natural and social environments, might undermine correlative systems in several ways. If, for example, as in China throughout most of the Period of Disunion, two or more dynasties hold sway simultaneously, then the "state analogy" mode of correlative thought might be seriously undercut. In this case, there is no single terrestrial counterpart of celestial constellations or powers. In such a situation, the orthodox cosmologist could always argue that the political changes that had produced cosmological imbalance were the products of an anomalous situation that was bound to pass. The correlative cosmologist could then proceed with his system building in the confidence that his schema reflected the normal state of affairs, even if not the one prevailing at the moment.

In Han China, however, quite a few correlative schemata, even some not based on the state analogy mode, were closely tied to the functions of the imperial government. Some such systems, especially those formulated by Dong Zhong-shu (c. 179–104 B.C.), Liu Xin (c. 46 B.C. –A.D. 23), and Ban Gu (A.D. 32–92), were devised in the first place as part of an effort to consolidate and legitimate the peculiar Han embodiment of the imperial ideal. When the dynasty fell, many of the systems of correspondence formulated by Han systematizers were rendered irrelevant to the current political and social situation.[1] Perhaps for this reason, political and social entities rarely figure very prominently in the correlative systems devised by the major cosmologists of the Period of Disunion. The latter were instead much more concerned with drawing medical, alchemical, and astrological correspondences, or with pairing the ideas associated with the newly introduced Buddhist religion with more familiar ones gleaned from native philosophical traditions. Thus, although the changes of the Period of Disunion seem to have sped the decline of one mode of correlative thought, they may well have stimulated the development of other modes. In any case, the basic assumptions underlying correlative thinking, particularly the belief in general homologies among various realms of the cosmos, do not appear to have been seriously called into question.

Inasmuch as the natural environment generally alters much more slowly than do political and social configurations, one would not expect the history of post-Han cosmology to have been greatly influenced by the course of geological, biological, or meteorological change. However, the historical movement of the Chinese people southward during the post-Han era had the effect of telescoping some such changes into a period of only a few centuries. For in the new lands south of the Yangzi, "the cycle of seasons as manifested in the life and death of plants and animals" was not so marked as in the North China homeland.[2] Since this cycle was basic to some of the systems of correspondence formulated in late-classical times, particularly to the *Yueling* schema for correlating imperial rituals and activities with the seasons of the year, its absence might well have inspired some to question systems based on the idea of seasonal change. Further, the expansion southward, by acquainting the medieval Chinese with a wide variety of new fauna, flora, and other natural objects, may have led them to view some of the old quinary and nonary orders as anachronistic. The new immigrant to the subtropics might wonder how the classical enumerators of the nine lakes, nine mountains, five animals, and five grains could have failed to include many of their more spectacular southern variations.

Thus far, I have not found evidence that any medieval cosmological critic reasoned in just this way, though the early Qing scholar Mao Qi-ling (1623–1716) did fault earlier cosmographers for having failed to include important mountains and marshes in their nonary enumerative orders.[3] But China's historical "march to the tropics" did lead several seventeenth-century commentators to question the current applicability of the classical North-China-centered nine-province and field-allocation schemes. There is evidence, moreover, that geographical expansion brought about a subversion of established cosmological schemata at least twice in Western history as well, in the Hellenistic Age and in the Age of Discovery. Perhaps such expansion led medieval Chinese, as well as the Elizabethans, to feel that "the world they lived in was becoming ever more difficult to fit tidily into a rigid order."[4] If so, it is possible that a vague unease with the apparent disjunction between established systems of correspondence and the diversities of the natural environment of the South prompted post-Han commentators to seize on other, more fashionable pretexts for challenging these systems. On the other hand, the disquieting spectacle of the luxuriant chaos of the South might well have driven some to take mental refuge in the schematism of an archaic world view.

The second of our two logically possible solvents of correlative thinking, its inner developmental logic, seems destined to remain confined to the realm of Ideas, for it is difficult to imagine how systems of correspondence, particularly relatively simple numerological ones, could evolve, or devolve through any such logic. How, indeed, could such systems develop at all except through the addition of new correlative sets, for example, by keying the five colors or five flavors to an already established series based on the five phases?

Rarely, however, does a correlative system develop so smoothly. One might even use this illustration, simple though it seems, to explain at least two of the complications that logically arise as numerological systems of correspondence develop. In the first place, once the basis of the system has been established, the sets that are added must conform. For example, even if the commonsensical notion in the culture concerned is that there are six colors and four flavors, the cosmologist must disregard what he has come to think of as the "natural" enumeration in the interest of completing the schema. Inasmuch as the schema, the matrix, abhors both a lacuna and a remainder, "nature" or "common sense" must be contorted each time one adds a new correlative set, except on those rare occasions when the set is coincidentally in perfect accord with the outlines of the schema. Thus as new sets are added, as the numerologist attempts to make the order truly universal, the schema becomes increasingly artificial and further removed from nature and common sense.[5]

At this point the schema is most vulnerable to criticism. For instead of reflecting the world view of a civilization, the system of correspondence, by virtue of its developmental logic, may come to be at odds with it. However, if the cosmologists persist, if they come to dominate the media, they may eventually restructure common sense to fit the outlines of the schema. They may convince people that there really are five and only five colors, five flavors, and even five seasons. This appears to have happened, to some extent, in traditional China, where the quinary cosmology apparently came to structure certain facets of ordinary perception.

A second problem is that the individual terms in the sets should correspond in some meaningful fashion. It is not enough to reduce the number of colors to five; one must also pair the individual colors with, for example, the five phases. Of course, some correlations can be drawn in a commonsensical manner without straining the intellect. Fire may be correlated with red, wood with green, and earth with yellow. But what of metal with white and water with black?

A slightly more complex illustration of the "forced fits" which sometimes resulted from the development of correlations based on the five phases appears in the writings of Lü Kun (1536–1618), a Neo-Confucian philosopher of the Ming era. According to Lü, "Water is soft when still and hard when in motion; metal is soft when in motion and hard when still; wood is soft when living and hard when dead; fire is hard when living and soft when dead."[6] To my mind, the first three of these correlations are natural. But the fourth strains the imagination, though a plausible explanation is conceivable. Yet Lü could not have omitted it without leaving an inadmissible gap in the schema as a whole. Nor could he have altered the attributes of "fire" without unbalancing the overall symmetry of the system.

The above examples indicate that as a correlative schema expands from the more or less natural pairings that inspired its formation, correspondences among its increasingly diverse sets are less easily justified. After a certain level of complexity is reached, the correspondences may become emptied of all cosmological content and reduced to the level of pure numerology, a state approached in the writings of Shao Yong (1011–1077). At this point, the manipulation of numerological ciphers within a system of correspondence may become a sort of esoteric game played by commentators who are increasingly uninterested in cosmology. Having been thus reduced to the absurd, correlative systems become quite vulnerable to criticism, providing that they have not been so widely accepted as to restructure common sense. Even though this developmental process is quite slow and insidious, proceeding over the course of centuries and rarely providing the main focus of articulate criticism, it is probably the most universal solvent of correlative modes of thinking. For both Qing Chinese and Renaissance Europeans wearied of the excessively arbitrary character of correlative numerology in its later stages, as is discussed later in chapters 6 and 7.

Even had the particular trends not emerged that led to the concerted critique of systems of correspondence in the early Qing era, correlative thought might well have eventually developed (or devolved) to the point where it could no longer be taken seriously. It might have ended in the same manner as the European great chain of being, the later elaborations of which "ended by making it ridiculous and hence unacceptable in any form."[7] Or perhaps it would have collapsed under the weight of its own success, as did the "helpless humor theory" in Europe when called upon to explain such diverse phenomena as "the fecundity of peoples, the rise of religion in one geographic area, the distribution of insanity, of leprosy, of cruelty in war."[8]

PHILOSOPHICAL CRITICISM OF ANALOGICAL THINKING

Throughout most of the middle period of Chinese history, however, systems of correspondence had hardly developed to this point. Hence, medieval skeptics and critics of correlative thought were generally constrained to take it quite seriously. Such critics seldom if ever simply dismissed correlative systems as too fanciful to be worthy of attention.

Yet even before the formulation of any but the most rudimentary of these systems in China, a few of the classical philosophers did devise arguments that might well have been used to challenge correlative modes of thinking. Zhuangzi, for example, opposed the classification of things by established categories. The attributes that we normally associate with things, he argued, are purely the products of convention, custom, and prejudice, for things in themselves, or from the point of view of the Dao, are neither lofty nor lowly, neither large nor small, neither durable nor ephemeral. Hence, to call Mount Tai large, the tip of an autumn hair small, or Pengzi (who lived for eight hundred years) old[9] is to be led by popular prejudice and to display a lamentable ignorance of the natural equality of things. Inasmuch as Zhuangzi rejected the accepted criteria for classifying things, he removed any basis for the drawing of analogies, a necessary preliminary to most modes of correlative thinking, as one usually bases a correspondence drawn between two things, like the ruler and the pole star, on a quality which they are presumed to share, such as axiality. But if such attributes as axiality are equally characteristic of all things, then there is no basis for pairing any two particular things.

Zhuangzi himself did, to be sure, frequently analogize. But such analogies as Zhuangzi drew were usually quite unconventional—so unconventional, in fact, that they were probably meant to confute or parody analogizing as it was normally practiced, as when Zhuangzi locates the Dao in excrement and urine, or compares a high ministry of state to a rat's rotting carcass.[10] Zhuangzi, in any case, likened his own teachings, including presumably his analogizing, to rabbit snares and fishnets which may be cast aside once their object is obtained.[11]

Zhuangzi's animus against conventional modes of analogizing also appears in Chinese Zen (Chan), as well as in the teaching of a few other classical philosophers, particularly Huizi. In Zen, the transcendence of customary ways of likening things even seems to be an important prerequisite of enlightenment. The chief difference, as told in a famous story in the *Platform Sutra*, between the almost enlightened and the fully enlightened is that the latter eschews the drawing of analogies.[12] The almost enlightened head monk, Shen Xiu, expressed his understanding of Buddhist truth as follows:

> The body is the Bodhi tree,
> The mind is like a clear mirror.
> At all times we must strive to polish it,
> And must not let the dust collect.[13]

The fully enlightened patriarch-to-be, Hui Neng, replied in the following way:

> Bodhi originally has no tree,
> The mirror also has no stand.
> Buddha nature is always clean and pure,
> Where is there room for dust?[14]

Many Zen *koan*, riddles designed to inspire an enlightened state of mind, may also be understood as confutations of conventional analogizing. Partly for this reason, most *koan* are not meant to be "solved," inasmuch as this might require one to fall back on the old analogizing habit of mind that constitutes a formidable barrier to enlightenment. Thus, the novice missed the point if, on being told that the Buddha was "three pounds of flax," he tried to figure out how the two could correspond.

Classical Daoist and Zen Buddhist critiques of analogical thinking, radical though they implicitly were, do not seem to have inspired much direct criticism of correlative cosmology in China. Apparently few critics of correlative schemata were willing to go to the extent of repudiating the drawing of analogies, without which thought or speech, as conventionally practiced, would be difficult. Major cosmological critics in Chinese intellectual history generally preferred more empirical arguments against established systems of correspondence.

COSMOLOGICAL CRITICISM IN THE LATER HAN

A few such critics appeared as early as the later Han era. One or two of them, particularly Wang Chong, are even celebrated for their opposition to facets of the established cosmology, including the conception of cosmic resonance, the political use of portents, and numerological interpretations of the *Classic of Change* and its appendices. Thus the Later Han, the era in which both correlative thought and geometrical cosmography matured, was also by some accounts the epoch in which cosmological skepticism first emerged. But just how skeptical were the skeptics? Was their world view really in radical opposition to that of such Later Han cosmological systematizers as Ban Gu and Zheng Xuan (A.D. 127–200)? Did they call into question the fundamental premises or only secondary elaborations of correlative thought?

The obvious place to begin a study of these issues is in the *Lunheng* (Discussions Weighed in the Balance), the chief surviving work of the most celebrated critic of early Chinese cosmology in all Chinese history, Wang Chong. These essays, by virtue of their deliberate iconoclasm, their attacks on apparently irrational superstitious beliefs, their logical mode of argument, and their direct uncluttered style, have greatly appealed to modern historians of Chinese thought, especially to those of a positivist persuasion. But Wang Chong's essays are perhaps most renowned for their criticism of established cosmological conceptions, especially the idea of resonance between heaven and man, the notion that the powers of the cosmos respond to human appeals or are influenced by human activities. Indeed, several of the essays in the *Lunheng* are devoted principally to examining aspects of this particular idea.

Wang raises a number of objections to both the theory of resonance in general and to one of its major ramifications, the idea of moral reward and retribution, that heaven rewards the good and punishes the evil. Against the latter idea, he argues that the virtuous often experience great calamities while the wicked prosper. Even the exemplary sage kings Yao and Tang had to deal with catastrophic floods and droughts during their reigns. On the other hand, the legendary arch-villains of ancient Chinese history, *Jie* and *Zhou*, are not noted for having encountered natural catastrophes during their reigns.[15] Among commoners, too, "there are cases of virtuous men being taken sick and dying early and of wicked men being strong and healthy and living to an old age. A man's getting sick and dying is not because of immoral conduct."[16]

Wang also argues more generally against the idea that man can either influence or communicate with heaven. First, Wang points out, man is so tiny in proportion to the heavens that it is almost inconceivable that his petty actions or appeals could in any way affect their movements. Second, since heaven is so distant from man, and in any case lacks ears, how could it hear human appeals? Finally, attempts to communicate with heaven through divination rather than through speech ignore the fact that heaven, which is living, cannot be contacted through such inert media as milfoil stalks and tortoise shells. Moreover, the cosmos, though animated, is not anthropomorphic or even corporeal, but rather is composed essentially of *qi* or "pneuma." Even if man could somehow make his queries, prayers, and appeals known to heaven, the latter could not respond in any intelligible or effective way.[17]

Although cosmic resonance between heaven and man was the main object of Wang's criticism, he also challenged other aspects of correlative cosmology. For example, he criticized the popular idea that the five phases succeed one another in the order prescribed by the "mutual production" and "mutual conquest" series by arguing that the cosmic *qi* is unitary and cannot be split into five separate parts.[18] Wang reduced to absurdity correlations based on the mutual conquest order of the five phases, as in the following example:

If we examine such theories with respect to animals, we will also find cases in which there is no "mutual conquest" effect. The horse is connected with the *wu* [terrestrial] branch [paired with fire], the rat with the *zi* [paired with water], the cock with the *yu* [paired with metal], and the rabbit with the *mao* [paired with wood]. Water conquers fire; so why don't rats pursue horses? Metal conquers wood; so why don't cocks peck rabbits?[19]

Quite a few passages from the *Lunheng* indicate that Wang Chong was generally quite critical of the prevailing cosmology. But other parts of the *Lunheng* reveal that Wang, even while rejecting resonance theory, was a cosmological conservative in certain respects. In some ways Wang was an even more consistent correlative thinker than were many of his less iconoclastic contemporaries, whom he sometimes criticized for not having applied correlative modes of reasoning strictly enough:

The Confucians say that the Way of husband and wife takes its pattern from heaven and earth. They know that the rule of husband and wife is modeled on that of heaven and earth; but they do not know how to infer from the Way of husband and wife to discuss the nature of heaven and earth.[20]

How, then, does Wang himself proceed from his knowledge of the "Way of husband and wife" to an understanding of the "nature of heaven and earth"? He infers, for example, that "inasmuch as husband and wife do not deliberately give birth to children, so heaven and earth do not deliberately give birth to men." Just as a child may come into the world without its father knowing about it, so men may come into being of whom heaven is ignorant.[21] Paradoxically, then, Wang uses the idea of correspondence between heaven and man to refute the notion that heaven is interested in man.

Wang employs the conception of structural correspondence between heaven and earth in a similar way to criticize the notion that heaven is equipped to respond to human appeals or intervene in human affairs. For heaven is like earth in that it lacks the physical instruments through which it might communicate with man:

How do we know that heaven has no mouth and eyes? We know it through the earth. The earth (di) has earth (tu) as its embodiment; and earth has no mouth or eyes. Heaven and earth are like husband and wife. Since the earth has no mouth and eyes, we know that heaven also lacks mouth and eyes.[22]

Wang also invokes the structural correspondence between heaven and earth to debunk ancient myth. He argues, for example, that there could never have been ten suns in the sky, as related in one early myth recorded in the *Zhuangzi*. For in that case, there would have to be ten corresponding kinds of fire on the earth. Further, celestial and terrestrial bodies must correspond in form and substance as well as in number. Thus, since water and fire do not assume a spherical shape on the earth, the sun and moon, the heavenly quintessences of water and fire, must not be spherical either.[23]

In sum, while Wang Chong vigorously criticized conceptions of cosmic resonance, he upheld the notion of structural and numerological correspondence between heaven and man in an even more literal fashion than did many of the principal Han cosmologists. Wang's rejection of resonance theory might even be attributed in part to his particularly literalist approach to correspondences, as manifested in his insistence that heaven cannot communicate with man since it lacks a mouth and eyes. Wang still maintained that auspicious omens, such as phoenixes and unicorns and the Yellow River Chart and Luo River Writing, appeared on earth in response to sagely rule. Even rulers of his own era, Wang argued, had received favorable signs from heaven, though "present-day auspicious omens are not necessarily the same as those of old."[24] While denying that heaven and man could communicate directly, Wang maintained that something in the cosmos responds to or resonates with moral government.

Wang Chong's comments on the schematic cosmography associated with Zou Yan also reveal an iconoclastic spirit coupled with a conceptual conservatism. The greater part of Wang's essay on Zou's cosmographical system is devoted to attacking it on various grounds, for example arguing that Zou could have never actually verified the existence or dimensions of the distant regions included in his schema. But Wang stops short of denying the validity of schematic cosmography, never faulting Zou's conception in principle as unrealistically or unnaturally stylized. In fact, Wang Chong himself seems to accept a schematic, perhaps even geometrical, conception of ancient China when he posits that "in Zhou times, the nine regions extended 5,000 *li* from east to west and 5,000 *li* from north to south."[25]

Some historians have interpreted the cosmological skepticism that appears in some sections of Wang Chong's work as part of a greater skeptical tradition that flourished in the Later Han and persisted through succeeding centuries. Thus Joseph Needham has written that "So important was the Chinese skeptical tradition" of which Wang was representative "that Wang Chong was doubtless not the only critic of the five-element theories" or related cosmological conceptions. However, Needham names only a few other critics, some of whom seem to have confined themselves to attacking common superstitions.[26] Further, he does not specify just what Wang's relationship was with these later figures in the "skeptical tradition." In any case, Needham's confidence in the great importance and radical character of the tradition is not shared by the leading authority on medieval Chinese nature lore, E.H. Schafer, who remarks that "even among the skeptics, who seem to have been few," correlations based on the five phases seemed "natural and obvious."[27]

But what of the Later Han itself, supposedly the age in which the skeptical tradition emerged? Were any of Wang Chong's near contemporaries more critical than he was of any aspect of correlative cosmology? On the contrary, few if any of them went nearly so far as Wang. Xun Yue (A.D. 148–209), while echoing some of Wang's criticisms of moral reward and retribution, "also criticized those who denied outright any correspondence between cosmos and man." Xun Yue was fascinated with number and mysticism and approved of such divinatory arts as physiognomy.[28] Xun Yue's predecessors Huan Tan (40 B.C. –A.D. 30) and Zhang Heng (A.D. 78–139), while rejecting the numerological constructions associated with the apocryphal "charts and tallies" texts (tu chen), both affirmed the general principle of the political interpretation of portents.[29] Finally, Wang Fu (A.D. 76–157), though expressing doubts about the possibility of contacting ghosts and spirits through divination, nevertheless maintained that man's actions could influence the cosmos. He also endorsed the general conception of correspondence between parts of the human body and those of the cosmos.[30] None of these noted Later Han thinkers went so far as to repudiate the principle of cosmic resonance, much less to challenge the more fundamental elements of correlative cosmology.

The above discussion hardly exhausts the list of possible Later Han critics of correlative thought. But it does include several of the more prominent and original thinkers of the age, as well as some of the most noted for their critical approach to traditional learning. However, one slightly later figure, Wang Bi (A.D. 226–249), deserves some attention for his alleged opposition to one particular mode of correlative cosmology—that based on the figures associated with the *Classic of Change*.

Wang is perhaps most celebrated in the history of Chinese thought for his contributions to the third-century revival of philosophical Daoism, particularly for his famous commentary on the *Laozi*. But he is also noted for having eschewed the numerological (shushu) approach to the *Change* so popular in the Han, as well as for having established the moral-philosophical (yili) school of *Yijing* interpretation. One scholar, Walter Liebenthal, goes so far as to credit Wang's opposition to astronomical and numerological glosses of the *Yijing* with having effected "the destruction of Han Byzantinism and the propagation of a world view that dared to interpret the world as a whole."[31] It is doubtful that Wang Bi could have single-handedly overthrown Han cosmology or whatever else Liebenthal might have meant by "Byzantinism." But the evidence for his rejection of *Yijing* numerology is worthy of examination.

Wang and his disciple Han Kang-bo undeniably interpreted key passages in the *Classic of Change* and its canonical appendices in quite a different way from that followed by Han numerologists. An example, explicated by Mou Zong-san, of a passage on which Wang's gloss departs from the established Han interpretations, is the statement in the "Great Commentary" that "the number of Great Expansion is 50 of which 49 are used."[32] According to Han numerologist Jing Fang, "the 50 refer to the 10 days, the 12 [terrestrial] branches, [plus] the 28 lunar lodges—altogether 50." Another Han commentator, Ma Rong (A.D. 79–166), also derived the number 50 in a numerological fashion, combining the Great Ultimate (1), the yin and yang (+2), the four seasons, the fives phases, the twelve months, and the twenty-four solar periods, and then commenting that the one remaining is the pole star that does not move itself but serves as the axis for rotation for all the other stars. Wang Bi, however, eschewed the standard interpretations and posited that the one that remains is the Great Ultimate of the *Change*, and ultimately the void. Although the term "Great Ultimate" appears elsewhere in the "Great Commentary," Wang's interpretation of this particular passage is evidently based on Laozi's statement that "being is produced from nonbeing," as Mou Zong-san remarks.[33]

Wang and his disciple Han Kang-bo did not, however, directly attack the Han interpretations of the sentence in question, much less devise a general critique of the systems of correspondence based on the figures of the *Change*. Although his commentary may have marked a departure in *Yijing* interpretation, this does not mean that Wang Bi was ipso facto a radical critic of correlative cosmology. About the farthest Wang ever went toward criticizing particular correlations based on the *Change* was to label them superfluous. Wang commented, for example, that "If the meaning of something is 'firmness' [the definition of the *qian* hexagram given in one of the appendices to the *Change*], why must [one correlate it with] a horse? If the category of something is 'compliance' [the *kun* hexagram in the same source], why must [one correlate it with] a cow?"[34] In other words, if one already knows the basic meaning of "firmness" and "compliance," why trouble oneself with symbolic correlations?

COSMOLOGICAL CRITICISM IN THE ELEVENTH CENTURY

After the Later Han era, the next widely recognized cluster of cosmological critics appeared in the eleventh century. Several Tang-era scholars, including Lü Cai (600–665), Liu Zhi-ji (661–721), and Niu Seng-ru (779–847), as well as Liu Zong-yuan (773–819), did criticize a few particular applications of correlative cosmology. Niu, for example, argued that political administration should proceed independently of interpretations of the heavenly mandate, "that abandoning human affairs and inquiring after the Way of Heaven, abandoning the near and seeking the far have no advantage for instruction."[35] But in contrast with most of these Tang cosmological critics, Northern Song scholars such as Ouyang Xiu (1007–1070) and Su Xun (1009–1066) directly challenged some of the basic modes of Han correlative cosmology. Had the views of these eleventh-century critics prevailed, and had their studies been expanded in scope, the cosmological reformation of the early Qing might well have been anticipated in the Northern Song. However, the rise of Neo-Confucianism in that era reaffirmed many of the basic tenets of the perennial cosmology, even disseminating them more widely in Chinese culture. Thus eleventh-century criticism did not have a lasting impact on the intellectual world of late traditional China.

At least two important motives figure in eleventh-century scholars' critiques of Han cosmology. The first of these arose from the revived classicism of the era. Inasmuch as few of the Confucian classics contain more than the most rudimentary anticipations of correlative cosmology or geometrical cosmography, classical purists in the eleventh century and later had reason to denigrate as heterodox the cosmological commentary formulated in the Han. Second, systems of correspondence had, in some cases, been extended far enough by Song times to be encumbered by the forced fits and arbitrary pairings that arose from efforts to develop simple schemata into world-embracing cosmological designs. Thus eleventh-century commentators were able to point to disjunctions and disharmonies.

Just as a pair of late-Tang thinkers, Han Yu (768–824) and Li Ao (fl. 798), are customarily identified as precursors of Northern Song Neo-Confucianism, so a ninth-century figure, Liu Zong-yuan, anticipated eleventh-century cosmological criticism. Like many Tang literati, Liu only occasionally discussed topics that were "cosmological" by any strict definition of the term. But he did explicitly challenge at least one major mode of correlative cosmology formulated in late antiquity, that matching the seasons of the year with imperial rituals and activities, as codified in the canonical *Yueling* (Monthly Ordinances) chapter of the *Record of Rites*. Liu's primary objection to this system was that its emphasis on conducting political affairs according to the order prescribed by cosmological correlations departed from the Way practiced by the sages. For the latter was primarily concerned with benefiting the people and expediting government business, not with cosmological issues. Further, Liu pointed out, to limit such essential functions of government as broadcasting virtue and harmony, bestowing kindness, and nurturing the young to one season of the year, as prescribed by the *Yueling* schema, would be quite irresponsible.[36]

Liu was particularly critical of the custom, also based on *Yueling* prescriptions, of scheduling rewards and punishments according to the season of the year. Such a practice, he argued, might actually discourage virtue and encourage vice:

> If those who do good in the autumn and winter are made to wait until the spring or summer to be rewarded, then they will necessarily be lax. If those who do evil during the spring and summer are made to wait until the autumn or winter to be punished, then they will necessarily be relaxed. When the good are lax and the evil relaxed, then people of the world will be driven into vice.[37]

Liu Zong-yuan also composed a noted commentary on the *Tianwen* (Queries on the Heavens), a series of rhetorical questions on astronomy and cosmography forming part of the *Chu Ci* (Songs of Chu). Liu's replies to the "Queries" reveal him as a critic of such established cosmographical conceptions as the idea that the heavens are supported by eight pillars and that there are nine heavens.[38]

Ouyang Xiu's criticism, even more than that of Liu Zong-yuan, appears to have been inspired chiefly by a desire to free the original teachings of the Confucian sages from the encumbrances of cosmological commentary. Ouyang, in fact, condemned cosmology in general as unclassical and as hardly worthy of the attention of a Confucian scholar. Thus in his *Yitong Ziwen* (A Child's Queries on the *Change*), he commented that "the sage is concerned with human affairs. He seldom speaks of the encounters between heaven and man."[39]

Ouyang could hardly deny, however, that the canonical appendices to the *Classic of Change*, especially the "Great Commentary" traditionally attributed to Confucius, were principally concerned with cosmological issues. But he met this difficulty by denying that the appendices were composed by the sages or that they faithfully represented classical ideas. Rather, he argued, they were compiled from diverse sources by later students of the *Change* as a way of supporting their own interpretations. Yet the appendices were not, on his account, to be utterly condemned or completely ignored, since some of the teachings of the sages had found their way into this highly composite arrangement of texts. The task before the orthodox student of the "Great Commentary" was to salvage what sagely wisdom could be gleaned and to reject the rest for having "harmed the classics and deluded the world."[40]

Ouyang Xiu proceeded to do just that, to attempt to distinguish between orthodox and heterodox elements in the appendices, in his own commentaries on the *Change*. For example, he made a special point of downgrading the "numbers of the great expansion" passage in the "Great Commentary," which had served as focus for much Han numerological commentary on the *Change*. He concluded his discussion by remarking that "those who wish to be superior men study the words of the sages; those who wish to be diviners study the 'numbers of the great expansion.'"[41]

Ouyang Xiu's noted discussion of the "legitimate line of succession" (zhengtong) in Chinese political history criticizes the correlative schema that identifies individual dynasties with one of the five phases. According to Ouyang, the theory that dynasties succeed one another according to the "mutual conquest" order of the phases with which they are paired contravenes the teachings of the Confucian sages, who held that moral and political factors, not cosmological cycles, determine the rise and fall of dynasties:

> From antiquity, the rise of kings has necessarily [depended on] the abundant virtue by which they received the heavenly mandate [to rule]. In some cases their achievements and benefits spread to the populace. In some cases they successively and gradually completed kingly enterprises. So how can one one-sidedly designate [such rulers] by one particular virtue [or phase]? When Tang and Wu arose [and founded the Shang and Zhou dynasties], the reason that they corrected what was harmful and delivered the people was because they could not do otherwise. Hence, the statement that [because of]

the revolutions of the five phases there are good kings, and that [a king] declines by virtue of that [phase] or excels by virtue of this [phase] is the affair of astrologers and diviners. Thus to say that the rise of rulers necessarily hinges on the five evolutive phases (*wuyun*) is an erroneous and absurd proposition.[42]

Here again, the chief point in Ouyang Xiu's brief argument against an established theory is its heterodoxy, its unclassical provenance, not its internal contradictions or even its disjunction with reality. Such an argument, however, was hardly conclusive in eleventh-century China for at least two reasons. First, the level of philological expertise common in the era did not generally permit the definitive separation of the classical core of the Confucian tradition from later accretions. Usually, the skeptic could only register suspicions concerning the heterodoxy of a given text. Second, even if a particular cosmological idea could not be found in the classics, the imaginative cosmologist could always claim to have received it through a secret transmission which led back ultimately to some ancient and honorable authority. This was one of the ways which, in fact, some of Ouyang's contemporaries, the great Neo-Confucian cosmologists of the Northern Song, Zhou Dun-yi (1017–1073) and Shao Yong (1011–1077), justified their peculiar cosmological constructions. It is hardly surprising that Ouyang Xiu's opposition to traditional cosmology, strident though it was, did not effect an intellectual transformation in the eleventh century.[43]

At least one aspect of Ouyang Xiu's cosmological criticism, his rejection of the theory of resonance between natural phenomena and political developments, did, however, help to establish a precedent in official historiography. For the standard dynastic histories of China composed before Ouyang's *New Tang History* (Xin Tangshu) generally included a treatise on the five phases which correlated events in the natural and political realms. But the later standard histories either failed to include a treatise on the five phases or downplayed the theory of resonance.[44] Perhaps one reason why Ouyang's critique of cosmic resonance was more influential than those of earlier commentators was the wide range of arguments he arrayed against the doctrine. His point that Confucius, in composing his exemplary history the *Spring and Autumn Annals*, did not explicitly correlate natural phenomena with political events might well have made a special impression on classicists in late-traditional China.

Although Ouyang Xiu is probably the most famous of the eleventh-century critics, his contemporary Su Xun (1009–1066) anticipated

more closely the type of argument favored by seventeenth-century cosmological commentators. For unlike Ouyang, Su devoted some attention to
exposing forced fits and numerological disjunctions. For example, Su
pointed out that Yang Xiong's one-to-one correlation of the 729 *zan* in his
numerological system with the days and nights of the year leaves a small
remainder, since $365\frac{1}{4} \times 2 = 730\frac{1}{2}$, not 729. Yang Xiong, as noted earlier,
had attempted to make up the ¾ day difference ($729/2 = 364\frac{1}{4}$) by creating
two extra *zan*. But inasmuch as two *zan* correspond to one whole day, Yang
overshot the mark by ¼ of a day, as Su Xun observed. The discrepancy
might seem small; but if this method were used over a long period, Su
pointed out, the winter solstice would eventually be made to change places
with the summer solstice.[45]

Su Xun did not pursue his search for discrepancies in Yang Xiong's
system simply for the fun of exposing disjunctions. He had a larger purpose
in mind, which was to discredit the conflation of calendrical numerology
with studies based on the *Classic of Change*, for inasmuch as "in astronomy
numbers are paramount and in the *Change* the Way is paramount," the two
subjects (or orders of reality) should be kept distant.[46]

Other leading eleventh-century savants, notably Sima Guang
(1019–1086) and Shen Gua (1031–1095), did not criticize forms of correlative cosmology so consistently, as did either Ouyang Xiu or Su Xun. Sima
Guang on the one hand roundly condemned geomancy, a science thoroughly imbued with correlative thought, on the grounds that it was both
impractical and unclassical. Positing that the ancients "emphasized expediting human affairs" in the burial of the dead, he accused his contemporaries of blindly following the dictates of yin-yang cosmology even to the
point of postponing interment for long periods.[47] On the other hand, Sima
Guang hardly repudiated correlative cosmology in general; he composed a
numerological work, the *Qianxu* (Secret Vacuity), on the same order as
Yang Xiong's *Taixuan Jing* (Classic of Great Mystery).

Shen Gua, like Sima Guang, did not devote his main intellectual
energies to a critique of correlative cosmology. But several of the notes in
his best-known work, the *Mengqi Bitan* (Dream Brook Essays), are concerned with numerological correspondences. In general, Shen took a
skeptical view of them, as one might expect in view of his generally
empiricist turn of mind and his proposals for radical reform of astronomy
and cosmography. He criticized Sima Qian's correlation of the twelve
pitchpipes with the twenty-eight lunar lodges as an example of an "arbitrary

pairing." Elsewhere, Shen pointed out the irregularities that had issued from medical cosmologists' attempts to link bodily states to meteorological cycles rigorously through, for example, correlating the five evolutive phases (wuyun) with the six seasonal pneumas (liuqi). But Shen Gua's apparent distrust of numerological abstractions by no means led him to repudiate systems of correspondence in general. Shen endorsed a form of the *najia* system, which correlated the trigrams of the *Change* with the ten heavenly stems and the twelve earthly branches, as a means by which one might "fathom the patterns through which the cosmos is nurtured."[48]

The four discussed above were not the only Song and Yuan critics of correlative cosmology. The great twelfth-century scholar Zheng Qiao (1108–1166) challenged the five-phase theory of dynastic succession, arguing that the *wuxing* were only physical elements which did not affect temporal affairs. Ma Duan-lin (1254–1324/5) proceeded to question the theory of resonance between natural oddities and political affairs.[49] Even a few of the major Neo-Confucian philosophers of the era criticized aspects of the perennial cosmology, as illustrated in the next chapter. Yet none of these figures nor even the eleventh-century skeptics, with the possible exception of Ouyang Xiu, seem to have set out to critically analyze Han cosmology in general. Moreover, there are few, if any, cases in which the theme of cosmological skepticism may be traced throughout the works of a well-known scholar of the Song era. Whatever anticipations of particular Qing criticisms might be found here, cosmological criticism was not one of the major themes in the intellectual history of the Song.

COSMOLOGICAL CRITICISM AND CONSERVATISM
IN POST-HAN MATHEMATICAL ASTRONOMY

One other major group of possible cosmological critics in medieval China merits attention: post-Han mathematical astronomers. Technical treatises on mathematical astronomy may not appear to be a likely source for cosmological commentary. But in China, even more than in the ancient and medieval West, cosmology was quite closely related to astronomical science. Most major modes of correlative cosmology that developed in China, particularly those based on man-cosmos, state-cosmos, and *Yijing* correspondences, as well as the field allocation and Ming Tang schemata, were based on a rudimentary knowledge of astronomy and the calendar. Indeed, the point of many of the systems of correspondence was the schematic correlation of some aspect of man's world, such as the human body, the imperial state, or political geography, with the patterns of the cosmos as manifested in the constants, periods, and configurations of the astronomical heavens. For the heavens were man's widest window on the cosmos, the clearest medium through which he could view the fundamental order of space and time.

Thus it is not surprising that post-Han mathematical astronomers frequently addressed cosmological issues. But why was some of their commentary critical in the sense that it challenged, though usually only implicitly, facets of the established cosmology? How could disjunctions between astronomy and cosmology have arisen in the post-Han era? After all, such Han systematizers as Yang Xiong had taken care to reconcile their cosmological schemata with the current state of knowledge in astronomy and calendrical science. Concurrently, mathematical astronomers in the Han had endeavored to justify their calculations of calendrical constants and periods by reference to cosmologically based numerologies. But as astronomical science progressed in the post-Han era, such knowledge and such calculations came increasingly to be revealed as outmoded. This process should logically have led to a critique of Han cosmology, or at least should have moved later cosmologists and astronomers to revise the established cosmology to the extent necessary to bring it fully into accord with new astronomy. However, these possibilities were not fully realized until the seventeenth century, for reasons that will become apparent.

As Nathan Sivin has explained in his "Cosmos and Computation in Early Chinese Mathematical Astronomy," a disjunction between astronomical knowledge and cosmological conception appeared as early as the Han.[50] Astronomers of that era came to recognize that the movements and periods of the astronomical heavens did not conform precisely to the simple cyclical models constructed through numerologies. They discovered that solar and lunar eclipses and planetary conjunctions, in particular, could not be predicted over a long period by a simple counting off process. Lunar eclipses did not invariably recur once every 135 months, a figure which Han cosmologists had justified by reference to an *Yijing* numerology.

The apparent incapacity of even more complex cyclical models to forecast celestial events accurately in the long run led astronomers, in the Later Han, to conclude that unfathomable subtleties or unpredictable irregularities in the structure of the cosmos made a perpetual astronomical system an impossibility. That opinion was cogently expressed by Jia Kui (A.D. 30–101), who remarked that since "the ways of the heavens are uneven and irregular, there are bound to be remainders [in any calculation]; remainders also have variations which cannot be made uniform." As a result, even "the Taichu (Grand Inception) astronomical system [of the former Han] cannot tally with [the ephemeredes of] the present, while the new astronomical system cannot provide correct computations back to the beginning of the Han era. Any particular astronomical system can only [apply] for a period of three hundred years."[51]

Inaccuracies of calculation, then, issued not so much from mathematical astronomers' lack of skill as from unpredictable changes in cosmic patterns. As Du Yu (A.D. 228–294) explained, "The revolutions of the sun and moon are anomalous with each movement, unendingly anomalous, and thus out of kilter with the [periods of the] calendrical system."[52] These discrepancies between calendar and cosmos, initially almost undetectable, would eventually accumulate to the point where major inaccuracies appeared. If a long enough period had elapsed since the last astronomical reform, the new moon, for example, might not fall on the first day of the calendrical month. At that point, official astronomers would be obliged to undertake a major reform of the astronomical system in use to bring it into accord with new configuration of the heavens. In calculating the ephemeredes for a new era, mathematical astronomers obviously could not rely on the same correlative numerologies that had been used to generate astronomical constants and periods in earlier ages. They could not, for example, "derive" the number of years in the standard intercalation cycle by adding the final yin and yang numbers (10 + 9 = 19) noted in the "Great Commentary" to the *Change*, for the intercalation ratio of seven intercalary months for every nineteen years had been discovered to be inexact. Rather, they increasingly found it to be necessary to abandon numerology and to proceed empirically, to measure the rate at which the discrepancies between calculations and phenomena had widened since the last reform in order to make the proper adjustment.

Such early medieval theorists as Du Yu seem to have regarded the historical appearance of these disjunctions as rather mysterious, as evidence that the cosmos was in a sense animated.[53] But other astronomers in this and subsequent eras proceeded to explain rationally several of the anomalies through their discovery of specific quantifiable irregularities in celestial movements. The most celebrated of these was the "annual difference"[54] (*suicha*) between the tropical and sidereal years, the discovery of which is usually credited to Yu Xi (fl. A.D. 307–338). Yu noted that the sun as observed at the winter solstice (the shortest day) of each new year appeared to have moved very gradually backward on the ecliptic (the sun's apparent annual path through the heavens) against the background of the fixed stars. The sun, in other words, did not appear in exactly the same place in the heavens from one winter solstice to the next. More precisely, the tropical year, the time from one winter solstice to the next, was slightly shorter than the sidereal year, the time it took the sun to return to the same position on the ecliptic with respect to a given star.

The discovery of the "annual difference," though offering a rational explanation for the appearance of one discrepancy, also, as E.H. Schafer put it, "permanently dislocated the traditional belief in cosmic equilibrium by detaching the calendar [which was based essentially on the tropical year] from the fixed field of stars." According to Henri Maspero, it may even be said to have marked an epoch in the history of Chinese mathematical astronomy, in that "it put an end to Chinese astronomers' secular dream of devising a perfect calendar." In positing a distinction between the tropical and sidereal years, "it separated two things that the Chinese had always believed to be two faces of the same reality, the calendar and astronomy."[55]

Almost as damaging to the Han view of astronomical order were the discoveries of the inequalities of solar and lunar motion, that, in modern terms, both the sun and the moon traverse unequal degrees of angular distance in equal moments of time.[56] The solar inequality was the more disturbing of the two, since it meant that the lengths of the four seasons, as measured by the intervals between solstices and equinoxes, were not the same. This discovery also made it possible to conceive of a distinction between astronomical and calendrical time, more specifically between true and mean solar time.

Even after the discovery and the measurement of these and other astronomical anomalies in the Period of Disunion, some astronomers continued to insist that all astronomical movements were perfectly cyclical and to deny that basic irregularities could exist in celestial motions. The tenacity of the Han world picture is illustrated by the prominent astronomers and cosmologists of the Six Dynasties and early Tang eras who repudiated the idea of the annual difference. Dai Fa-xing, for example, opposed the conception on both empirical and classical grounds, arguing that the regularities in solar motion observed over the previous thousand years disproved the theory. To clinch his argument, Dai cited Mencius' statement that we can "while sitting in our places, go back to the solstice of a thousand years ago."[57] Even the renowned early Tang astronomer Li Chun-feng (602–670) did not accept the theory of the annual difference, though Yi Xing finally gained general assent for the idea in the next century.

By the mid-Tang, leading mathematical astronomers thus acknowledged the existence of several specific irregularities in celestial movements, even if contemporary cosmologists took little note of the development. Among Tang astronomers, the most renowned advocate of the new view of the heavens was Yi Xing, one of the most eminent figures in the history of Chinese science. Like Jia Kui, Du Yu, and He Cheng-tian (370–447), Yi Xing sometimes seems to have regarded irregularities in the movements of celestial bodies as not entirely susceptible to rational explanation. Though he attempted to measure the rate of progress of the annual difference, Yi Xing also remarked that fluctuations in the divisions of astronomical space and time "cannot be approached through calculatory astronomy." As a result, it was inevitable that with time, discrepancies between an astronomical system and the celestial movements it was supposed to forecast would appear, no matter how knowledgeable the mathematical astronomers. Once these discrepancies became noticeable, it was necessary to reform the system. According to Yi Xing, the great merit of the sagely astronomers of high antiquity was not that their superior calculations made possible a perpetual calendar—for that was impossible—but that they recognized the need for periodic calendar reforms. Realizing their own limitations and the unpredictability of the phenomena with which they dealt, the ancient astronomers deliberately devised systems appropriate only for their own era.[58]

Although there was later some debate on the question of whether a perpetual calendar was possible, most major astronomers after Yi Xing seem to have regarded the prospect as remote. While such later writers as the editors of the *Song History* (*Songshi*) deplored the seemingly endless series of calendar reforms that punctuated the later history of calendrical astronomy in China, including sixteen in the Song era alone, they admitted that the celestial phenomena codified in astronomical systems were so complex and obscure that it was impossible to avoid cumulative error.[59] The editors of the "Treatise on Astronomy" (*Lizhi*) in the *Yuan History* (*Yuanshi*) argued: "In general, the heavens have irregular movements, but mathematical astronomy depends on fixed methods. Thus over a long period discrepancies are inevitable. Since discrepancies [appear], then reform [of the astronomical system] is inevitable."[60]

In sum, post-Han mathematical astronomers became increasingly aware that astronomical systems, far from being natural reflections of celestial movements, were only artificial approximations of them. This view was obviously not at all in accord with the general world picture devised by Han cosmologists who held that regularity, equilibrium, and congruence among various orders of reality prevailed in the cosmos. Yet quite a few prominent post-Han astronomers continued to uphold aspects of correlative cosmology, even in their writings on astronomy. Perhaps the most notable survivals of correlative constructions in the works of medieval astronomers are the numerological "derivations" of astronomical and calendrical constants. As I noted earlier, these derivations rested on the assumptions that astronomical periods are regular and fixed and that there is a fundamental numerological correspondence between astronomical periods on the one hand and the figures associated with the *Change*, or harmonic proportions and intervals, on the other. Of course, the actual use of numerologically based simple periodicities in calendrical construction was increasingly abandoned from the Later Han. But as Yabuuti Kiyosi has noted, "the fundamentally metaphysical assumptions that all astronomical phenomena could be expressed in terms of periodicities long survived its utility."[61] In the "Treatise on Harmonics and Astronomy" (*Lüli Zhi*) in the Liu-Song history (*Songshu*), for example, such simple periods as the round number of days in the year are derived numerologically by relating them to harmonic figures. Thus "one pitchpipe produces five tones; and the twelve pitchpipes [altogether] make sixty tones. Accordingly multiplying 6 × 6 = 36, the 360 tones thereby correspond to the [round number of] days in the year. Therefore the numbers of astronomy and harmonics correspond to the ways of heaven and earth.[62] Dai Fa-xing, proceeding from similar assumptions, maintained that numerology was just as valid as a basis for calendar construction as empirical observation.[63]

The most renowned medieval Chinese exponent of astronomical numerology was Yi Xing, who was said to have based his astronomical system, the Dayan (Great Expansion), on the figures associated with the *Change*.[64] It is doubtful that Yi Xing ever really used *Yijing* numerologies as the basis of his astronomical calculations. But he did rationalize numerologically such factors in his system as intercalation constants,[65] thereby tying them to a larger metaphysical reality.

Yi Xing also professed a belief in the mutual resonance of astronomical and political bodies. On at least one occasion, he argued that the failure of a predicted eclipse to occur as scheduled was the result of imperial virtue having influenced the heavens. Extending his argument, Yi Xing contended that during the age of Great Peace in high antiquity, there were no solar eclipses, comets, or any other such celestial concomitants of a degenerate age.[66] Yi Xing even attempted to establish a systematic basis for explaining cosmic resonance that is strikingly reminiscent of those composed by Han cosmologists:

> Now when the five affairs are activated at the middle level [of the cosmos], then the auspicious omens of the five phases respond on the lower level, and changes in the five planets become manifest at the upper level. When the sound goes forth then the echo harmonizes; when the form moves then the shadow follows. Therefore, if the king violates the justice of the constant rules, then stars and celestial markers run off course because of it. If he ruins the arrangement of the normal principles, then celestial affairs are disordered because of it; when they run off course and are disordered, then can they be set in order by the rules of mathematical astronomy?[67]

Yi Xing thus argued that the normal order of the heavens, as calculated by astronomers, might be suspended by imperial virtue or vice. In other words, both mathematical astronomy and portent astrology have their proper realm. As Yi Xing expressed the distinction, "[When the celestial bodies] follow their proper courses, then they are assimilable to mathematical astronomy; [when they] veer off course, then they are assimilable to divination."[68]

Yi Xing also embraced other forms of correlative cosmology. For example, he characterized the sun, which suffers no waxing or waning, as that astronomical body which follows the Way of the prince. The moon, on the other hand, adheres to the Way of the vassal in that its light brightens and dims according to its distance from the sun. When the full moon infringes on the ecliptic, the sun's apparent path, "this is called the vassal's violating the glory of the prince; in that case the yang [bright or active force associated with the sun] eclipses it."[69]

In sum, astronomers of the post-Han era, despite their empirical discovery of anomalies in celestial movements, often embraced aspects of correlative cosmology as unreservedly as did Han cosmologists. Though one might think that the failure of calculations based on correlative numerologies to predict celestial movements would have disposed astronomers to repudiate the type of thinking on which these numerologies were based, this does not seem to have occurred. The survival of correlative cosmology in what should have been its unfriendliest quarters may be ascribed in part to its pervasiveness in traditional Chinese culture, but also, paradoxically, to the compartmentalization of scientific knowledge in post-Han China. In contrast with the situation in Han times and later in the Qing period, mathematical astronomy in the Tang, Song, Yuan, and Ming eras was generally quite isolated, both socially and intellectually, from most other branches of learning. Indeed, by the laws of some dynasties, calendrical astronomy was a state monopoly, the legal practice of which was limited to a corps of official astronomers attached to the imperial Bureau of Astronomy. Thus the cultivated Confucian scholar in Song or Ming China might have found the study of the subject not only intellectually distasteful and morally unrewarding, but possibly politically dangerous as well. Official astronomers in late imperial China, on the other hand, increasingly lacked the wider intellectual interests and contacts of their Han and early medieval predecessors. By Ming times they may well have merited the contempt shown them by Confucian literati and by serious private students of astronomy as well.

As a result, neither cosmologists and philosophers on the one hand, nor mathematical astronomers on the other, were generally inclined or able to apply the discoveries of astronomy to wider fields of knowledge. Both lacked the capacity to use the empirical findings of this science to formulate a general critique of the established cosmology. The Tang astronomer Yi Xing was apparently a rather rare case of a talented medieval astronomer fully conversant with the current metaphysics. But even he did not use his science to criticize the prevailing cosmology. The great Song Neo-Confucian cosmologist and metaphysicians, on the other hand, were hardly in a position to apply current science toward the critique of cosmology. For their knowledge of astronomy was, in some cases, almost a millennium out of date. Thus, through an empirical basis for a thorough critique of Han cosmology was laid out as early as Tang times, not until the seventeenth century was such a critique articulated. This challenge, however, can only be understood in the context of the history of cosmological thought in Song to Ming Neo-Confucianism.

Chapter Four

Correlative Cosmology in the Neo-Confucian Tradition

The eleventh century is a paradoxical age in the history of Chinese cosmology. While it witnessed the appearance of perhaps the most significant cluster of cosmological critics in Chinese history before the seventeenth century, it also saw the revitalization of traditional cosmology in Song Neo-Confucianism. In fact, the great Neo-Confucian cosmologists of the Northern Song era, Zhou Dun-yi (1017–1073), Shao Yong (1011– 1077), and Zhang Zai (1020–1077), were contemporaries of most of the critics, including Ouyang Xiu (1007–1070), Su Xun (1009–1066), and Shen Gua (1031–1095).

Eleventh-century cosmologists, as well as their Southern Song, Yuan, and Ming successors, did not limit themselves to simply reaffirming Han cosmology. Besides modifying much of what they inherited, Song and Ming thinkers broadened the scope of cosmological discourse. They considered such questions as the proper cosmic role of the sage and the relationship between "pattern" (li) and "pneuma" (qi), issues which transcend the bounds of "correlative thought." On the other hand, this topic does provide a useful framework for discussing Song cosmology within the broader historical context of the development of Chinese cosmological thought from the later-classical era.

Inasmuch as Song-Ming Neo-Confucianism was quite a diverse philosophical tradition extending through some six centuries of Chinese intellectual history, even the correlative aspect of Neo-Confucian cosmological thought can hardly be discussed in a summary fashion. For various Neo-Confucian cosmologists were inspired by different models and motives in their correlative thinking. Thus it is necessary to distinguish among different clusters of Neo-Confucian cosmologists. The most convenient division is fourfold. The first distinct group consists of the great cosmologists of the Northern Song, especially Zhou Dun-yi, Shao Yong, and

Shao's twelfth century follower Cai Yuan-ding (1135–1198). These are the figures who drew most directly on Han cosmology and whose cosmological ideas were, partly for that reason, attacked most vigorously in the early Qing era. Next to appear were the main figures associated with the Cheng-Zhu or *lixue* school of Song Neo-Confucianism, including Zhang Zai, Cheng Yi (1033– 1107), and Zhu Xi (1130–1200), as well as their Southern Song, Yuan, and early Ming successors. Third were the Neo-Confucian thinkers of the School of Moral Mind (xinxue), most notably Lu Xiang-shan (1139–1193) and Wang Yang-ming (1472–1529). Fourth, the noted Neo-Confucian philosophers of the late Ming, especially Lü Kun (1536–1618), Liu Zong-zhou (1578–1645), Huang Dao-zhou (1585–1646), and Sun Qi-feng (1585–1675), constitute the last significant cluster of correlative cosmologists in the high intellectual history of premodern China and furnished the immediate background for the seven-teenth-century critique. This fourfold division does not cover all the important philosophers in Neo-Confucianism, but it does encompass representatives of the major trends in cosmological thought. With the possible exception of the late-Ming group, it also corresponds roughly to scholastic divisions customarily used by historians of Neo-Confucian philosophy.

THE ELEVENTH-CENTURY COSMOLOGICAL REVIVAL

Just as Zhou Dun-yi, Zhang Zai, the Cheng brothers, and their successors are supposed to have renewed Confucianism's "orthodox line of transmis-sion" after a hiatus of more than a thousand years, so the Neo-Confucian cosmologists of the eleventh century drew directly on the thought of their remote Han predecessors, particularly Yang Xiong (53 B.C.–A.D. 18) and Dong Zhong-shu (c. 179–104 B.C.). Several prominent eleventh-century cosmologists, especially Sima Guang (1019–1086), deliberately modeled some of their own works on Han classics such as Yang Xiong's *Taixuan Jing* (Classic of the Great Mystery).[1] In fact, the *Taixuan Jing*, more than any other single source of Han cosmology, set the pattern for the work of the eleventh-century cosmologists, particularly Shao Yong. For Shao's *Huangji Jingshishu* (Book of the Supreme Rules Ordering the World), like Yang Xiong's "classic," outlined a comprehensive cosmological schema expressed in figurative and numerological terms borrowed from the *Classic of Change* and its appendices.

The comprehensiveness of Shao's schema bespeaks an epistemological optimism also characteristic of the work of such Han cosmologists as Yang Xiong. For Shao and several of his Han predecessors apparently believed that the essential aspects of various orders of reality could be incorporated into a system so complete as to be practically a simulacrum of the cosmos.

Shao Yong, however, apparently regarded his system not as merely a model of cosmic order. Rather, his schema *was* that order, or at least corresponded with it so closely as to virtually eliminate distinctions between sign and substance. According to Michael Freeman, Shao Yong's cosmological charts "are not theories about the universe but the universe itself set down on paper."[2]

Shao Yong's numerology is based essentially on four and its multiples. Deriving the number four by combining the greater and lesser yang (2) and the greater and lesser yin (+2) associated with the *Change*, Shao proceeded to identify four heavenly bodies, four earthly substances, four kinds of biological creatures, four sense organs, four ways of transforming the world, four kinds of mandates of heaven, and so forth.[3] Shao also correlated quaternary sets, using his correspondences to explain various forms of change in the cosmos. In matching the four periods of ancient history with the four seasons, for example, Shao likened historical transitions to seasonal changes. Shao and his follower held that all forms of change in the world could be expressed in terms of four and its powers. As Cai Yuan-ding explained, "In general the transformations of heaven and earth, the interactions of the myriad things, and the vicissitudes of past and present all do not depart from [the number] sixteen. In sixteen the Way of heaven and earth is completed."[4]

Shao Yong applied his quaternary correlations so widely that they often appear to be quite awkward, especially when a resonant relationship is involved. An example of such a forced fit may be found in Shao's account of how four basic meteorological conditions affect the four corresponding types of biological creatures: "Rain transforms things walking; wind transforms things flying; dew transforms things grassy; and thunder transforms things woody." Although some sense might be made of the second and third pairings in his schema, the rationale of the first and fourth is less easily grasped. On the other hand, none of the pairings in Shao's description of how heat, cold, day, and night affect the four aspects of a thing's being appear to be very commonsensical: "Heat changes the nature of a thing; cold changes the condition of a thing; day changes the form of a thing; night changes the substance of a thing."[5]

The monotonous lengths to which Shao extended his quaternary numerology might better be conveyed through a more extended quotation from the *Huangji Jingshishu*. Witness, for example, the first few lines of Shao's disposition of four of the five classics with respect to the four seasons:

> By observing spring, we know that by which the *Change* exists; by observing summer, we know that by which the *Documents* exist; by observing autumn, we know that by which the *Songs* exist; by observing winter, we know that by which the *Spring and Autumn Annals* exist. The *Change* of the *Change* means to produce life; the *Documents* of the *Change* means to produce growth; the *Songs* of the *Change* means to produce harvest; the *Spring and Autumn Annals* of the *Change* means to produce storage. The *Change* of the *Documents* means to increase life; the *Documents* of the *Documents* means to increase growth; the *Songs* of the *Documents* means to increase harvest; the *Spring and Autumn Annals* of the *Documents* means to increase storage...[6]

In this case, as in many others, Shao "works through all the possible permutations of each relationship," a procedure that requires many pages filled with the mechanical repetition of phrases. "Its effect on the reader," as Freeman has noted, "is not to convince him on particular points and thus lead him to see the whole, but to overwhelm and even lull him by its cosmic totality." Shao thus established cosmological linkages not so much by induction or deduction, but "simply by force of the rhythmic repetition."[7]

Shao applied his quaternary numerology to the classification of practically everything under heaven. But where astronomy and the calendar were concerned, Shao found it necessary to introduce another numerological order, one based on the twelves and thirties as outlined in the preface to the *Huangji Jingshishu*.

> 12 hours make a day; 30 days make a month; 12 months make a year; 30 years make a generation; 12 generations consisting of 360 years make a revolution; 30 revolutions consisting of 10,800 years make an epoch; 12 epochs consisting of 129,000 years make a cycle.[8]

This series, far from being based on any astronomical system—as Yang Xiong's was purportedly keyed to the Tai Chu (Grand Inception) of the former Han—is only a highly schematized calendrical numerology. It is quite fanciful in its higher reaches and ignores such elementary calendrical irregularities as that the lunar month is not exactly thirty days long and that twelve lunar months do not equal a solar year. Nevertheless, Shao's calendrical numerology does resemble that of Yang Xiong in that it assumes a general correspondence between a *Yijing*-based numerology and the natural divisions of time.

Shao's astronomical oversights notwithstanding, several important figures in the Song-Ming Neo-Confucian tradition hailed him as a master astronomer whose achievements in that science were unparalleled.[9] But few later cosmologists built on his work. Perhaps they felt that there was little need for further elaboration of a mode that Shao himself had practically exhausted. Or maybe they sensed the arbitrariness of some of Shao's schemata. In either case, Shao's philosophical and cosmological ideas exercised only limited influence on the development of Neo-Confucian thought. Shao, as Michael Freeman notes, "had many friends but few followers."[10]

The noted twelfth-century Neo-Confucian cosmologist Cai Yuan-ding, however, did occasionally apply the type of quaternary numerology developed by Shao Yong, especially in his studies on the system of the *Change*.[11] But in his *Fawei Lun* (A Discourse Disclosing Subtleties), Cai focused on structure or anatomical correspondences among various fields of knowledge and orders of reality. For example, he correlated medical and geomantic anatomy in the following manner:

In general, there is no difference between geomancers' investigation of circulation tracts and doctors' investigation of circulation tracts. Good doctors investigate the yin and yang of circulation tracts [of the body] and accordingly use medicines. Good geomancers investigate the rise and fall of circulation tracts [of the earth] and accordingly establish grave sites. The principle is the same [in both cases].[12]

In the same vein, and in the same source, Cai likened the contours of the moral world with those of the atmospheric. He commented, for example, that just as the cosmos is morally uneven (buqi), having both good and evil fortune, so the *qi* that concentrates about the mountains and rivers is mixed and variegated.[13]

Even in his categorizations of meteorological phenomena, however, Cai sometimes used the quaternary form developed by Shao Yong. He identified four meteorological transformations of water, explaining each in terms of a specific mode of interaction between the yin and yang *qi*. "When yang envelops yin then there is sleet; when yang harmonizes with yin then there is snow; when yin envelops yang then there is hail; when yang enters yin then there is frost."[14]

Any one of these correlations seems implausible, even inexplicable, when considered in isolation, and might well have seemed so to Cai's contemporaries. But the list as a whole has a greater intellectual attraction, both by virtue of its conceptual and linguistic symmetry and by dint of its comprehensiveness, of its having apparently exhausted the types of frozen meteorological phenomena and the possible modes of interaction between yin and yang. In this case, as in others, statements that appear to be implausible by themselves seem almost self-evident when placed in the context of a correlative schema. Partly for this reason, odd or isolated statements were sometimes "proven" by building a schema around them or by inserting them into existing systems of correspondence. Thus the substantiation of particular cosmological propositions may well have been a significant motive for the construction of correlative systems in the eleventh and twelfth centuries.

What other motives might have inspired Song cosmologists to construct systems of correspondence? Of the half-dozen reasons for the earlier development of correlative schemata, the syncretic motive also seems to have played a significant role in the Song period. Major Neo-Confucian thinkers did not, of course, generally present themselves as syncretists or eclectics but rather as restorers of a purified classical Confucianism. Nevertheless, the early Neo-Confucian cosmologists frequently incorporated ideas from other traditions into their systems. The first sentence of the earliest key cosmological document of Song Neo-Confucianism, Zhou Dun-yi's *Taiji Tushuo* (Explanation of the Diagram of the Great Ultimate), might be interpreted as a syncretic statement. It asserts the identity of the "Non-ultimate" (wuji) of the *Laozi* with the "Great Ultimate" (taiji) of the Confucian "Great Commentary' to the *Change*.[15] The cosmogonic order which follows this statement includes such diverse entities as yin-yang, the five phases, and the four seasons, all drawn from different classical texts, if not from distinct philosophical traditions.

Some of Shao Yong's correlative schemata are also broadly syncretic, or at least eclectic, in that they relate assorted figures and ciphers extracted from diverse cosmological texts. For example, building on the work of Han cosmologists, particularly Liu Xin (c. 46 B.C. –A.D. 23) and Kong An-guo (c. 156 B.C. –c. 74 B.C.), Shao split the main elements of the cosmological

universe into two corresponding sets, one centered around the Hetu
(Yellow River Chart) and the other on the Luoshu (Luo River Writing).
With the Hetu Shao associated roundness, the stars, the rules of mathe-
matical astronomy, the sage king Fu Xi, and the eight trigrams; and with the
Luoshu he grouped the cosmographical correspondents of the above,
squareness, the earth, the rules of geographical mensuration, the sage king
Yu, and the nine-square grid form.[16] The classical sources of these various
entities run almost the entire gamut of late-Zhou and early Han cosmological literature, ranging from the "Great Plan" chapter of the *Documents
Classic* to the *Dadai Liji* (The Elder Dai's Record of Rites).

Apart from indicating the range of Shao Yong's cosmological sources,
this simple system of correspondence schematizes elements of correlative
thought and geometrical cosmography. In fact, correlative cosmology was
often associated with the members of the Hetu set listed just above, and
geometrical cosmography with those of its Luoshu complement. Geometrical cosmography, for example, was concerned with the measurement of
the earth, with the modeling of spatial patterns after the nine-square grid
form and was often traced to the sage king Yu. The Luoshu itself was
supposedly the primordial cosmogram on which most of the others,
particularly the well field and Ming Tang schemata, were based.

CORRELATIVE COSOMOLOGY IN THE CHENG-ZHU SCHOOL

In contrast to Shao Yong and his followers, Neo-Confucian thinkers of the
Cheng-Zhu school eschewed the construction of systems of correspondence meant to comprehend the cosmos as a whole. But they still aimed at
understanding general patterns, particularly those of an ethical or moral
nature. This understanding was to be realized through "investigating
things" (gewu) to discover the moral principles in them. Generally speaking,
the major philosophers of the Cheng-Zhu school took current affairs and
books, especially the classics and histories, as "things" most worthy of
investigation, though Cheng Yi once remarked that things were best
investigated in oneself.[17] But they also occasionally turned their attention
toward natural phenomena for the ethical principles that they, too, supposedly manifested. Those who did so, particularly Zhang Zai, Cheng Yi, and
Zhu Xi, naturally assumed the existence of a fundamental homology
between the patterns of the natural world and those of the human or moral
sphere.

But rather than systematizing such correspondences, Song *lixue* thinkers generally invoked a particular natural pattern to illustrate its moral correspondent. Zhang Zai commented that "the nature of heaven in man is like the nature of water in ice; though it may differ by its being frozen or melted, as a thing it is unitary."[18] The early Qing Cheng-Zhu scholar Zhang Li-xiang (1611–1674) drew a similar parallel, remarking the "the four seasons change and are yet able to complete themselves over the long run. Thus [is] the gentleman with respect to the Way—he wishes that he might daily renew it."[19]

Neither of these correspondences, however, appears to have been drawn solely to illustrate an argument. For both Zhang Zai and Zhang Li-xiang seem to have assumed that the patterns of the moral or sagely mind really are immanent in nature as well. The late Ming scholar Gao Pan-long (1562–1626) expressed this viewpoint most succinctly, remarking that "the patterns of the mind and the patterns in nature are one."[20]

In sum, though few of the major philosophers in the Cheng-Zhu tradition were cosmological systematizers, some of their basic cosmological assumptions were quite conservative. For like Dong Zhong-shu, they apparently assumed that the principles of one realm of the cosmos could be known by inference from those of a corresponding realm. Dong Zhong-shu applied this idea in a much more systematic fashion than did Song and Ming Neo-Confucians, correlating, for example, the dimensions and parts of the heavens, the earth, the human body, and the imperial government. But he shared with Song *lixue* thinkers the general belief that various realms were homologous with respect to one another, though he used this idea not so much to establish a cosmological basis for Confucian ethics as to formulate a model for imperial government.

Several philosophers of the Cheng-Zhu school did call into question one or two basic presuppositions of correlative cosmology. In the first place, some of these thinkers regarded the structure of the world as far less regular and determinate than did either Han cosmologists or eleventh-century numerologists. They were more apt to note anomalies and asymmetries in cosmic patterns. This aspect of their cosmic vision is reflected to some degree in the landscape painting of the Southern Song, which is generally characterized by "asymmetry and arbitrary juxtaposition of the large units,"[21] presenting quite a contrast to the monumental symmetry of the great Northern Song landscapes. Asymmetry does not, of course, preclude cosmological order in general; but it does undermine the type of order conceived by most earlier correlative thinkers and geometrical cosmographers.

Cheng-Zhu philosophers' enhanced appreciation of anomaly in the cosmos may be attributed in part to their having acquired some inkling of the astronomical discoveries made several hundred years earlier. Thus Cheng Yi said of the "annual difference" between the tropical and sidereal years "that the yin and yang in their expansion and contraction are uneven and cannot but [produce] anomalies."[22] Zhu Xi devised a cosmogonic explanation for irregularity in general, maintaining that "when the myriad things came into being, it was as if they were flung out from a millstone; some were coarse and others fine; and because of this they were nonuniform."[23] The empirically oriented early Ming Cheng-Zhu scholar Hu Ju-ren (1434–1484) similarly remarked that "When two pneumas interact, they cannot do so in a uniform fashion. Therefore, the things to which they give birth have many irregularities." As a result, plum blossoms, for example, might bloom in the second month in one year and the twelfth in another.[24]

Major thinkers associated with the Cheng-Zhu school did not, however, proceed from their recognition of cosmic irregularities to a general critique of correlative cosmology. Far from denying the existence of cosmic correspondences, most of them continued to assume that homologous patterns structured such diverse realms as the moral mind, the Confucian classics, the natural world, and the course of human events. But one major Song thinker of the orthodox line of transmission, Zhang Zai, did challenge the notion of correspondence between man and cosmos in at least one case. He denied, in a brief passage in his commentary on the "Great Commentary" to the *Change*, that the moral constitution of the cosmos and the sage are at all similar:

> Laozi says that heaven and earth are not humane and that they regard the myriad things as straw dogs. This is correct. [But Laozi also says that] the sage is not humane and that he regards the people as straw dogs. This I must take exception to. For how could the sage have inhumanity about him? What he most abominates is inhumanity. How could heaven and earth have any inclination regarding humanity? For they only rouse the myriad things. But for the sage, humanity is everything. By this he is able to broaden the Way.[25]

Zhang Zai proceeded to argue that the Way of man should not be confused with the Way of heaven, implicitly calling into question one mode of correlative cosmology. Zhang did not apply this conclusion to the criticism of any particular system of correspondence. Nevertheless, his comments perhaps helped to inspire his seventeenth-century disciple, Wang Fu-zhi (1619–1692), to mount a more decisive critique of correlative cosmology.

Seventeenth-century cosmological critics might have also taken note of Zhu Xi's critical comments on *Yijing* correspondences. For despite his having composed such numerologically oriented works as his commentary on the *Zhouyi Can Tongqi* (Homology of the Triad to the Zhou Change), he also faulted such established constructions as the correlation of the 365 days of the year with the 384 lines of the 64 hexagrams. Zhu proceeded to criticize Han cosmologists' interpretations of the *Change* in more general terms, commenting that they "on the one hand have nothing to do with the basic sources of moral principles, and on the other do not rely on strictures concerning human affairs. Thus why is it necessary to take great pains and make great efforts in order to pursue them?"[26]

However, Zhu Xi and other Song thinkers associated with this school generally endorsed and even developed other types of numerological correspondences, particularly those based on the five phases. Zhu Xi paired four of the five phases (metal, wood, water, and fire) with the four Confucian norms or virtues (humanity righteousness, propriety, and wisdom).[27] He interpreted this pairing in light of Neo-Confucian metaphysical categories, associating pneuma (qi) with the four phases and pattern (li) with the four norms. Elsewhere, Zhu discussed the numerological discrepancy between the four Confucian norms and the four Mencian endowments or innate moral qualities (siduan) on the one hand, and the five phases on the other. Zhu's approach to the problem is reminiscent of Dong Zhong-shu's in that he singled out the odd phase, earth, as a sort of substratum for all the rest. Earth, Zhu commented, "is what water and fire anchor in and what metal and wood rely on. It resides in the center and resonates with the four directions. It is one substance and yet contains the myriad categories [of things]."[28] Zhu Xi thus justified the correlation of only four of the phases with four Confucian norms and Mencian endowments by imputing extraordinary qualities to the fifth phase.

Wang Ying-lin (1223–1286), one of the greatest and most prolific scholars of Song times, also devoted special attention to adjusting numerological discrepancies in correlative pairings. In a discussion of the medical correlation of the five evolutive phases (wuyun) with the six seasonal pneumas (liuqi), Wang commented that the fire phase must appear twice in each cycle for the proper order to be maintained.[29] Wang confronted a similar numerological discrepancy in his correlation of the five directions (including the center) with four meteorological phenomena (heat, cold, wind, and cloudiness), though he adjusted it in a different way. Having paired south with heat, north with cold, east with wind, and west with cloudiness, Wang did not assign any particular correspondent to the center, explaining that it "gets the proper balance of heaven and earth and the harmonious proportions of yin and yang."[30]

Cheng Yi, like Wang Ying-lin, discussed the problem of coordinating corresponding sets of four and five. However, Cheng focused his attention on pairing the five Confucian norms (wuchang) with the four Mencian endowments. Just as Dong Zhong-shu and Zhu Xi devised ways of dealing with the odd phase, earth, and Wang Ying-lin with the odd direction, center, so did Cheng Yi with the fifth norm, "belief" or "trust" (xin). Cheng argued that belief had no corresponding Mencian endowment, since "it was because there was disbelief that there appeared [the word for belief]. Thus the four endowments do not speak of 'belief.'"[31] Conversely, one who properly cultivates the other four norms (humanity, righteousness, propriety, and wisdom) will automatically and effortlessly have belief as well. As A.C. Graham explains, Cheng's ingenious reduction of this fifth of the five Confucian norms, "Within the nature there are four norms [which correspond to the Mencian four endowments]; the fifth, xin, is simply having the other four. As long as benevolence [or humanity] is really inside me, I am benevolent without having to ask questions or make statements about it."[32]

Cheng Yi thus made a significant philosophical point in the course of adjusting a numerological discrepancy. Cheng's discussion may in this respect be compared to Plato's correlation of the three social classes of his ideal city with the four virtues. For Plato, having matched wisdom with the philosopher-rulers, courage with the soldiers, and temperance with the farmers and craftsmen, argued that the fourth virtue, justice, "belongs to no particular class but to all three."[33]

CORRELATIVE COSMOLOGY IN THE LU-WANG SCHOOL

One might expect philosophers associated with the Neo-Confucian School of Moral Mind (xinxue) to have been less sympathetic to traditional cosmology and numerology than were their Cheng-Zhu counterparts. For *xinxue* epistemology generally regarded the moral mind as the ultimate source of truth and value, and deprecated texts, traditions, and commentaries as at best footnotes to points immanent in the purified mind and at worst serious hindrances to moral and spiritual cultivation. Further, the leading *xinxue* philosophers, especially Lu Xiang-shan, generally focused what classical studies they did undertake on the Confucian Four Books, especially the *Mencius*, texts that contain few traces of correlative cosmology. How could such thinkers have taken seriously the numerological constructs devised by Han and Northern Song cosmologists, constructs apparently not based on the teachings of Confucius and Mencius nor immanent in the moral mind?

Notwithstanding the apparent disjunction, some pages from the works of Lu Xiang-shan and Wang Yang-ming read as if they might have been extracted from Shao Yong's *Huangji Jingshi Shu*. Wang Yang-ming even reproduced a calendrical numerology quite similar to Shao's except that he began with the largest unit, the cosmic cycle of 129,600 years, and counted his way down by twelves and thirties to the smallest, the twelve-hour day.[34] Lu Xiang-shan's numerological interests are illustrated in one of his "miscellaneous works" in which he listed various kinds of things enumerated by threes, fours, and fives. The first of these enumeration orders reads as follows:

> Heaven, earth, and man are the three powers. Sun, moon, and stars are the three heavenly bodies. The trigrams are completed in three lines. Tripods stand on three legs. A statement attributed to Laozi likewise says that the one gives birth to the two, the two to the three, and three to the myriad things. Thus three is the beginning of change.[35]

Lu associated the numbers three and five with change, three with its beginning and five with its completion. But he did not clearly explain why some things should be counted in threes, others in fives, and still others in fours. Lu did indicate that things conventionally divided by fours, such as the seasons and the directions, are basically quinary in their inner structure. One ordinarily spoke of only four directions (east, west, south, north) because of the physical difficulty of dividing space into five quarters. But counting the center, there are really five instead of four. Even the Mencian four endowments (siduan), said Lu, might be supplemented by a fifth, "belief" or "trust" (xin) of which Confucius spoke on several occasions.[36]

Lu used correlative numerology to establish calendrical and musical constants. He also related the figures of the *Change* to various aspects of the physical world. For example, he accounted for the peculiar qualities of water through his explication of one of the trigrams:

Water's creation number is one and its completion number is six. Its trigram is *kan* (☵). *Kan* is yang on the inside [an unbroken line] and yin on the outside [two broken lines, one above and one below]. Water's form is soft and weak, because it has a yin exterior. But it was originally produced from yang. Thus the Daoists refer to water as yin rooted in yang.[37]

Such disquisitions are rather rare in the works of leading Song and Ming philosophers of the Lu-Wang school. But that they appear there at all in such undiluted form shows the pervasiveness of correlative cosmology in the thought of late-traditional China.

CORRELATIVE COSMOLOGY IN LATE-MING NEO-CONFUCIANISM

Cosmological skepticism did not flourish in early and mid-Ming China. On the contrary, the various divinatory and magical arts, based ultimately on correlative cosmology, enjoyed almost unprecedented support from both state and literati during this era.[38] Even Liu Ji (1311–1375), one of those fourteenth-century scholar-officials most celebrated by modern historians for his rationalism, once suggested to the first Ming emperor that he select the date on which to fight a naval battle on the basis of five-phases reckoning. Liu also held that the moral conduct of a ruler could prevent prodigies from appearing.[39] The theory of correspondence between ruler and cosmos found another influential early Ming advocate in Song Lian (1310–1381). According to John Dardess, Song held that "to the extent that the ruler's mind embodies and imitates nature, his state is well ordered and no opposition can be mounted against it."[40] Finally, Ming students of the *Classic of Change* continued to cultivate numerological cosmology.[41]

The celebrated late-Ming philosophers Liu Zong-zhou and Huang Dao-zhou, near contemporaries though they were of the seventeenth-century cosmological critics, also reaffirmed forms of correlative cosmology. Liu, the last major moral philosopher in the Ming *xinxue* tradition, attempted to reconcile *xinxue* epistemology with the cosmology associated with the *Change* through a system of correspondence. This system is based on the proposition that the figures of the *Change*, as well as the forms of heaven and earth, are immanent in the human mind. To facilitate recognition of the mental simulacra of these forms and figures, Liu included drawings of them in his "Explication of the Diagrams Associated with the *Change*." One of the simplest diagrams, a circle circumscribed around an *X*, represents the four pneumas (siqi) of the mind, and homologously the four seasons of the heavens and the four directions of the earth. A more complex one depicts the mental form of the sixty-four hexagrams with their 384 lines.[42]

Liu also elaborated more established types of numerological correspondence. He paired the "seven governors" (the five planets plus the sun and moon) of the heavens with the seven emotions in man. Extending the analogy, Liu commented that just as the heavenly bodies must move both leftward and rightward, both advance and retrogress before the year is complete so "if one does not use reversals, how can one be a sage?"[43] The paths of proper moral cultivation, in other words, are congruent with those of the heavenly bodies.

Liu's contemporary Huang Dao-zhou, probably the last great cosmologist in the Song-Ming Neo-Confucian tradition, applied his correlative thought not so much to the philosophy of mind as to the sciences, especially astronomy and calendrical studies. In this, he resembled Shao Yong, whom he praised as the most accomplished of astronomical theorists. Huang, in fact, seems to have patterned his calendrical numerology after Shao's in that he successively built up larger calendrical untis through multiplying smaller ones alternately by twelve and thirty. But Huang also expressed admiration for earlier astronomical schemata. He remarked, for example, that the *Tai Chu* (Grand Inception) astronomical system of the Former Han era was especially precise because it was keyed to the intervals of the standard bells and pitchpipes. Similarly, the Dayan (Great Expansion) system of the Tang era was superior because the lengths of its periods had been determined from the divination procedure explained in the "Great Commentary" to the *Change*. Both these approaches, and others as well, Huang maintained, could produce an accurate calendrical system, though some form of numerological manipulation was presumably required.[44] For inasmuch as the structure of the cosmos was numerologically correlative, then calendrical, harmonic, and divination units must all correspond, allowing one to infer the measurements of one from those of another.

The influence of correlative cosmology in the late-Ming Neo-Confucian thought is manifest in the works of other noted philosophers of the period. Sun Qi-feng, for example, systematically correlated the five phases (or planets) with the five earthly directions and the five Confucian virtues. He paired the virtue of humanity with the eastern quarter and the wood phase. Sun presented this simple system of correspondence to establish the point that man forms a triad with heaven and earth, that he performs a vital function in the cosmos as a whole.[45]

Finally, Lü Kun, another prominent Neo-Confucian of the late Ming era, ought, perhaps, to be classified as a transitional figure in the history of cosmological thought. For some of his cosmological views have more in common with those of the major early Qing cosmological critics than with correlative thinkers in the Song-Ming Confucian tradition. But Lü did affirm the general idea of resonance between heaven and man as well as the conception of man as microcosm. Though he generally eschewed correlative numerology, Lü sometimes paired homologous structures and processes in various cosmic realms. He remarked, for example, that just as there are two types of heaven, the heaven of pattern and the Way and the heaven of pneuma and regularity, so there are two corresponding types of human nature: the moral and the material. Lü also showed the same penchant for parallelistic classification common among Han and Song cosmologists. For example, he paired the ages of ancient history with particular moral and ethical qualities, matching the third age, that of the three kings, with propriety and righteousness.[46] In short, whatever doubts Lü Kun expressed regarding particular modes of correlative thought or geometrical cosmography, he seems to have assumed that various orders of reality, including heaven and man, history and morality, and space and time, were roughly parallel in their overall structure. Further, Lü almost always expressed his correlative thoughts in such a rigidly parallelistic syntax that it appears as if his pairing of any two sets implicitly draw in a third, that of language.

Thus the major late-Ming Neo-Confucian philosophers, far from having abandoned correlative cosmology, generally reaffirmed and even extended it. Some of these figures were among the most conservative correlative thinkers in the Neo-Confucian tradition. The influence of correlative cosmology in the late Ming was increased by the teachings associated with the syncretic Unity of the Three Teachings (sanjiao heyi) movement of that era, as well as by the steady popularization of such divinatory arts as geomancy.[47] Illustrations of correlative numerology appear even in popular literary works of the late Ming. The following passage from chapter one of Wu Cheng-en's *Journey to the West*, for example, describes a numerological microcosm reminiscent of the Ming Tang:

There was on top of that very mountain an immortal stone, which measured thirty-six feet and five inches in height and twenty-four feet in circumference.

The height of thirty-six feet and five inches corresponded to the three hundred and sixty-five cyclical degrees, while the circumference of twenty-four feet corresponded to the twenty-four solar terms of the calendar. On the stone were also nine perforations and eight holes, which correspond to the Palaces of the Nine Constellations and the Eight Trigrams.[48]

Thus the sixteenth century, in China as well as in Europe, witnessed perhaps the most extravagant development and widest dissemination of correlative cosmology in history, even though cosmologists of that era were not particularly innovative theorists. The long-term devolutionary trends in Chinese cosmological thought discussed earlier were not, by themselves, sufficient to have produced the wave of cosmological criticism that arose in the early Qing era. For if those trends were the only ones motivating such criticisms, then one would not expect to see any marked transitions, but only a gradually rising tide of skepticism.

Chapter Five

Early Qing Scholars and the Seventeenth-Century Intellectual Transition

The seventeenth century, along with the third and eleventh centuries, ranks as a major transitional era in the history of postclassical Chinese thought. The trends of this period brought such significant departures from the Neo-Confucian tradition that had dominated Chinese intellectual life for nearly five hundred years that one hesitates to call many of the principal figures of the Qing "Neo-Confucians." Some of these departures, such as the intensive cultivation of classical philology and mathematical astronomy, helped to inspire early Qing criticism of Han and Song cosmology. Hence a brief account of established interpretations of the early Qing intellectual transition should help to elucidate why seventeenth-century scholars were in a better position than their predecessors to challenge correlative cosmology.

SOME INTERPRETATIONS OF THE EARLY QING INTELLECTUAL TRANSITION

Qing scholars were the first to propose that the seventeenth century, especially in its middle decades, was a turning point in the history of Chinese thought. Even some figures whom later historians identified as the chief instigators of this seventeenth-century transformation expressly repudiated the dominant philosophical trends of the preceding few hundred years, and announced their intention of charting new courses of learning. Gu Yan-wu's (1613–1682) denunciation of what he regarded as the impractical idealism and speculative metaphysics that had supposedly dominated Neo-Confucian thought is perhaps the most celebrated expression.[1] But other noted early Qing scholars, such as Wang Fu-zhi (1619–1692), Yan Ruo-ju (1636–1704), Hu Wei (1633–1714), and Lu Long-qi (1630–1693), similarly condemned the teachings of both the Ming philosophers of the School of Moral Mind and the major Song cosmologists, and proposed to reestablish classical studies on a new basis. Of course, such condemnations of the immediate past and calls for a return to a purer antiquity might well be regarded as conventional responses to political and social upheaval. Nonetheless, probably at no time in Chinese history from the Han era, with the possible exception of the third century A.D., did leading Chinese thinkers so explicitly condemn the thought and culture of the immediately preceding era. Indeed, such expressions have tended to obscure the continuities that do exist between Ming and Qing intellectual history, and also to exaggerate the sharpness of the early Qing intellectual transition.

The noted nineteenth-century historians of Qing thought, particularly Fang Dong-shu (1772–1851), Jiang Fan (1761–1831), and Tang Jian (1778–1861), interpreted the seventeenth-century intellectual transition in scholastic terms. In their view, such figures as Hu Wei, Yan Ruo-ju, Lu Shi-yi (1611–1672), and Lu Long-qi were especially notable for having inaugurated the Han Learning (Hanxue) and Song Learning (Songxue) movements, the two dominant trends in mid-Qing scholarship.[2] The adherents of these two schools disagreed on which group of earlier scholars, Han or Song Neo-Confucian commentators, offered the surest way to comprehension of the classics and the governing of the world. But both, even most mid- and late-Qing partisans of the Song school, generally maintained that the classics, not the moral mind, human affairs, or the patterns of nature and history, were the chief repositories of truth and value, and that textual studies, not simply mindful reading and reflection, were required to ferret out this truth.

In the early twentieth century, such noted historians as Pi Xi-rui and Liang Qi-chao continued to regard the Qing as a distinct phase in the intellectual history of China and to argue that such great seventeenth-century savants as Gu Yan-wu, Huang Zong-xi (1610–1695), and Wang Fu-zhi effected a transformation in the history of Chinese thought.[3] The interpretation of early Qing thought that Liang helped to establish, the view that its practical, empirical, and textualist orientation constituted a sharp break with the metaphysical modes associated with Song and Ming Neo-Confucianism, has remained influential up to the present. While recognizing isolated precursors of seventeenth-century "real" or "solid learning" (shixue) in the Song, Yuan, and Ming, later historians of Qing scholarship, such as Qian Mu and Hu Shi, persisted in treating the seventeenth century as an era of fundamental reorientation.

Recent historians, however, have generally been less inclined to stress the distinctiveness of Qing scholarship and the abruptness of the seventeenth-century transition.[4] While recognizing the innovations fostered by such celebrated early Qing savants as Gu Yan-wu and Huang Zong-xi, contemporary investigators have traced important aspects of Qing thought back to Song, Yuan, and Ming antecedents. According to several recent commentators, major currents in Neo-Confucian thought, and not just isolated Song, Yuan, and Ming thinkers, may be linked with some of the dominant trends in Qing scholarship. Wing-tsit Chan, for example, has pointed out that Neo-Confucians of the Song era anticipated early Qing savants' procedure of basing philosophical conclusions of their studies of mundane affairs.[5] Another leading contemporary historian of Chinese thought, Yu Ying-shih, has traced important trends in early Qing scholarship back to the sixteenth century, especially to the works of such scholars as Yang Shen (1488–1599), Mei Zu, and Wang Ting-xiang (1474–1544).[6] But even Yu, though he emphasized the continuities between Song-Ming and Qing thought, has argued that an important shift in philosophical priority took place in the seventeenth century, particularly with such figures as Huang Zong-xi and Liu Zong-zhou (1578–1645). This shift, says Yu, was directed away from what the Neo-Confucians called "honoring the moral nature" (zundexing) and inner cultivation (neisheng zhi xue) toward "following inquiry and study" (dao wenxue) and world ordering (waiwang zhi xue).[7] Tang Jun-yi argues similarly in his conceptual history of Chinese thought from antiquity to the mid Qing, identifying some of the same seventeenth-century scholars as the figures most responsible for the turn toward classical scholarship and statecraft studies in the seventeenth century.[8]

Thus even those recent historians who have set Qing intellectual history within the larger context of the development of late-traditional Chinese thought often interpret the seventeenth century as an era of transition between Ming emphasis on moral cultivation and the Qing accent on empirical research. The chief point at dispute is not so much the question of the existence of an intellectual transition as of how significant were its antecedents.

METHODOLOGICAL CONSIERATIONS

At least one major methodological objection might, however, be raised to a few of the more general accounts of the seventeenth-century intellectual transformation, one that has serious implications for the present study. This is that they seem to be based primarily on research into the works of rather small numbers of scholars, particularly Gu Yan-wu, Huang Zong-xi, Wang Fu-zhi, Yan Yuan (1636–1704), and Fang Yi-zhi (1611–1671). That these scholars departed from Neo-Confucian orthodoxy in significant ways is well established. But is there convincing evidence that they represented a broad intellectual movement in seventeenth-century China? Is it possible to establish that their views were shared by most of their scholarly contemporaries? Inasmuch as the modern historians who themselves rediscovered these figures were initially attracted to some of them by their atypicality, it might be difficult to do this.

Even if these scholars were unrepresentative, is it possible to establish that their influence was so great as to have effected a change in the general intellectual climate, to have inspired a transformation in Neo-Confucian thought? This approach seems more promising. For at least two famous seventeenth-century scholars who are foci of modern interpretations of Qing intellectual history, Gu Yan-wu and Huang Zong-xi, were highly regarded and widely followed both in their own day and in the mid and late Qing. Indeed, several major trends in Qing intellectual history, especially statecraft studies, classical phonology, historical geography, and studies of the history of thought and scholarship, are sometimes traced to these figures. On the other hand, several other early Qing scholars on whom much modern commentary is focused, particularly Yan Yuan, Fang Yi-zhi, and Wang Fu-zhi, did not greatly influence the general course of Qing intellectual history. This is not to say that they are not worthy objects of study. A figure in intellectual history may be highly significant without being either representative or influential. But unless it can be established that he was either one or the other, then it is difficult to credibly use his works to gauge the intellectual climate of the age in which he lived.

Inasmuch as this book argues that the early Qing marked a transformation in at least one aspect of Chinese thought, cosmology, it will be necessary to demonstrate that cosmological criticism in the early Qing was articulated by more than a small assortment of unusually perspicacious individuals. We must establish, in other words, that we are not dealing with just another tiny cluster of cosmological critics such as appeared in the eleventh century. There are at least three ways of verifying that we are concerned with a broad intellectual movement of considerable significance.

One of these, explored in chapter 7 below, is to examine the relevant works of a few key mid- and late-Qing scholars in order to determine whether or not early Qing cosmological criticism really "took." If later scholars did, indeed, echo the criticism of their early Qing predecessors, or if they at least took it as a point of departure, then one may conclude that seventeenth-century savants did reform Chinese cosmological thought. If, on the other hand, mid-and late-Qing cosmological commentary paid little heed to seventeenth-century criticism, it would be reasonable to liken the latter to the still-born eleventh-century critique.

A second way of determining that a general reformation in cosmological views occurred in the early Qing is to establish that this movement was the logical outcome of important trends in the intellectual history of the sixteenth and seventeenth centuries. For in that case, seventeenth-century savants need not have been unusually creative to have faulted correlative thought. And, conversely, such iconoclasts as Li Zhi (1527–1602), being largely unsympathetic to the general trends stimulating cosmological criticism, would not have especially distinguished themselves as cosmological critics. Most of chapter 6 will be devoted to examining such trends.

The most obvious and arduous means of determining that cosmological criticism in the early Qing constituted a general intellectual movement is to establish that such criticism was articulated by a wide range, or at least a representative group, of early Qing scholars. Given the enormous quantity of the scholarly literature dating from that era, and in view of the underdeveloped state of the field of Ming-Qing intellectual history, there is no sure basis for determining who were representative scholars. Thus the most practical course is to examine the relevant works of those whom Qing and modern historians have identified as the intellectual leaders of the time. It is especially important that this group be as diverse as possible, that the sample represent most of the major philosophical and scholastic tendencies of the age. Moreover, if a common intellectual tendency can be shown to have animated otherwise diverse schools of thought, then there are solid grounds for believing such a trend to have been a general one in the intellectual life of the age.

EARLY QING COSMOLOGICAL COMMENTATORS

It is hard to imagine how any general study of early Qing intellectual history could ignore the works of those three scholars most celebrated by modern historians of the era: Gu Yan-wu, Huang Zong-xi, and Wang Fu-zhi. However, the first of these figures, Gu Yan-wu, seldom discussed cosmological topics, his broad scholarly interests notwithstanding. Gu even deliberately avoided cosmological and metaphysical issues, commenting that Confucius himself did not often broach such subjects as heaven or human nature and destiny.[9] But Gu's most famous work, the *Riji Lu* (Record of Daily Knowledge), does include some notes on astronomy, geography, and the figures associated with the *Classic of Change* and its appendices.

Huang Zong-xi, most celebrated for his political thought and his critical anthologies of Song to Ming Neo-Confucian philosophy, was also a quite accomplished student of the classics and of mathematical astronomy. Indeed, Li Yan, the noted historian of Chinese mathematics, has identified Huang as one of the three most illustrious seventeenth-century students of the Western mathematical sciences.[10] Among Huang's commentaries on the classics, his *Yixue Xiangshu Lun* (A Discussion of the Images and Numbers Associated with the Study of the *Change*) is a particularly valuable repository of cosmological criticism.

Wang Fu-zhi wrote a large number of works in which the theme of cosmological criticism is pervasive. These range from his earliest philosophical work, the *Zhouyi Waizhuan* (Outer Commentary on the *Zhou Change*) to his later historical commentaries, including the *Du Tongjian Lun* (Discussion of the Comprehensive Mirror [of Sima Guang]). Few of Wang's writings were printed until the middle of the nineteenth century, however, so that his critiques of Han and Song cosmology were not very influential in his own day.

Apart from Huang Zong-xi and Gu Yan-wu, the early Qing scholars most celebrated by the nineteenth-century historians of Qing thought were the figures they identified as the seventeenth-century founders of the rival schools of Han and Song learning (Hanxue and Songxue). Those major early Qing scholars commonly associated with the Han Learning, Yan Ruo-ju, Hu Wei, and Mao Qi-ling (1623–1716), all composed works commenting on aspects of Han and Song cosmology. Indeed, the principal scholarly achievements of Yan and Hu, Yan's critique of the old-text version of the *Documents Classic* (Shangshu Guwen Shuzheng) and Hu's *Yitu*

Mingpian (A Clarifying Critique of the Diagrams Associated with the *Change*), are concerned with the two classical texts that figure most prominently in Han cosmological and cosmographical speculation.[11] Further, the three works generally regarded as Hu Wei's most significant, the *Hongfan Zhenglun* (Rectifying Discussion of the "Great Plan"), the *Yugong Zhuizhi* (Boring the "Tribute of Yu"), and the *Yitu Mingbian* are all critical commentaries on important classical sources of Han cosmology. Mao Qi-ling also wrote cosmologically critical commentaries on such texts, notably the *Shangshu Guangting Lu* (Record of a Broad Understanding of the *Documents of Antiquity*).

Those figures whom nineteenth-century historians identified as the early Qing precursors of the School of Song Learning, Lu Shi-yi, Zhang Li-xiang (1611–1674), and Lu Long-qi, did not devote extensive studies to the classical sources of Han and Song cosmology.[12] But they did include brief essays and notes on astronomical, geographical, and cosmological topics in their philosophical notebooks and literary collections. Lu Shi-yi's *Sibian Lu* (Record of Thinking and Sifting), for example, discusses the nonary cosmograms formulated in the Han era, including the well-field, nine-province, field-allocation, and Ming Tang schemata. Li Guang-di (1642–1718), among other major early Qing scholars who adhered to the Cheng-Zhu school of Neo-Confucianism, wrote more extensively on cosmological topics. However, Li, in contrast to nearly all the early Qing figures named so far, generally reaffirmed the major tenets of Han and Song cosmology.

At least two mathematical astronomers, Mei Wen-ding (1633–1721) and Wang Xi-shan (1628–1682), were also among the leading cosmological commentators of the early Qing era. In view of the cosmologically subversive discoveries of the medieval Chinese astronomers, it is not surprising their seventeenth-century successors distinguished themselves as cosmological critics. Among the astronomers of the era, Mei Wen-ding and Wang Xi-shan are not only the most highly regarded,[13] but also the only early Qing specialists in the sciences prominently discussed in general histories of Qing thought. Mei and Wang composed extensive studies of traditional Chinese mathematical astronomy, unlike Xu Gang-qi (1562–1633) and Li Zhi-zao (d. 1630), the late-Ming propagators of the European mathematics and astronomy introduced into China by Jesuit missionaries. Many of the works of Mei and Wang were aimed at reconciling the traditional legacy with aspects of Western astronomy. In the course of promoting this

reconciliation, both Mei and Wang had occasion to compare the cosmological presuppositions of Western and Chinese astronomy.

The early Qing scholar who is currently most widely known for his
scientific studies is Fang Yi-zhi, whose knowledge of the mathematical
sciences was rudimentary.[14] However, Fang's interest in astronomy, geography, and *Yijing* studies, as well as his syncretist intellectual heritage, did lead
him to comment on cosmological questions. Thus Fang's *Wuli Xiaozhi*
(Small Notes on the Principles of Things), *Tongya* (Comprehensive
Refinement), and *Dongxi Jun* are significant sources for the history of early
Qing cosmological thought.

The dozen-odd figures named above do not exhaust the list of major
early Qing scholars or possible cosmological critics. We may also draw on
the writings of Huang Zong-yan (1616–1686), Gu Zu-yu (1631–1692), Yan
Yuan, Liu Xian-ting (1648–1695), and Li Gong (1659–1733). Works by a
few mid- and late-Ming scholars, particularly Wang Ting-xiang and Gui
You-guang (1506–1571), are also valuable repositories of cosmological
criticism. Indeed, Wang was probably the most prolific, incisive, and
consistent critic of correlative cosmology in all of Chinese intellectual
history up through the eighteenth century (with the possible exception of
Wang Fu-zhi). Finally, several mid-and late-Qing scholars are also relevant
to the present study.

Having properly identified most of the Qing commentators that will
constitute our sample, we might examine again the question of whether it is
representative enough to reflect the cosmological thought of the era. Some
doubts might be expressed on this issue. The sample might be biased,
inasmuch as it is largely limited to those scholars regarded by late-Qing and
modern historians of Qing thought, from Fang Dong-shu, Jiang Fan, and
Tang Jian in the nineteenth century to Pi Xi-rui, Liang Qi-chao, Qian Mu,
Jiang Wei-qiao, and Hou Wai-lu in the twentieth, as most important. They
do, however, constitute a diverse group and represent a number of different
scholastic persuasions and approaches to scholarship. One would expect
such a varied assortment of historians to have, among them, identified most
of the early Qing scholars who were important from several different points
of view.

A much more compelling objection to our roster of early Qing
cosmological commentators is that, like most surveys of Qing thought, it
includes only classicists, historians, Neo-Confucian philosophers, geogra-
phers, and mathematical astronomers. Surely early Qing specialists in other

branches of learning, such as medicine, alchemy, and geomancy, must have written extensively on cosmological topics, as the cosmological conceptions formulated in the Han era influenced those studies at least as much as they did mathematical astronomy. Indeed, medical theory in traditional China might well be conceived as a cosmology applied to the study of the human body, geomancy as cosmology directly applied toward analysis of landforms and building sites, and so forth. Why, then, exclude them from consideration specialists in such significant and relevant branches of learning?

Aside from the relative obscurity of the surviving Qing literature in other cosmologically related branches of learning, there are a few a priori reasons for focusing on the works of classicists, astronomers, and Neo-Confucian thinkers. First, these figures apparently had a much wider audience among their literate contemporaries than did alchemical, geo-mantic, or even medical theorists, if for no other reason than that the principal education curriculum in the Ming-Qing period consisted mainly of classical texts with Neo-Confucian commentaries. Qing classicists and Neo-Confucian thinkers could assume that literati of the day had a general familiarity with the issues and texts with which they dealt. They could also reasonably expect that a well-substantiated challenge to an established exegetical tradition would command the attention of many of their literate contemporaries.

Second, classical and Neo-Confucian studies, and to a lesser degree research in the exact sciences, enjoyed great prestige among Qing scholars as well as official support and encouragement. Accomplishment in these fields, moreover, was a means of acquiring power as well as prestige (through a classically oriented examination system which led to civil service appointment) and wealth (through attracting the support of patrons of scholarship). Achievements in most other fields of learning were not generally so munificently rewarded or highly regarded. Indeed, some of the cosmologically oriented sciences, especially alchemy and geomancy, were denigrated, even ridiculed, by prominent Qing scholars.[15] Hence, one would expect that many of the most talented and ambitious young literati in Qing China would have avoided such studies and pursued the more approved branches of learning. Although an unusually large concentration of talent in one particular field hardly assures intellectual innovation in that field, it might well make it more likely.

A third and final a priori reason for focusing on classicists in particu-lar is that the classics, in conjunction with their Han commentaries and extensions, were the ultimate textual sources of both correlative cosmology and geometrical cosmography in the Chinese intellectual tradition. As such, they would most likely have attracted the attention of those who were most interested in exploring the textual and philosophical roots, as opposed to the later ramifications, of the established cosmology. Inasmuch as Han cosmologists evidently took considerable liberties with such texts as the *Documents* and the *Change*, early Qing commentators had a solid textual basis for criticizing Han cosmology that was not generally available to specialists in other branches of learning. They had the means of proving that important aspects of traditional cosmology and cosmography were based on the systematic distortion (or creative reinterpretation) of classical passages. In contrast, the "classics" in other fields, including medicine, alchemy, and geomancy, were products of the Han and later eras. These texts, unlike the Confucian classics, were already thoroughly imbued with the cosmological ideas established in the Han, giving later specialists in these studies little in the way of a textual basis for criticizing correlative thought. Thus one would expect classicists to have mounted the most incisive critique of correlative cosmology in the early Qing era.

Chapter Six

Intellectual Origins
Of Early Qing
Cosmological Criticism

Historians of Western science and culture have been known to attribute the demise of Aristotelian cosmology, Ptolemaic cosmography, and theories of correspondence in seventeenth-century Europe to the rise of the new astronomy. It has been suggested that Galileo's telescopic discoveries by themselves snapped several key links in the chains of correspondence that were supposed to bind the cosmos together, and annulled the cardinal distinction, in Western cosmological thought, between sublunary and superlunary worlds. Essential supports in the edifice of cosmological theory having been removed, the whole is then supposed to have fallen like a house of cards.

It is unlikely, both on priori grounds and on the basis of the evidence in such classic studies as Tillyard's *Elizabethan World Picture* and Huizinga's *Waning of the Middle Ages*, that traditional Western cosmology met its end so swiftly and simply. It is even more unlikely that the Qing critique of Han and Song cosmology could be adequately explained as an effect of so simple a cause. Even the eleventh-century criticism of correlative cosmology, limited though it was, can be plausibly accounted for only by positing several different factors.

This is not to say that movements in intellectual history are inherently complicated, or that the more factors that can be introduced into a discussion of origins, the better will be the explanation. But Chinese cosmology in particular is so structurally complex, conceptually elastic, and variously ramified into almost every branch of traditional Chinese culture that it is hard to imagine any single point from which this world of discourse could be moved.

THE LIBERATION OF THE SCIENCES
FROM MORAL METAPHYSICS

The origins of early Qing cosmological criticism may be traced to trends in the intellectual history of the late-Ming and early-Qing, particularly the assimilation of cosmologically subversive technical and empirical studies such as classical philology, mathematical astronomy, and historical and physical geography into the mainstream of Confucian scholarship. The Ming origins of the movement are obscure, but it seems to have been accelerated by the Jesuit introduction of aspects of European learning into seventeenth-century China, as well as by the revival of statecraft studies in that era. The formation of networks of patronage for the support of various classical and technical studies in the early Qing further encouraged Confucian scholars to develop expertise in the subjects.

But didn't Neo-Confucian savants in pre-Qing times also pursue studies in astronomy, geography, and philology? If so, then what was peculiar about Qing scholars' cultivation of scientific and exegetical subjects?

Pre-Qing scholars in the Confucian tradition, as well as scholastics in the medieval West, did indeed pursue such studies. But both Neo-Confucian and Christian scholastics, the major guardians of the dominant traditions within the respective cultures, generally pursued the study of the sciences as ways toward the illumination of higher truths. In the West, the idea that science and philosophy should serve as handmaidens to theology may be traced back to late antiquity.[1] The subordination of the sciences to theology in the medieval West culminated in the writings of the thirteenth-century schoolmen, especially Saint Thomas Aquinas, for whom "almost the whole of philosophy is directed to the knowledge of God," and Saint Bonaventure, "who regarded all forms of knowledge and learning as subservient to theology and useful solely in that ancillary function."[2] By the high middle ages, even such purely scientific issues as those having to do with projectile motion and atmospheric pressure were "indirectly or directly supervised by theology."[3]

Even in the Western middle ages, however, a handful of investigators continued to pursue studies of the natural world independently of any religious purpose. By the fourteenth century, according to Gordon Leff, "a distinctive body of scientific, mainly mechanical, theory arose with its own independent principles and procedures, which were self-contained and not subservient to higher nonphysical principles."[4] But not until the seventeenth century did a major philosopher in the Thomist tradition, Francis Suarez (1548–1617), repudiate the idea that science should be the handmaiden of theology. Suarez argued that "one cannot prove the existence of God by arguments drawn from 'physics.' In order to show that God exists it is necessary to have a recourse to metaphysical arguments."[5] In separating physics from metaphysics, Suarez, however, was not so much proclaiming the intellectual autonomy of the sciences as he was denying that they could illumine truths of religion.

The Song Neo-Confucian contemporaries of the great Christian schoolmen also generally subordinated specialized branches of learning, especially the sciences, to higher concerns, though to moral or ethical philosophy rather than theology. Zhu Xi (1130–1200), for example, indicated that the principles of both literature and history were rooted ultimately in the realm of ethics.[6] Although the "investigation of things" (gewu) might reveal certain patterns or principles (li) in various aspects of history, nature, or literature, these principles generally had some moral or metaphysical import. Such studies as the six canonical arts (liuyi), the constituent principles of which were not necessarily of a moral or metaphysical character, were also to be cultivated as a means toward a Confucian end, either rectifying the mind or governing the world.

Other major Song Neo-Confucian philosophers also conceived of the sciences as lamps lighting the way to moral illumination. Even Zhang Zai's extensive comments on astronomy were intended "as a means of manifesting the principles of human nature and destiny."[7] Zhang maintained limiting oneself to the quest for empirical knowledge would fetter the mind, making it difficult to attain the aim of thoroughly plumbing moral nature.[8]

Prominent philosophers of the Ming era continued to advocate the moral- metaphysical approach to the natural world and to the sciences. Lü Kun (1536–1618), Gu Xian-cheng (1550–1612), and Gao Pan-long (1562–1624), for example, believed that empirical knowledge was at most a way station on the path to virtue and to the acquisition of moral knowledge.[9] On the other hand, Wang Ting-xiang (1474–1544) and Liu Zong-zhou (1578–1645) did advance the place of empirical study in the Neo-Confucian scheme of things, for they maintained that it was essential to moral enlightenment and not just one means of approach. Thus Wang commented that "no matter how clever the spiritual nature is, it must rely on seeing, hearing, thinking, and reflecting to be knowledgeable."[10]

However, even within the Neo-Confucian tradition, there were those who emphasized learning for the sake of world ordering or statecraft as opposed to self-cultivation. Scholars who emphasized statecraft, such as Ye Shi (1150–1223) and Wang Ying-lin (1223–1286), were more inclined to concede, at least tacitly, some degree of intellectual autonomy to these specialized studies. They did not so readily assume that the constituent principles of astronomy or geography were at bottom moral-metaphysical. For this assumption would hardly have facilitated the practical tasks, such as revising the calendar and constructing waterworks, that students of statecraft set for themselves. Neo-Confucian statecraft scholars were, however, generally in the minority until the seventeenth century, though a significant cluster of them did appear in the thirteenth century. They also concentrated studies not in the physical or philological sciences, but in such fields as fiscal administration, agrarian policy, and military affairs, branches of learning that were more directly related to problems of government.

Outside the Neo-Confucian tradition, some savants apparently cultivated the sciences mainly for amusement or intellectual interest, though they seldom admitted as much. Scholars of this sort include a few of the great astronomers of the Six Dynasties era as well as some of the celebrated mathematicians of the Song and Yuan periods. However, as Shigeru Nakayama has pointed out, the mathematical sciences of traditional East Asia "were not considered scholarly unless they made a contribution to 'self cultivation, husbandry, and the pacification of society.'"[11] This was especially true for the period following the crystallization and dissemination of Neo-Confucian ideology in the Song. Thus the more technically oriented students of the sciences who did not aim toward any of the proper Confucian ends listed by Nakayama became increasingly isolated from the intellectual mainstream.

Seventeenth-century scholars in the Confucian tradition, however, largely ended this long isolation. Almost every noted savant of the early- and mid-Qing seriously pursued the study of at least one science, with astronomy, mathematics, and geography being the most popular. Although not all became experts, a few, such as Mei Wen-ding (1633–1721) and Tai Zhen (1724–1777), composed scientific works that were considered definitive in eighteenth-century China. Not since the Han, if ever in Chinese intellectual history, were leading thinkers so knowledgeable and interested in current scientific studies. And certainly never before in Chinese intellectual history had a large group of self-proclaimed Confucians focused so much of their attention on such subjects.

Early-and mid-Qing Confucian scholars, however, tended to present their scientific studies as a restoration of an ancient intellectual unity, not as a departure from tradition. They maintained that Confucianism and science, particularly mathematical astronomy, were naturally complementary as well as classically connected, though Song and Ming Neo-Confucians had severed the link between the two. A number of noted early Qing savants either lamented or condemned their Neo-Confucian predecessors' ignorance. Huang Zong-xi (1610–1695), for example, complained that of the major Song philosophers, "many did not understand the methods of mathematical astronomy. Zhu Xi and Cai Yuan-ding were overly fond of numerology, and thus what they spoke of were theories of resonance which had no practical application."[12] Huang's younger contemporary Wang Xi-shan (1628–1682) argued that post-Tang estrangement of Confucian scholarship and mathematical astronomy harmed both:

> From Song times astronomy split into two branches. There was the astronomy of the Confucian scholars and the astronomy of the professional astronomers. The Confucians were not acquainted with mathematical astronomy, and thus invoked empty principles to establish their theories. The specialists were not acquainted with theoretical astronomy, and thus held to a fixed method in predicting celestial phenomena. But apparently no one mastered the foundations of the celestial configurations and movements. [13]

In arguing that cosmic patterns could be apprehended only by concurrently cultivating Confucian philosophy and mathematical astronomy, Wang Xi-shan and his contemporaries liberated the latter from the epistemological domain of the former. In other words, they maintained that astronomical phenomena should not be understood simply as manifestations of Neo-Confucian principles. For there were patterns proper to the heavens that had to be investigated through empirical observation and mathematical calculation before there could be any question of developing a cosmological schema. To the extent that these patterns were found to contravene the fundamentals of Han and Song cosmology, cosmology could be challenged on solid empirical grounds. Moreover, since astronomical patterns were important illustrations of established cosmological principles, the revelation of discord between the two was especially damaging. Astronomy, formerly the handmaiden of Neo-Confucian cosmology, became one of its most formidable critics.

Not all early Qing scholars, however, readily acknowledged the inherent value of empirical studies. Scholars associated with the School of Song learning were especially reluctant to abandon the Neo-Confucian moral-metaphysical approach to knowledge. Lu Shi-yi (1611–1672), for example, commented that the objects of the botanical world, insignificant in themselves, were notable only insofar as they manifested in visible form the workings of yin and yang and the five phases. They constituted a proper study for the Confucian scholar so long as he examined them for the metaphysical principles they revealed and did not simply observe their peculiarities or seek to increase his knowledge of things as such. For in the latter case, the investigator would be guilty of "trifling with things and losing his purpose." By neglecting the great precept that "the principles of the cosmos are [the same as] the principles of my mind," he would forfeit the opportunity to rectify the mind through the investigation of things (gewu).[14]

But even Lu Shi-yi acknowledged that there were certain areas of learning, such as astronomy, the principles of which were neither immanent in the mind nor necessarily of a moral-metaphysical character. These subjects, Lu admitted, would have to be approached through empirical study. The student of astronomy, for example, would find it necessary to investigate the divisions of celestial space and the movements of the heavenly bodies.[15] By thus excluding certain subjects from the ambit of Neo-Confucian moral knowledge, while nonetheless maintaining that such studies were worthy of being cultivated by the orthodox scholar, Lu Shi-yi implicitly admitted a break in the continuum of knowledge.

Even those few early Qing scholars who vigorously reaffirmed the subordination of the sciences to Neo-Confucian moral-metaphysics betray evidence of this break. Diao Bao (1630–1669) on the one hand emphasized that studies of astronomy and geography were justified only as means of advancing toward those moral aims related in the *Change* under the *qian* (heaven) and *kun* (earth) hexagrams. Yet he admitted that most of his contemporaries approached these sciences from a technical point of view:

The men of today who talk of "astronomy" all emphasize the calculation of the ephemerides. But I say that just as "celestial movements are strong, so the gentleman strengthens himself without ceasing." This is the "astronomy" of Confucius. The men of today who talk of "geography" all emphasize the investigation of territorial limits. But I say that just as "terrestrial contours are compliant, so the gentleman liberalizes virtue and carries all things." This is the "geography" of Confucius.[16]

CLASSICAL AND EXEGETICAL STUDIES

The branch of learning which in early Qing times inspired the widest critique of Han and Song cosmology was not, however, astronomy but classical studies. That such studies did not stimulate much cosmological criticism until the Qing may seem peculiar. Scholars had been composing commentaries on the classics ever since the Han era. Indeed, some of the commentaries are landmarks in the history of Chinese thought. However, one reason why they are so considered is that many of them were media for the expostulation of independent philosophical viewpoints. Such famous commentators as Wang Bi (226–249) and Zheng Yi (1033–1107) often treated passages from classical texts more as preambles for their own philosophical reflections than as objects of philological inquiry. For example, much of Wang Bi's commentary on the *Classic of Change* is informed by the world view of philosophical Daoism, as Mou Zong-san has pointed out.[17] Even had they been intent on pure exegesis, few pre-Qing classical scholars had developed the philological procedures required to distinguish clearly between classical ideas and systematizing commentary.

Hence, Qing classical scholars were generally distinctive in at least two respects: their high degree of philological expertise and in their purely exegetical aim. Works by two notable early Qing cosmological critics, Yan Ruo-ju's *Shangshu Guwen Shuzheng* (Inquiry into the Authenticity of the Old Text Version of the *Documents of Antiquity*) and Hu Wei's *Yitu Mingpian* (Clarifying Critique of the Diagrams Associated with the *Change*), are good examples of successful efforts by Qing scholars to distinguish the authentic classical core of a canonical text from later accretions and interpretations. Inasmuch as major early Qing classicists focused their attention particularly on those two classics, the *Documents* and the *Change*, which Han and Song cosmologists had used most extensively in the formulation of their systems, they were especially well equipped to challenge the latter on textual grounds.

Early Qing commentators applied their philological expertise directly to the criticism of Han and Song cosmology. One way in which they did this was by examining the classical sources of particular schemata, such as the *najia* system and the Hetu and Luoshu cosmograms. In cases where the pre-Han antecedents were diffuse and enigmatic, as with the Hetu-Luoshu set, early Qing commentators were able to expose the systematizing nature of Han commentary, the fact that it studiously conflated unrelated and decontextualized passages drawn from diverse texts. In instances in which the schema in question lacked all but the most tenuous classical basis, Qing exegetes could accuse its architects of outright heterodoxy.

Where a key term was in question, as with heaven (tian), yin-yang, or the five phases (wuxing), Qing classicists adopted an approach that was more strictly philological. Through examining and comparing the earliest extant appearances of these terms in such texts as the *Documents* and the *Songs*, they were able to establish that the characters originally lacked the cosmological senses imputed to them by later commentators, especially Han and Song cosmologists. By stripping terms like *wuxing* of their postclassical meanings, Qing commentators seriously undermined cosmological thought.

Qing scholars' approach to the classics was also distinguished by their relative purity of intention, by the single-mindedness of their quest to reconstruct the ancient meanings of the early texts. Inasmuch as earlier commentators also announced this to be their aim, how can it be established that seventeenth-century classicists were more sincere in making such claims, or more persistent in following through on them?

One way is by recalling that Qing commentators, in contrast with most of their Neo-Confucian predecessors, came to view the classics, and not the moral mind, the patterns of nature and history, or the course of human affairs, as the chief repository of truth in the universe. Whereas the Song rationalists took the classics as only one of a number of sources of ultimate principle (li), and Ming idealists even reduced the classics to the position of footnotes to the moral mind, Qing classicists were well aware of the heterodoxy and confusion bred by the search for *li* in extraclassical sources. They were therefore more inclined to insist on a relatively objective, authoritative criterion of truth, a condition that could best be met through reliance on the classics.[18] For since the Confucian classics reposited the thought of the wisest men who had ever lived—the sages of antiquity—they might almost be said to have an eternal validity. Thus early Qing scholars hoped that interpretations of *li* based on classical exegesis would be so authoritative as to end forever the kind of sectarian strife that had flourished in the late Ming. Such an expectation may well have inspired Gu Yan-wu's famous statement that the ancients studied *li* by studying the classics.[19]

An important concomitant of Qing commentators' single-minded classicism was their opposition to syncretic thought. For inasmuch as the latter assumed that value could be found in a multiplicity of sources from different intellectual traditions, it denied the unique authority of the Confucian classics. Although early Qing antisyncretism may have been aimed principally at discrediting the syncretic religious and philosophical movements that figured prominently on the mid- and late-Ming intellectual scene, it was also directed against the noncanonical elements in Han and Song Neo-Confucian cosmology. Considerable portions of Hu Wei's *Yitu Mingpian* and Huang Zong-xi's *Yixue Xiangshu Lun* (A Discussion of the Images and Numbers Associated with the Study of the *Change*) are devoted to tracing how various diagrams and numerologies from heterodox sources came to be incorporated into Neo-Confucian cosmology. The object of this procedure was not just to discredit such bases of Song cosmology as Zhou Dun-yi's "Diagram of the Great Ultimate" (taiji tu), but more broadly to desyncretize the Neo-Confucian tradition, to purge it of all elements that were not strictly canonical.

Since intellectual syncretism was one of the major motives inspiring the formulation of correlative systems in the Han and Song, classicist desyncretization threatened the raison d'être of some systems. If even one or two of the correlative sets in a system of correspondence could be shown to have extraclassical origins, then the whole schema was questioned. Thus Hu Wei's exposure of the noncanonical origins of the astronomical and alchemical elements in the *najia* system must have made the whole arrangement seem suspect, as Hu himself implied.[20]

Early Qing scholars' enhanced exegetical expertise and single-minded classicism thus gave them both means and motives for challenging Han and Song cosmology. But to what extent did these scholars succeed in discrediting this cosmology and recovering the classical world view? A provisional answer to this question might be proposed on the basis of sixteenth- and seventeenth-century reinterpretations of a few key terms in the perennial cosmological lexicon.

The sixteenth-century figure who proposed the most thorough, deliberate revisions in this lexicon was Wang Ting-xiang. Wang, in fact, attempted to imbue almost every major cosmological term used by Han and Song metaphysicians with what he believed to be its original concrete meaning. He argued, for example, that in antiquity the *wuxing*, as used in the "Great Plan" chapter of the *Documents Classic*, did not refer to cosmological categories but to material elements that the ruler was obliged to regulate in order to nourish the people.[21] For example, "water" (shui) referred to the aqueous element that the sovereign was supposed to put in order by building and maintaining irrigation works.

As for the correlative system based on the *Change*, Wang indicated that the eight trigrams, a key to most of them, were originally modeled on assorted phenomena and not meant to be integrated into a comprehensive system for explaining change in the universe. Finally, Wang objected to the prevailing use of the yin-yang duality for interpreting such cyclical changes as the alternation of the seasons, pointing out that proximate, material causes, such as the annual movement of the sun, were sufficient to account for such phenomena.[22]

Several early Qing classicists argued along these lines. Huang Zong-xi, for example, commented that whereas many of his Confucian contemporaries interpreted "heaven" (tian) to mean cosmic "pattern" or "principle" (li), references to "heaven" in the *Change* and the *Songs* showed that the ancients conceived it as a sovereign power which was able to give birth to humankind and cause disasters.[23] This radical redefinition of "heaven" implicitly challenged such widely accepted dichotomies as that between "heavenly principles" (tian li) and "human desires" (ren yu). Hu Wei's redefinition of the terms *xiang* and *shu*, which Han and Song cosmologists generally took to mean "image" or "simulacrum" and "number" or "regularity," respectively, undermined systems of correspondence based on the figures of the *Change*. According to Hu, these terms originally denoted only the concrete objects used in the process of divination, particularly the hexagrams and milfoil stalks.[24] They did not refer to the numerological systems or cosmographical figures with which later cosmologists linked them. Finally, Wang Fu-zhi (1619–1692) dissociated the classical *wuxing* from the cosmological schemata which postclassical philosophers used to explain the phases of change in the universe, echoing Wang Ting-xiang on this point. According to Wang, the original *wuxing*, as described in the "Great Plan" chapter of the *Documents*, referred only to materials used in economically productive activities.[25]

Early Qing exegetes' concrete reinterpretations of key terms in the perennial Chinese cosmological lexicon in some cases approximated the classical meanings of such terms. Even so, it is possible that some of these commentators were pursuing what H.D. Harootunian, following Kenneth Burke, has called an "archaicizing strategy" in a deliberate effort to "recover the individuality of things in their essential particularity, uniqueness, and concreteness."[26] Indeed, Wang Ting-xiang, like the *Kokugaku* (National

Learning) scholars of eighteenth-century Japan studied by Harootunian, once stated his aim of "putting straight the simple and concrete vision of high antiquity," and of "wiping out the absurd usages of later ages."[27]

If Wang and other cosmological critics of the era were deliberately "archaicizing," then they probably took the rejection of correlative cosmology as a point of departure. For what reason could there be for devising systems of correspondence in a world in which things could only be known in their "essential particularity, uniqueness, concreteness"? Indeed, such cosmological schemata were often the most formidable barriers separating the archaicizer from the archaic.

THE HISTORICIZATION OF NATURE

Most prominent early Qing scholars, whether or not they pursued an archaicizing strategy, did acknowledge that both the shape of the world and the sphere of human knowledge had changed since ancient times. As the heirs of a continuous scientific tradition some two thousand years old, Qing savants were in good position to note the existence of secular changes in the natural world and to appreciate the progressive development of some of the sciences. The situation should logically have given rise to two additional sources of cosmological criticism in the late-traditional era. First, if the patterns of the cosmos had altered appreciably since antiquity, then the schemata that Han cosmologists had devised for explaining these patterns were out of accord with current physical reality. Second, if the cosmologically related sciences, such as astronomy and geography, had really progressed so far in the fifteen hundred years from the Later Han to the Qing, then why rest content with a cosmology based on a woefully outdated science? Why not update the world picture by reference to more recent developments?

Of course, secular change in the natural world, as well as progressive development in scientific knowledge, can take many forms, not all of which necessarily subvert an established cosmology. Thus it is necessary to recount just what types of change Qing savants recognized, and then consider how that recognition might have inspired cosmological criticism in the seventeenth and eighteenth centuries.

The idea of cosmic change was not unknown in pre-Qing China. Even such classical texts as the *Laozi* and the "Great Commentary" record rudimentary cosmogonic speculations. [28] The third chapter of the *Huainanzi* contains a more extended account of the successive stages of cosmic evolution, proceeding from the Dao which gives birth to the void, which in turn produces the universe of space and time, which then gives rise to pneuma (qi) and so on.[29] Such cosmogonic ideas, never really very elaborate, underwent little development after the Six Dynasties period, even when Neo-Confucian cosmologists appropriated them in the Northern Song era.[30] In any case, traditional Chinese cosmogony was largely unconcerned with long-term change in the patterns of nature, focusing instead on the remote ahistorical formation of the cosmic order.

However, from as early as Tang and Song times, poets and philosophers came to recognize other forms of long-term change, besides the cosmogonic, in the natural world. By the Song era, even the idea of geological change was common currency, having been endorsed by such eminent thinkers as Shen Gua (1019–1086) and Zhu Xi.[31] But though they occasionally acknowledged cosmic change on a grand geological scale, most Song, Yuan, and early Ming Confucian thinkers seem to have generally assumed that the face of nature, the patterns of sky and earth, had altered very little since the end of the classical era. Though dynasties had waxed and waned and institutions had changed since ancient times, the astronomical and geographical realms ordered by the Han cosmographers had, so it seemed, remained fairly stable.

Seventeenth century scholars, however, especially students of those sciences related to cosmology, discovered that the patterns of the heavens and the earth had altered appreciably even in historical times. The famous early Qing geographer Gu Zu-yu (1631–1692), for example, felt that the extent of the geographical changes that had occurred since the composition of the "Tribute of Yu" chapter of the *Documents Classic* required the formulation of new geographical measures to replace outmoded ancient ones.[32] One of the major themes of seventeenth-century comments on the "Tribute to Yu" in general was that the nine regions of the realm described in that classic had been radically transformed since antiquity, necessitating revision in the original schema. Barbarian encroachments and the collapse of irrigation works in the Northwest and the transformation of the Southeast from a marshy wilderness to the most prosperous and densely populated region of the realm were the developments that such seventeenth-century commentators as Lu Shi-yi, Lu Long-qi, Wang Fu-zhi, Gu Yan-wu, Yan Ruo-ju, and Liu Xian-ting most frequently cited as having altered the ancient geographical order.

Even the patterns of the heavens, early Qing savants recognized, had altered perceptibly. One of the most disturbing causes of such changes, the "annual difference" between tropical and sidereal year lengths (suicha), had been noted by Song Neo- Confucians. But Qing students of astronomy admitted other alterations as well, including historical variations in the orbital periods of planets (especially Jupiter) and in the obliquity of the ecliptic with respect to the celestial equator.[33] For Lu Shi-yi, secular changes in the patterns of the heavens were significant enough to require the periodic adoption of new cosmological systems. According to Lu, the traditional Chinese world conceptions, the "covering heaven" (gai tian) and the "rounded heaven" (hun tian), were to be rejected not so much because they were empirically inaccurate or theoretically uniformed as because they were out of date. On the other hand, the Western world systems introduced into seventeenth-century China by Jesuit missionaries were relatively precise, since they were newer,[34] and thus presumably reflected more recent cosmic developments. Ruan Yuan (1764–1849), in the mid-Qing, extended this argument, commenting that even recent Western cosmological models would eventually be rendered obsolete by the future evolution of the cosmos. Something of this sort, Ruan suggested, had already occurred, as indicated by the substitution of Keplerian ellipses for Ptolemaic epicycles in Western planetary theory.[35]

Lu Shi-yi posited the existence of secular change in the acoustical realm, as well as the astronomical and geographical, arguing that the lengths and tones of the pitchpipes had altered appreciably since antiquity. Lu contended that since the tonic of the pipes, the *huang zhong*, was theoretically attuned to the pneumas which arose from the earth at the winter solstice, the beginning of the tropical year, then the annual differ-ence between the tropical and sidereal years affected the pitch of this and the other canonical pipes.[36] This implied that the "watching the pneumas" (hou qi) correlative system which keyed the twelve pitchpipes with the pneumatic emanations that supposedly rose out of the earth, each in a certain season, had to be adjusted with every calendar reform. The recogni-tion of such difficulties undermined confidence in the *hou qi* correlative system and facilitated its ultimate rejection by late-Ming and early-Qing commentators.[37]

A final historical change in natural patterns which stimulated seven-teenth-century criticism of established cosmological ideas was the great wave of epidemics in late-Ming times, as described in an article by Helen Dunstan. That even an unprecedented concentration of epidemics could have aroused cosmological criticism in late traditional China may seem strange unless one recalls that in Chinese medical theory, pestilence was generated by the unseasonable appearance of a particular cosmic phase or pneuma. When the six seasonal pneumas (liuqi) and the five phases (wuxing) succeeded one another in proper seasonal order, without anomaly or deviation, then epidemics would be very rare. The experience of the great late-Ming epidemics seems, however, to have led at least one prominent medical theorist of the time, Wu Yu-xing (1582–1652), to challenge the established notion that pestilence arose when the progression of the phases did not mesh with the course of the seasons. According to Wu, as translated by Dunstan, "Explanation of the prevalence of diseases cannot be confined to consideration of the year and the seasons, for it is not something that can be determined by the procession of the Five Agents [= five phases] or the vagaries of the Six Qi, which is how we know that the Qi [which causes disease] are arbitrary with regard to time." Wu went on to say that "febrile epidemic diseases occur in all four seasons and from one year to the next without a break."[38] While Wu continued to use the traditional cosmological vocabulary, he challenged what was perhaps the most basic presupposition of traditional medical theory, the idea of correspondence between the phases and periods of the cosmos at large with those relating to health and disease.

Seventeenth-century savants recognized secular change in human culture and institutions as well as in the natural world. This recognition could not have been purely a product of the events surrounding the fall of the Ming and rise of the Qing, since it was anticipated by a few prominent savants of the mid and late Ming. Thus Wang Ting-xiang wrote that "what was suitable in ancient times cannot be suitable in modern times. Ultimate pattern (or principle) brings about what is appropriate to the times. All that is past is like straw dogs; and is it not rotten and broken as well?"[39] Lü Kun (1536–1618) commented that even the sages, were they to be reborn, could not restore the ancient ways in the circumstances of the present, but "would be obliged to conform to the times and yield to circumstances."[40]

A prime example, cited by several seventeenth-century commentators, of a sagely institution that had succumbed to the forces of historical change was the "feudal system" that supposedly prevailed under the Western Zhou in high antiquity. According to the great early Qing geographer and traveler, Liu Xian-ting (1648–1695), "Destroying the feudal system and creating the prefectural system definitely [issued from] historical circumstances which could not have made it otherwise."[41] Gu Yan-wu indicated that even the sages could not have halted the ultimate demise of the feudal system, and would, in fact, have opted for the prefectural system had they been reborn in a later age.[42] Such an orientation could hardly have disposed Liu, Gu, or those of like mind to look sympathetically on systems of cosmological correspondence which were generally rather static.

THE PROGRESS OF SCEINCE

Seventeenth-century scholars' recognition of the progress of science, particularly of mathematical astronomy, may have also contributed to cosmological criticism in the early Qing era. It is at least reasonable to expect Qing commentators to have been wary of schemata based, in part, on such relatively simple science as prevailed in the Han. That most major early Qing scholars believed astronomy to have progressed appreciably from Han times may be easily established.[43] What is in question is the extent to which these scholars regarded Han cosmology as tainted by association with an obsolete science.

The idea that astronomy had advanced since antiquity appeared at least as early as Tang times in the treatises on harmonics and astronomy included in the standard histories compiled during that era. By the Song period, the idea of the secular advancement of astronomical science had apparently entered into the mainstream of intellectual life, as illustrated by its acceptance by such authorities as Ouyang Xiu (1007–1070), Shen Gua (1031–1095), and Zhu Xi.[44] However, most of these commentators confined themselves to noting that recent astronomical systems facilitated a more precise calculation of the ephemeredes, and did not attempt to analyze why or whether the science of mathematical astronomy had developed concep-tually since Han times. Too, while affirming that astronomy had progressed in postclassical times, Tang, Song, and Yuan commentators on the history of astronomy generally upheld the idea of an astronomical fall from high antiquity, which was said to have taken place either with the Qin burning of the books in the late third century B.C. or several centuries earlier when the demise of the Western Zhou court had forced the dispersal of the officials charged with managing calendrical affairs.[45] So perfect was the astronomy of the ancients and so great the loss resulting from these disasters that even the finest of post-Qin calendrical systems, it was thought, had never approached the excellence of those formulated in high antiquity.[46]

In contrast to most earlier commentators, seventeenth-century scholars generally maintained that the development of astronomy in the centuries following the Han was not simply a matter of gradual refinement in predictive technique. They contended that a theoretical development had also occurred, albeit not one that had resulted in any revolutionary breaks with the past. Further, they questioned whether the astronomy of high antiquity, only fragments and brief notices of which were extant, was superior to that of later ages. For this idea ran contrary to their notions, illustrated especially clearly in the writings of Mei Wen-ding, of how and why astronomical science developed over time.

Mei was probably the most prolific seventeenth-century Chinese commentator on the history of astronomy. Like his Western contemporary Francis Bacon, Mei regarded the cumulative development of the science as, in part, a product of time; as records of observational data lengthened over centuries, later astronomers were increasingly able to discern patterns that the ancients could not have detected. The annual difference between the tropical and sidereal years, for example, could have been discovered only on the basis of several hundred years of accumulated data.[47] Modern astronomical systems, Mei noted, also incorporated certain conceptual improvements over ancient systems. The Season Granting (shou shi) system promulgated in the Yuan period, for example, located the epoch of the system, the zero point from which cyclical phenomena were calculated, in the relatively recent past (the winter solstice of December 1280) instead of at some hypothetical moment in the remotest antiquity when all the relevant cycles were simultaneously at point zero. As a result, the *Shou Shi*, remarked Mei, was the most accurate of all historical astronomical systems.[48] Mei and several of his contemporaries believed that the *Shou Shi* also excelled all previous astronomical systems in that it discarded the numerological apocrypha associated with such earlier systems as the Grand Inception (Tai Chu) of the Former Han and the Great Expansion (Da Yan) of the Tang. Its periods and constants were based on actual calculation and observation, and not derived from harmonic intervals or *Yijing* numerologies. The *Shou Shi* jettisoned almost all vestiges of correlative cosmology, an innovation which seventeenth-century cosmological critics considered to be especially praiseworthy.[49]

Mei Wen-ding's conception of the way in which astronomy progressed implied that the ancients, lacking access to the observational data collected over many centuries, could never have discerned the subtle patterns and minute irregularities detected by later astronomers.[50] The ancients, however, were to be given credit for having marked off the celestial-cartographical background against which later astronomers, in the fullness of time, were to discern more elusive patterns and motions. For Mei, it was almost as if the sages, having a premonition of the existence of subtleties that they themselves were unable to codify, bequeathed a method by which these might eventually be discovered.[51] The purport of the sagely astronomers of high antiquity was thus most faithfully adhered to by those modern investigators who endeavored to reform the science on the basis of the best available data rather than by classicists who attempted to reconstruct, from the fragments still extant, the systems supposedly used by the ancients.

Several other early Qing scholars, including Huang Zong-xi, Lu Shi-yi, Lu Long-qi, Li Guang-di, Wang Xi-shan, and Yan Ruo-ju, also noted that the science of astronomy had developed cumulatively, with the tradition having culminated in the *Shou Shi* system promulgated in the Yuan era. A few of these figures, particularly Yan Ruo-ju, outlined cases in which the science had progressed conceptually. Yan remarked that at least two theories of lunar motion had been proposed since antiquity. The more primitive and schematic "nine road" (jiu dao) model had been superseded by the relatively precise conception that the moon moves along a single continuous path, the "white road" (bai dao), that is inclined to the ecliptic, which it intersects at the lunar nodes. Yan did not, however, condemn the nine-road theory as false, but said only that it was relatively crude. A comprehensive theory could not, in any case, have been formulated in antiquity, since ultimate patterns (li) become manifest only gradually over the course of several thousand years.[52] The science of the moderns was necessarily superior to that of the ancients.

But was the cosmology of the ancients also obsolete by virtue of its having been based on subsequently superseded science? At least one major eighteenth-century scholar, Dai Chen, argued that it was. According to Dai, the numerological cosmology outlined in Yang Xiong's *Taixuan Jing* (Classic of the Great Mystery) was deficient and outmoded insofar as it was based on the calendrical system then in use, the Grand Inception (tai chu).[53] Conversely, such early Qing savants as Mei Wen-ding condemned the *Tai Chu* and other early astronomical systems for their use of cosmologically oriented numerology, as noted above.

THE OVEREXTENSION OF CORRELATIVE COSMOLOGY

The overextension of correlative cosmology in late-medieval and Renaissance Europe, as described in such classic accounts as those by Huizinga
and Tillyard, suggests a final possible inspiration for cosmological criticism
in Qing China. According to Huizinga, the allegorical mode of thought
which in the high middle ages provided a means by which one might "soar
towards the ineffable" had degenerated, by late-medieval times, to the point
of complete exhaustion. Even though "the representation of the Universe in
a grand system of symbolical relations had long been complete" by the
fifteenth century, allegorists continued to play at "adding ever new figures
that were like petrified flowers." The development of correspondences once
conceived as a means of mounting from the material to the spiritual, or as
"the mind's road to God," became little more than "arithmetical exercises" or
"intellectual pastimes." Examples given by Huizinga of such pastimes
include Jean Froissart's correlation of all the details of love with the parts of
a timepiece. Oliver de la Marche's matching of each article of female
costume with a particular virtue, and Jean Gerson's mixing of Latin
grammar with theology: "The noun substantive is the man; the pronoun
means that he is a sinner." Thus even theological correspondences were
extended to the point of absurdity, so much so that they were ridiculed by
Martin Luther and other religious reformers.[54]

E.M.W. Tillyard's account of the waning of medieval world views
focuses on England in the Elizabethan age. Like Huizinga, he notes that
correspondences became increasingly artificial after the high middle ages.[55]
However, Tillyard does not view this development as necessarily degenera-
tive. On the contrary, the Elizabethan perception of tensions between the
world they knew and the elaborate "chains of correspondence" passed down
from medieval times, Tillyard implies, inspired some fine moments in
Elizabethan drama. Sometimes, however, the correspondences, or rather
their miscarriage, were objects of jest. In Shakespeare's *Twelfth Night*, for
example, Sir Toby pairs a zodiacal sign, Taurus, with the wrong parts of the
body, the legs and thighs instead of the neck and throat. But it is not the
error itself that is ludicrous but rather, according to Tillyard, "Sir Toby's
being right in a way he did not mean." Tillyard concludes his comments on
this scene with the observation that "the serious and ceremonial game of
the Middle Ages," the drawing of correlations, "had degenerated into a
farce."[56]

A farcical element also perhaps appears in Menenius' famous account, in Shakespeare's *Coriolanus*, of the traditional body-state analogy. Menenius pairs the leaders of the state not with the head but with the belly, an identification that "distorts the old analogy, and thereby abuses the ideal."[57] The same might be said of Thomas Hobbes' extended comparison of the body politic with the sea monster, Leviathan, instead of with the human body. This analogy, as a modern commentator on Hobbes has remarked, was so unconventional[58] that it must have been perceived more as literary fantasy than as cosmological fact.

Is there also evidence that the unconventional extension of systems of correspondence in late-traditional times inspired cosmological skepticism in Qing China? It does seem the Qing commentators were generally less critical of the Han cosmologists responsible for the crystallization of correlative thought than of such later figures as Shao Yong (1011–1077) and Cai Yuan-ding (1135–1198), who elaborated correlative cosmology to the same unnatural lengths as did Huizinga's fifteenth-century allegorists. While some major early- and mid-Qing scholars endorsed certain aspects of Han cosmology, nearly all condemned Shao Yong for his numerological excesses.

Finally, were Qing savants, like some of Tillyard's Elizabethans, aware of the farcical possibilities of an overextended correlative cosmology? If a passage from chapter 31 of Cao Xue-qin's *Story of the Stone* is any indication, it appears that some of them were. In this passage, Shi Xiang-yun, one of the ladies in the household, attempts to explain to Kingfisher, an only modestly intelligent maid, how every relationship in the world has a yin and yang aspect. Thus "the sky is Yang and the earth is Yin; water is Yin and fire is Yang; the sun is Yang and the moon is Yin." This leads Kingfisher to ask "why is it that everything has Yin and Yang but we haven't?" Although Xiang-yun apparently considers this question unworthy of a serious reply, Kingfisher invents a solution of her own, telling Xiang-yun, her mistress, that "You're Yang and I'm Yin."[59] Xiang-yun, of course, laughs at this suggestion that a woman could be categorized as yang. But Kingfisher's point is a correct extension of the principle that the yang and yin describe a relationship, in this case that of master and servant, and not the essential qualities of a thing,[60] as a yang in one situation may well be a yin in another. Xiang-yun, a yin with respect to most things, could be a yang in relation to a servant. However, given the usual associations of yang, Kingfisher's suggestion seemed ridiculous to an educated eighteenth-century Chinese.

Thus Cao Xue-qin, like Shakespeare, found occasion to satirize correspondences elaborated to conclusions that contradicted common sense.

None of the intellectual developments discussed in this chapter—the liberation of the sciences from moral philosophy, the intensive cultivation of classical and exegetical studies, the ideas of secular change in nature and progressive development in science, or the extension of correlation to unconventional or unnatural lengths—was wholly unprecedented in the Qing era. However, all but the first and last of these were relatively new in the seventeenth century. Further, the confluence of all these trends swelled cosmological criticism in the era to an extent unprecedented in Chinese intellectual history.

POSSIBLE POLITICAL AND SOCIAL INFLUENCES

Might the political and social configurations of the period have also contributed to this outcome? Inasmuch as late-Ming and early-Qing cosmological critics were of diverse political and social orientations, it would be difficult to establish a purely "externalist" explanation of the cosmological reformation of that era. Might the impact of the Manchu conquest of 1644 have spurred cosmological criticism in seventeenth-century China? The possibility cannot be ruled out, though a number of major cosmological critics, particularly Wang Ting-xiang, flourished before the Manchus appeared on the scene. Mid- and late-Qing commentators, moreover, could have been but little affected by the experiences of the 1640's. Could Ming loyalism have somehow established a social or ideological nexus for early Qing cosmological criticism? A number of the premier cosmological critics of the late seventeenth century were, after all, Ming loyalists. But others, such as Yan Ruo-ju, Lu Long-qi, and Mei Wen-ding, were not, to say nothing of sixteenth- and eighteenth-century figures. Might the establishment of patronage networks for the support of classical and historical studies in early Qing times have promoted cosmological criticism in that era? The formation of what Benjamin Elman has called "a secular academic community, which encouraged original and creative scholarship," apparently facilitated critical studies of the sources of traditional cosmology.[61] But some of the most prolific and incisive early Qing opponents of Han-Song cosmology, particularly Wang Fu-zhi, did not receive significant community support for their works. Finally, might the chaos of the middle decades of the seventeenth century have so disoriented members of the intellectual elite as to lead them to critically reevaluate traditional cosmology? It does seem reasonable that massive dislocations in the outer world might have inspired changes in world view. But earlier ages of political and social upheaval in Chinese history, such as those centered on the third, tenth, and fourteenth centuries, did not foster any wave of cosmological criticism at all comparable to that of the seventeenth century.

Thus I have chosen to emphasize the intellectual origins of cosmological criticism. For there does at least exist substantial evidence that intellectual trends influenced Ming and Qing scholars' rejection of aspects of traditional cosmology. Of course, some social trends should be kept in mind. The wider dissemination of printing in the late Ming and early Qing,[62] for example, must have facilitated criticism by making available a broader range of classical and scientific texts to more scholars. The diffusion of print culture in the same era also perhaps obviated the need for systems of correspondence as mnemonic devices. This was the case in Stuart England, where correspondences based on plant forms "were no longer needed for memorizing moral lessons. When flowers were associated with virtues and vices, it was more for poetic than for pedagogic effect."[63] In late-Ming and Qing China, the easier availability of printed literature also perhaps reduced the inclination to associate the classical moral qualities with an easily memorizable paradigm of correspondences such as that based on the five phases. In other words, when print almost completely replaced memory as the primary agent of cultural transmission, then systems of correspondence lost one of their chief functions. Mental paradigms were no longer so important when printed literature became so widely diffused.

That such trends perhaps encouraged early Qing scholars to reject established schemata suggests that the intellectual developments described in this chapter should not be taken as a final explanation of Qing cosmological criticism. Moreover, these intellectual developments were seldom fully exploited by seventeenth-century commentators. Early Qing exegetes' exposé of the heterodox origins of aspects of traditional cosmology, for example, did not quite discredit it in the intellectual world of Qing China. For seventeenth-century classicists seldom pursued their anticosmological conclusions relentlessly to their logical end; moreover, later commentators frequently found reasons for ignoring the discoveries of mere philologists. Such a situation also prevailed in seventeenth-century Europe. For although in 1614 Isaac Casaubon had proven that the *Corpus Hermetica*, a prime source of Renaissance cosmological thought, was composed in late antiquity, Robert Fludd and others continued to use the *Hermetica* as if it reposited the original theology revealed to the sages of high antiquity.[64]

Thus in seventeenth century Europe, as in China of the same era, no single argument sufficed to overthrow the perennial cosmology, however conclusive such arguments seem when considered abstractly. Indeed, applications of traditional cosmology survived and even flourished throughout the Qing era. Yet the Qing break with the Han-Song cosmological tradition, though not abrupt or revolutionary, was more complete than is generally recognized. As C.T. Hsia has pointed out, one indication of the extent to which traditional cosmological ideas were rejected in the Qing is the fact that they were not major objects of attack by the early twentieth-century iconoclasts associated with the New Culture movement.[65] While a few of the intellectual leaders of the May Fourth generation, such as Wu Zhi-hui (1865–1953), occasionally ridiculed aspects of traditional cosmology and cosmogony, apparently they did not think it necessary to compose a comprehensive critique. For, as they may have known, the Qing inhabitants of the "Old Antique Shop of Confucius and Sons" had already done so.

Chapter Seven

Criticisms
Of Correlative Cosmology
In Late-Traditional China

Criticisms of forms of correlative cosmology in Western civilization may be traced as far back as the Presocratics. Xenophanes, for example, faulted Homer's anthropomorphic conception of the gods by arguing that "if oxen (and horses) and lions had hands or could draw with hands and create works of art like those made by men, horses would draw pictures of gods like horses, and oxen of gods like oxen."[1] Explicit criticism of the more developed varieties of correlative cosmology, however, appeared only intermittently in pre-Renaissance Europe. But in the early modern era, such criticism swelled to a crescendo. Indeed, if there was any point which the most famous religious and philosophical reformers of late-Renaissance and early modern Europe held in common, it was their opposition to correlative thinking. Figures as diverse as Girolamo Savonarola, G. Pico della Miran-dola, Martin Luther, John Calvin, Peter Ramus, Francis Bacon, Marin Mersenne, and Blaise Pascal challenged some of the presuppositions on which correlative cosmology was based. Perhaps the most celebrated critique was that mounted by Bacon in his condemnation of the "Several Kinds of Idols," old habits of thought which supposedly constituted the greatest barrier to scientific progress. The first set of such idols, the "Idols of the Tribe," were molded in the following way:

> The human understanding is of its own nature and prone to suppose the existence of more order and regularity in the world than it finds. And though there be many things in nature which are singular and unmatched, yet it devises for them parallels and conjugates and relatives which do not exist. Hence the fiction that all celestial bodies move in perfect circles, spirals and dragons being (except in name) utterly rejected. Hence too the element of fire with its orb is brought in, to make up the square with the other three which the sense perceives.[2]

Bacon thus characterized what I have called "correlative thought" and "geometrical cosmography" as products of the human imagination which do not correspond with anything that may be found in nature. Bacon highlighted this disjunction "between the spirit of man and the spirit of the universe" by remarking that "if that Supreme Architect had conducted himself in the fashion of a human builder, then He would have set the stars into some beautiful and elegant order very similar to the carefully worked paneled ceilings of palaces."[3]

The great Elizabethan poet John Donne admitted the existence of a similar disjunction between the order man imposed on the heavens and the actual movements of the heavenly bodies. Such motions, Donne acknowledged, were so "various and perplexed" that they seemed to manifest no sense of proportion, much less geometrical regularity:

> So, of the Stars, which boast that they do run
> In Circle still, none ends where he begun.
> All their proportion's lame, it sinks, it swells.
> For of Meridians, and Parallels,
> Man hath weav'd out a net, and this net thrown.
> Upon the Heavens, and now they are his own.
> Loth to go up the hill, or labour thus
> To go to heaven, we make heaven come to us.[4]

Early modern religious reformers of diverse persuasions criticized various forms of correlative cosmology, though not so deliberately as did Bacon or Donne. For John Calvin, so great was the disproportion between God and man, or between the divine and human realms, that the free grace of God was the only means of mediation between the two. Hence, the drawing of correspondences between these two realms was impious from a Calvinist perspective. Luther, while not insisting on the absolute incommensurability of the divine and the human, did pointedly ridicule the kind of allegorical correspondences common in Renaissance theology.[5] The Catholic reformer Savonarola also faulted such allegorical correlations, remarking, for example, that while the planet Mercury was customarily linked with Christianity because its movements are hard to understand, it might with equal justification be regarded as contrary to Christianity, "which is not as unstable as Mercury." (*laquale non e volubile come Mercurio*).[6] Savonarola's famous contemporary Pico della Mirandola likewise commented on the ease with which practically any proposition might be defended through analogical reasoning, since "nothing exists which it is impossible to imagine by an argument of this kind to have some similarity and dissimilarity with something else."[7] Even fire and water might be correlated by arguing that "water is like fire because it is cold and the fire is hot."

Finally, Pascal, like the Calvinists of the preceding century, attacked that particular mode of correlative cosmology based on the idea of proportionality between divine and human realms, though in such a dramatic fashion that some of his sayings on the subject have become proverbial. Indeed, the idea of the disproportion of God and man, of the divine and the human, though hardly original with Pascal, was at the very center of his philosophy. Even Pascal's famous "wager" may be viewed as a mathematization of this principle applied toward the question of whether or not the skeptic should stake his life on the possibility that God and Heaven exist.[8]

The Renaissance and early modern European critiques of correlative thinking just noted were philosophically oriented and not very concerned with exposing particular discrepancies or misfits in systems of correspondence. For having established that the structure of the cosmos is basically irregular (Bacon and Donne), or that analogical reasoning is inherently flawed because of its lack of rigor (Savonarola and Pico), or that the things of the human world bear no proportion to the divine or to the cosmos at large (Calvin and Pascal), why take the trouble to meticulously investigate particular schemata in order to reveal their faults? But Chinese cosmological critics, in contrast to most of their European counterparts, were especially concerned with exposing numerological discrepancies and other "forced fits" in particular systems of correspondence. Very few of them mounted a programmatic challenge to established cosmological conceptions. For the Neo-Confucian tradition within which most of these thinkers were placed encompassed few standpoints incompatible with correlative cosmology. The infinity of the divine and the absolute disproportion between the divine and the human, ideas widely articulated in medieval Christian scholastic philosophy, contravened some of the basic tenets of nearly every major school of Neo-Confucian thought.

Thus most Qing cosmological criticism was focused rather narrowly on the faults of particular schemata such as systems of correspondence based on the five phases and on the figures associated with the *Change*. Inasmuch as such discussions are usually both quite technical and of limited scope, they are easily overlooked by intellectual historians on the lookout for grander trends that anticipated the major ideological wonders of the modern world.

Nevertheless, more general critiques of correlative cosmology do occasionally appear in the writings of sixteenth- and seventeenth-century Chinese philosophers, including Wang Ting-xiang, Lu Kun, and especially Wang Fu-zhi. The last argued, in a way reminiscent of Bacon's critique of the "Idols of the Tribe," that the regular symmetrical patterns that man imposes on the world, or on "heaven," seldom have any correspondent in the structure of the cosmos itself. Like Bacon, Wang cited examples of such artificial models, including the arrangement of the "eight palaces and sixty-four hexagrams" invented by the Han cosmographer Jing Fang, the "Prior to Heaven" ordering of the sixty-four hexagrams formulated by the Neo-Confucian cosmologist Shao Yong, and the nonary numerology associated with Cai Chen. Wang criticized all these contrivances with the remark that "the cosmos does not have this sort of regularity; only what has been constructed by human effort has it. What is round and can therefore be measured with a compass, and what is square and therefore can be measured with a carpenter's square, are all man-made artifacts. Natural living things are not like this."[9] Wang did, however, admit that man-made cosmological constructions have some truth in them. For even though the structure of the universe is not, as Yang Xiong supposed, based on the number "three" and its multiples, nor, as Shao Yong thought, based on "four" and *its* multiples, nor as Sima Guang believed, based on "five" and *its* multiples, "one definitely cannot say that three, four, five, and nine are not the numbers of the heavens and the earth." There may be some cases in which particular numerological systems actually do accord with aspects of the cosmos. But such accord, Wang indicated, is quite limited and largely coincidental.

In his philosophical commentary on the *Documents Classic,* the *Shangshu Yinyi* (An Interpretation of the *Documents of Antiquity*), Wang related how such instances of coincidental accord between human and cosmic entities had facilitated the construction of systems of correspondence. "In heaven," he concluded, "there is yin and yang, and in man there is humanity and righteousness." Further, "the heavens have the five planets and man has five sense organs." But "their forms are different and their material unconnected; one cannot forcibly conjoin them."[10] There is, he continued, a basic disjunction between the cosmos as perceived and interpreted by man and the cosmos as it is in itself, or between the anthropomorphic heavens (ren zhi tian) and the phenomenal heavens (tian zhi wei tian). Though it is possible for man to apprehend the latter, he could not do it by way of inference from his own anthropomorphic or numerological fancies, which so often presume the existence of abstract regularity, symmetry, and correspondence where there is none.

General critiques of correlative cosmology such as those articulated by Wang Fu-zhi were rare in seventeenth-century China, but they seem to have been more common in Tokugawa Japan. Perhaps the main reason for this was the deliberate, systematic, and somewhat clumsy use of correlative schemata for political purposes by the Neo-Confucian ideologists associated with the Tokugawa house. This Tokugawa politicization of correlative cosmology made it an inviting target for intellectuals dissatisfied with the political and social system that it buttressed. Thus Andō Shōeki (fl. 1751–1764) complained that in the works of Tokugawa house intellectuals, "Heaven is equated with the principle of yang and is held in high respect, while the earth is equated with yin and held to be base. In this way, they distinguish between the high and the low, and proclaiming this to be the law, they claim to possess princely characters and place themselves above others."[11]

CRITICISMS OF FIVE-PHASE CORRELATIONS

Ming and Qing commentators' criticisms of correlative cosmology were less politically oriented than were those of their Tokugawa counterparts. These commentators were apparently more concerned with freeing the meaning of classical texts from cosmological interpretations than they were with the issue of political legitimacy, particularly in their discussions of five-phase correlations. Thus several sixteenth- and seventeenth-century scholars, beginning with Wang Ting-xiang, emphasized that the classical *wuxing* as described in the "Great Plan" chapter of the *Documents Classic* referred to material elements that the ruler was supposed to regulate for the benefit of the people. But later cosmologists, Wang lamented, had distorted the canonical purport of the *wuxing* in the course of correlating them with such diverse entities as the four seasons, the stars and planets, geographical patterns, and the organs of the human body. By the Tang era, the *wuxing* were used in fate calculation, and in the Song assimilated into yin-yang cosmology. Thus "heterodox theories [became] numerous and disorderly, and gradually [developed to] an extreme point."[12]

Wang Fu-zhi, in the following century, also argued that the intention of the sages as expressed in the "Great Plan" was to promote the people's welfare, not to establish a basis for cosmological speculation. "The five elements," he commented, "were natural materials produced by heaven for nourishing the people; to make good use of them is the way of the prince. . . But from the Han era, scholars did not investigate [this matter], and indiscriminately drew in the sayings of numerologists, pairing [things that were] unconnected. [These scholars] thus did not understand the purport of the 'Great Plan.' "[13] Finally, Li Gong (1659–1733), another major early Qing classicist, also faulted later cosmological commentators for having distorted the canonical sense of the *wuxing*. Li, moreover, commented that the classical *wuxing* (metal, wood, water, fire, and earth) first appear in the *Da Yu Mo* (Counsels of the Great Yu) chapter of the *Documents* where, together with grain, they are the "six repositories" (liu fu) or treasuries of nature, not the *wuxing*.[14]

Qing cosmological critics faulted five-phase correlative arrangements on other grounds as well. Chief among these were the numerological discrepancies between the *wuxing* and the other sets with which they were conventionally correlated, such as the four seasons and the eight trigrams. Thus Li Gong objected to the manner in which the phases were usually paired with the trigrams, asking "how is it that water and fire are each [allotted] one trigram, while metal, wood, and earth each have two [corresponding] trigrams."[15] Wang Fu-zhi similarly remarked that "the trigrams and the phases, one [numbering] eight and the other five, are numerologically uneven. Thus water and fire alone have only one trigram [a piece paired with them], while the others all have one trigram extra."[16]

But the numerological disjunction which drew the most criticism was that between the five phases and the four seasons. Wang Ting-xiang and Wang Fu-zhi were particularly concerned with the awkwardness of the various formulas devised by Han cosmologists for dealing with the fifth wheel in the pairing, the odd earth phase. Wang Fu-zhi condemned the most popular solution, the apportionment of the earth phase into four eighteen-day segments each placed at the end of one of the four seasons, for its "arbitrary establishment of limits." More generally, Wang argued, the existence of cosmic irregularities precluded any such schema being applied very widely or uniformly throughout the world:

> The transformations of heaven and earth are subtle by dint of their irregularity and are balanced by dint of their irregularity. Since the seasons originally number four, and the phases originally number five, of what use is "truncating a duck to augment a crane," making them come out in one track? . . . The

cosmos is not a printing block, and thus a myriad of transformations emerge from the [cosmic] brush. But narrow-minded people naturally do not understand [this].[17]

Wang Ting-xiang, while also noting the numerological awkwardness of the correlation of the four seasons with the five phases, emphasized that this schema failed to take into account well-known astronomical and meteorological phenomena. The seasons of the year, he pointed out, were known to be caused by the annual advance and retreat of the sun and were thus not related to the distribution of the five phases or pneumas.[18] Moreover, since the pneumas of the five phases were intermingled in the Great Void, each of them must be active at all times. But "if in spring only the wood phase is active," as the cosmologists say, "then who or what extinguishes the pneumas of water, fire, earth, and metal [during the season]?" Furthermore, how could the pneuma of wood suddenly disappear at the close of the last day of spring to be abruptly replaced by the pneuma of fire on the first day of summer? Common sense alone, Wang Ting-xiang maintained, should be sufficient to establish that the course of nature did not proceed in this fashion.[19]

While sixteenth- and seventeenth-century discussions of the five-phase correlations focused on such obvious discrepancies as that between the phases and the seasons, mid-Qing scholars probed more complex numerological arrangements in which the *wuxing* figured. The eighteenth-century editors of the general catalogue to the *Siku Quanshu* (Complete Library in Four Treasuries) reviewed an anonymous Ming work, the *Wuxing Kao* (Investigations of the Five Planets), which divided each of the twenty-eight lunar lodges into five segments, correlating the five phases with the segments in each lodge. The work, for example, paired water with the first three degrees of the "horn" (jiao) lunar lodge, and wood with the segment extending from the fourth degree to the eighth degree. Such an arrangement might have some basis, the editors imply, if all were approximately thirteen degrees. But inasmuch as the lunar lodges varied widely in length, it was impossible to pair degree segments with the phases in a simple and consistent manner.[20]

Besides exposing the unclassical provenance and numerological disarray of systems of correspondence keyed to the *wuxing*, late-Ming and Qing cosmological critics also faulted five-phase correlations for having misrepresented the physical reality that they were supposed to encode or describe. Wang Ting-xiang noted several such irregularities. He remarked, for example, that the pairing of the water phase with winter was a "forced fit" (qiang pei) inasmuch as winter was the dry season throughout much of China.[21] Moreover, various astronomical and meteorological phenomena, such the course of the seasons and the phases of the moon, were best explained through an examination of the physical patterns of the heavens rather than through the application of five-phase models. Thus Wang objected to the correlation of the five-phases with the phases of the moon on the grounds that "the moon's waxing and waning arises from its relative distance from the sun. How [therefore could it] have anything to do with the alternations of the five phases?"[22]

Other sixteenth- and seventeenth-century scholars who noted disjunctions between five-phase correlations and aspects of physical reality include Jiao Hong (1540?–1620) and Huang Zong-xi (1610–1695). Jiao faulted the general principle of one-to-one correspondence between the phases and particular physical events, an idea that he traced to the Han cosmologist Liu Xiang (77–6 B.C.). Pursuing this line of argument via a medical illustration, Jiao contended that individual diseases may be produced by the confluence of various factors and are not necessarily caused by the malignant development of a single *qi*.[23]

Huang Zong-xi similarly opposed the drawing of strict one-to-one correspondences between the *qi* of the five phases and heaven and earth. For inasmuch as the cosmic *qi* is really unitary, Huang reasoned, how could there be any sharp distinctions between those pneumas associated with the heavens and those paired with the earth? Thus "although wood, fire, metal, water, and earth are of five categories, they are of one pneuma [qi]; they are all heavenly. When they complete their forms and become the myriad things, they are all earthly."[24]

In sum, late-Ming and early-Qing cosmological critics condemned systems of correspondence based on the five phases for their (1) unclassical provenance, (2) numerological disarray, and (3) lack of accord with physical reality. At least two nineteenth century scholars raised yet another objection to five-phase correlations, especially to those which incorporated the yin-yang duality, namely that they were based on the arbitrary conflation of distinct classical traditions. According to Gong Zi-zhen (1792–1841), such arrangements arose from the melding of elements extracted from three separate classics, the yin-yang associated with the *Change*, the *wuxing* mentioned in the "Great Plan" chapter of the *Documents*, and the portent astrology of the *Spring and Autumn Annals.*[25] Pi Xi-rui (1850–1908) also traced the yin-yang and *wuxing* ideas to two distinct classical schools of thought which were combined only in the Han.[26]

Late-Ming and Qing cosmological critics thus attacked five-phase correlations along almost every conceivable line. Their contemporaries in Tokugawa Japan, while generally aiming their cosmological criticism at more stately structures, especially the Tokugawa political and social hierarchy, also occasionally faulted correspondences based on the five phases. Itō Tōgai (1670–1736), for example, reasoned that the correlation of the four Confucian virtues with the five phases, and the arbitrary addition of a fifth virtue to complete the set, resulted in the ossification of this sagely teaching: "Earlier it had been on the basis of actualities that the teaching concerning the four virtues had been formulated; now these virtues were taken as fixed and unchanging things within us." As a result of this and subsequent developments, Itō lamented, "the Way of the Sages was left in darkness and obscurity for more than a thousand years."[27]

CRITICISMS OF CORRELATIONS BASED ON THE SYSTEM OF THE CHANGE

A second major mode of correlative cosmology exposed to criticism in Ming and Qing times was that based on the images and numerologies associated with the *Classic of Change* and its canonical appendices, the "Ten Wings." Several earlier commentators on the *Change*, beginning with Wang Bi (A.D. 226–249), had, of course, generally eschewed the numerological approach to this classic, focusing instead on the moral- metaphysical principles supposedly embedded in it. But unlike Wang Bi, such early Qing scholars as Gu Yan-wu directly attacked *Yijing* numerology. Gu argued that the schematic figures devised by the major Han cosmological commentators on the *Change*, especially Xun Shuang (A.D. 128–190) and Yu Fan (164–233), had little basis in the canon. In Gu's view, "there was hardly any phrase in the 'Ten Wings' in which they did not seek such a figure; and consequently the purport of the *Change* was neglected."[28]

Although Gu Yan-wu did not adduce evidence sufficient to prove the heterodoxy of the various cosmological constructions devised by Han commentators on the *Change*, such as the *najia* and *guaqi* schemata, some of his contemporaries did. At least three of them, Huang Zong-xi, Hu Wei (1633–1714), and Huang Zong-yan (1616–1686), devoted major studies to tracing the origins of the various diagrams and numerologies associated

with the *Change*. Mid- and late-Qing scholars, such as Hui Dong
(1697–1758), Jiao Xun (1763–1820), Chen Li (1810–1882), and Pi Xi-rui,
continued this line of investigation, though they did not reject all the
cosmological schemata associated with the *Change*. Pi Xi-rui pointed out
that some of these systems, particularly the *najia*, could not be traced back
to Confucius, nor even to Jing Fang, the Han cosmologist.[29]

As with systems of correspondence based on the five phases, Qing
commentators criticized the *Yijing* correlative schemata on physical as well
as historical grounds. Inasmuch as several of these arrangements, particularly the *najia*, incorporated astronomical and calendrical units, scholars
interested in astronomy were well situated to identify disjunctions between
such units and the figures with which they were associated. Thus Huang
Zong-xi, besides establishing that the *najia* was devised by postclassical
commentators, pointed out that one of the keystone of the system, the
correlation of the eight trigrams with the phases of the moon, was astro-
nomically ill- informed. For the moon in the course of its monthly waxing
and waning does not, Huang noted, really resemble its supposed simulacra,
the trigrams. Moreover, while the position of the moon in the sky shifts
from night to night and month to month, the trigrams which are supposed
to represent the lunar circuit are invariable.[30]

Huang Zong-xi's astronomical criticism of the *najia* system was not
unique. The famous nineteenth-century classicist and historian Chen Li
pursued this line of argument in an even more literalist fashion. He pointed
out that since the eight trigrams all have three lines, none of them could
adequately depict the figure of he half moon as it appears on the eighth and
twenty-third days of the lunar month. Chen Li also noted that neither the
kan trigram (☵) which consists of a yang (=brightness) line within two yin
(=darkness) lines, nor the *li* trigram (☲) which is composed of a yin line
within two yang lines, could possibly be taken as a physical depiction of the
moon in any of its phases: "How could the moon possibly have brightness
within darkness or darkness within brightness?"[31] Unlike Huang Zong-xi,
Chen Li did, however, endorse the pairing of the other four trigrams, the
zhen (☳), *xun* (☴), *qian* (☰), and *kun* (☷), with certain phases of the moon.
The *qian* trigram with its three unbroken yang lines simulated the full
moon, while the *kun* trigram depicted the dark of the moon.

Late-Ming and early-Qing scholars also argued more generally
against the correlation of astronomical figures with those associated with
the *Change*. Wang Ting-xiang insisted that it was not possible to coordinate

the *Yijing* with astronomy and the calendar, since "the *Classic of Change* is man-made while the calendar accords with the dimensions of the heavens." Further, "while the movements of the heavens are constant, the Way of the *Classic of Change* alters. To assimilate heaven to man is called 'to upset and transgress'; and if the constant is assimilated to the changing, how could they tally?"[32]

Since the constitution of the heavens differed so fundamentally from that of the *Change*, no attempt to coordinate the two could succeed. In any case, Wang argued, the original figures of the *Change* as devised by the sages had nothing to do with astronomy or the calendar:

> The *Change* has the Great Ultimate; this gives birth to the two modes [yin and yang], and the two modes give birth to the four images; and the four images give birth to the eight trigrams. This is the sage's account of how the *Classic of Change* was drawn up; it is not a discussion of the originally subtle workings of cosmic transformations.[33]

Among Wang Ting-xiang's seventeenth-century successors, those who excelled in the study of mathematical astronomy were especially critical of the traditional practice of deriving astronomical constants and periods through numerologies based on the *Change*. Wang Xi-shan, in fact, attributed the frequency of calendrical reform in Chinese history, as well as the relative backwardness of the science of mathematical astronomy in China, to native astronomers' having generally based their calculations on the figures of the *Change* and on harmonic intervals.[34] According to Wang's contemporary Mei Wen-ding (1633–1721), even the paradigmatic astronomical systems in the Chinese tradition were based on such numerological schemata, the "Grand Inception" (tai chu) of the Former Han on the "bells and pitchpipes" and the "Great Expansion" (Da Yan) of the Tang on the Hetu (Yellow River Chart) and Luoshu (Luo River Writing) cosmograms associated with the *Classic of Change*. Only with the "Season Granting" (Shou Shi) system promulgated in the Yuan period were such correlative numerological constructions finally abandoned and calendrical constants and periods determined empirically:

> When it came to the Yuan era, Xu Heng and Guo Shou-jing for the first time pointedly took empirical measurements and verifications as the basis [of their calculations]. They did not again discuss mathematical astronomy in terms of the bells, pitchpipes, and *guaqi*. Thus in one stroke they eliminated the forced interpretations put forward by all the specialists. Therefore their

system was especially refined. This is the reason harmonics and astronomy parted ways.[35]

The progressive technical development and increased intellectual autonomy of the science of mathematical astronomy severed the link between cosmological numerology and astronomy. Indeed, early Qing scholar-astronomers such as Mei Wen-ding only confirmed this development which had been practically completed, on a technical level, hundreds of years earlier.

Mid- and late-Qing scholars, such as Qian Da-xin (1728–1804) and Ruan Yuan (1764–1849), extended seventeenth-century commentators' critique of numerological derivations of astronomical constants and calendrical periods. On the other hand, several noted early Qing scholars occasionally dabbled in cosmocalendrical numerologies. Even Wang Xi-shan, one of the most inveterate opponents of astronomical numerology, attempted to relate the figures associated with the *Change* to his reformed celestial cartography. He proposed that great circles of the celestial sphere be divided into 384 degrees, a figure which equals the total number of lines in the 64 hexagrams of the *Change*. The number 384, Wang indicated, was more consonant with the natural order of things in the universe than was either 360 or 365¼.[36]

Jiang Yong (1681–1762), a major eighteenth-century classical scholar and student of the mathematical sciences, also did not entirely abandon correlative numerology, though he applied it principally in his studies on mathematical harmonics. While faulting the twelfth-century cosmologist Cai Yuan-ding for having based his work in calendrical astronomy on Shao Yong's numerological *Huangji Jingshi Shu*, Jiang went on to pose simple numerological correspondences between the units of the pitchpipes and those of the calendar. He pointed out, for example, that the twelve months of the year match the twelve pitchpipes and that the number of units in the circumference of the tonic *huangzhong* pipe (730½) equals the number of days in two years (365¼ × 2).[37]

But even while affirming the existence of such numerological consonances, Jiang Yong criticized some of the more extravagant systems of correspondence drawn between the pitchpipes and the calendar, such as the "watching for the pneumas" (houqi) schemata. According to this arrangement, the twelve pipes were buried in the ground with only their tops exposed, sometimes covered with a thin layer of ashes. Each of the pipes was then supposed to resonate on the first day of the corresponding month (of which there were also twelve). Since the resonance was so subtle, one could sometimes detect it only by observing the ashes which, it was believed, would rise up when the earth intoned its corresponding seasonal note. Jiang Yong denied that such a device could work, arguing:

> The pitchpipes definitely have patterns which arcanely tally with the ways of the heavens. But if one expectantly buries [the pipes] in the ground in order to watch for [the emanations of] the pneumas, I fear that no result can be trusted. For the heavenly pneumas are diverse. Though one were to make the lengths and widths of the pipes all according to specifications, how could each pneuma resonate [in turn, causing] the ashes to rise? Never having observed such a phenomenon, I do not dare prejudge the matter. However, Xing Yun-lu [fl. 1573–1620] also profoundly doubted [the existence of] this phenomenon.[38]

Wang Fu-zhi, like Jiang Yong, was quite interested in the cosmological implications of harmonic theory, though he did not attempt to systematically correlate harmonic measurements and calendrical units. He remarked that though it is possible to devise correspondences between the two, consonance is not complete or exhaustive. For "if one takes the pitchpipes and the calendar to comprehend the numbers of all under heaven, then coincidentally there may be some accord; and yet [there will also] definitely be discord."[39] Wang Fu-zhi did maintain that the system of the *Change* comprehended both astronomy and harmonics. Yet he rejected some of the more elaborate constructions purportedly based on this proposition, such as the *guaqi* schema associated with the Han commentator Jing Fang, and the numerological systems propounded by the Song Neo-Confucian cosmologists Shao Yong and Cai Chen.[40]

CRITICISMS OF SHAO YONG

Direct criticism of Shao Yong's numerological cosmology may be traced as far back as the thirteenth century. The prominent Song Neo-Confucian scholar Huang Zhen, for example, faulted Shao Yong's numerological interpretations of the *Change* on the grounds that they were both unclassical and unconcerned with human affairs.[41] But by the seventeenth century, criticism of Shao and his school had expanded to the point of becoming a significant theme in the intellectual history of that era. Qing scholars of almost every major scholastic affiliation criticized Song cosmologists'

schematic correlations of the *Yijing* figures and numerologies with astronomical, calendrical, and harmonic units. Although Han Learning and Song
Learning scholars of the mid-Qing were at odds on many issues, both
condemned the cosmological numerology associated particularly with Shao
Yong.

Late-Ming and early-Qing criticism of Shao Yong and his school,
being quite uniform, may be recounted by citing those of a few typical
figures, beginning with those posed by the sixteenth-century anticosmologist Wang Ting-xiang. Wang, like several of his seventeenth-century
successors, remarked that Shao's numerological interpretation of the
Change distorted the basic meaning of that classic: "Although there are
numbers in the *Change*, the sages [in composing it] did not [aim to] discuss
numbers, but to discuss principles." Wang pointed out that Shao's
four-based numerological system failed to accord with either the purport of
the sages or the structure of the cosmos. For it did not take into account the
myriad irregularities of the processes of transformation in the universe.
Wang accused Shao's twelfth-century successor Cai Yuan-ding of having
similarly neglected incommensurable units, especially those that failed to
accord with his harmonic theory.[42]

Later scholars also charged Shao Yong with having ignored natural
irregularities. Huang Zong-xi noted that Shao's calendrical numerology
rounded off every unit to either twelve or thirty. But "how could he have
thus effaced remainders?"[43] The nineteenth-century editors of a supplement to the *Zhouren Zhuan* (Biographies of Mathematicians and Astronomers) similarly faulted Shao for having "only selected round numbers and
not taken note of remainders."[44] Of course, an admission of incommensurables would be practically inconceivable in any correlative numerological
schema; for such a step would contradict the *raison d'être* of the system,
demonstrating the congruence of different cosmic realms.

The mid-Qing scholar Zhang Hui-yan (1761–1802), advanced a more
comprehensive critique of Shao's numerology in his *Yitu Tiaopian* (Systematic Critique of the Diagrams Associated with the *Change*). Zhang began by
pointing out various contradictions between the classical *Change* and
Shao's *Huangji Jingshi Shu* (Book of the Supreme Rules of Ordering the
World), imputing a "Daoist" origin to the latter. He proceeded to fault Shao
for having correlated such diverse sets as celestial bodies, terrestrial
elements, calendrical periods, meteorological conditions, types of rulers,
and Confucian classics with the eight trigrams, remarking that there is no

canonical basis for these pairings. Finally, Zhang accused Shao and the major Song Neo-Confucian thinkers in general of presuming that the cosmos is more orderly than it is, of ignoring the existence of anomalies, especially in astronomy.[45]

Qing scholars' criticisms of Shao Yong and his ilk were not confined to numerology. Both Wang Fu-zhi and Ruan Yuan also faulted Shao's cosmogony for its arbitrary account of stages of cosmic evolution that were beyond the scope of empirical investigation.[46] On the other hand, at least one noted early Qing scholar, Fang Yi-zhi (1611–1671), commended Shao's approach to nature, and even endorsed aspects of his numerology.[47] Indeed, the procedure Fang followed in such later works as his *Dongxi Jun* is reminiscent of Shao's in that he aimed to derive metaphysical principles and cosmological ratios from his elementary knowledge of astronomy and other sciences.

CRITICISMS OF THE "YUELING" SYSTEM

Of the five or six basic modes of correlative cosmology developed in the Han era, the ones that late-Ming and Qing commentators criticized the most were those centered on the five phases and those based on the figures associated with the *Change*. However, a few commentators did attend to some of the other types of correlative cosmology developed in Han China. One of the most distinctive of these was that outlined in the *Yueling* (Monthly Ordinances) chapter of the *Liji* (Record of Rites). This *Yueling* schema, a slightly modified version of the opening sections of the first twelve chapters of the *Lüshi Chunqiu* (Master Lü's Spring and Autumn Annals), correlated various imperial activities with the months of the year, as was seen earlier.

According to Wang Ting-xiang, the formulation of such correspondences led the *Yueling* to some peculiar conclusions. For example, the text indicated that the last month of spring is the time when the sovereign should "solicit the services of celebrated scholars and honor the wise." But it would seem that every month is appropriate for such an exemplary activity. "Why only the last month of spring?" The text also prescribes that in the last month of summer, "one should not join with the feudal lords in raising armies or rousing the masses." But if rebellions or invasions occur in that month, "should one halt and not take any initiative?' Wang thus concurred with Liu Zong-yuan's opinion that the *Yueling* abounds in forced pairings.[48]

Wang Fu-zhi, in the following century, attempted to explain how the

Yueling, with its unorthodox correlative cosmology, came to be incorporated into one of the classics, the *Record of Rites*. Tracing the *Yueling* to the opening sections of the first twelve chapters of the *Lüshi Chunqiu*, Wang noted that the late-Zhou scholars who composed the work arbitrarily associated various heterodox ideas with the traditions of the former kings. But the spirit of this artificial system for coordinating the most minute particulars of imperial rituals with the seasons of the year did not accord with the actual practices of the sage kings. The latter, in fixing the times and seasons of the year, only sought to promote agriculture and husbandry, not to establish a cosmological basis for the conduct of government. This fact was obscured by the incorporation of the *Yueling* into the canon and the failure of later scholars to examine the provenance of this work. The canonization of the *Yueling* system, in turn, laid the basis for the further development of heterodox numerological schemata.[49]

Wang Fu-zhi also faulted the *Yueling* on more practical grounds. He remarked, for example, that the *Yueling*'s mechanical linking times of reward and punishment with the seasons does not take sufficient account of the vagaries of human affairs.[50] But despite his criticism, Wang Fu-zhi did not condemn the document unreservedly. He contended that the text, corrupted though it may have been by heterodox accretions, preserved a valuable record of the agrarian policies of the former kings. For this reason, he concluded, it should not be totally discarded.[51]

Apart from Wang Fu-zhi, few major early- and mid-Qing scholars seem to have criticized the *Yueling* system extensively. Even so, the commentary of these few scholars on the *Yueling* might have influenced Qing law. As Derk Bodde has pointed out in his study of law in imperial China, the Qing code of 1740 dramatically restricted the periods during which executions were prohibited, a taboo that had its classical basis in the *Yueling* system. According to Bodde, the periods of taboo, having remained virtually unchanged in the codes promulgated from the Tang to the Ming, after 1740 "shrink to mere symbolic vestiges of what they had been." But rather than attributing this development to the influence of Qing scholars' critique of the *Yueling* system, Bodde interprets it more generally as having arisen from "a weakening belief by Qing times in the doctrine of the oneness of man and nature." In any case, Bodde correctly regards the drastic shrinking of the periods of taboo in the Qing code not as an isolated development but as a measure of significant "changes in cosmological belief" which occurred in Qing times, changes which he sees manifested in

Qing landscape paintings and harmonic theory as well as in criminal law.[52]

DEVOLUTION OF ANATOMICAL CORRESPONDENCES

Qing scholars did not extensively criticize two other modes of correlative cosmology developed in late-Zhou and Han times, those relating man and cosmos and state and cosmos. Even those texts in which one would most expect to find attacks on the "state analogy" mode of thought, such as Huang Zong-xi's famous critique of imperial government, the *Mingyi Daifang Lu*, seldom broach the topic. In fact, the latter work rarely criticizes correlative thought of any kind, though it does, as Ian McMorran has pointed out, challenge "the currently established idea that loyalty to the emperor was analogous to the duty that a son owed his father."[53] On the other hand, while political thinkers of the early Qing era seldom directly attacked the state analogy, they rarely invoked it either. Perhaps they regarded the idea of the imperial state as microcosm as an intellectual relic hardly worthy of the attention of serious scholars.

A few major seventeenth-century scholars did pose structural and anatomical correspondences among celestial, terrestrial, and human bodies. However, they rarely set such correlations in the sort of larger systematic framework that appears in the *Huainanzi*, the *Chunqiu Fanlu* (Luxuriant Gems of the *Spring and Autumn Annals*), or the *Baihu Tongyi* (Comprehensive Discussions in White Tiger Hall). Unlike the Han systematizers, they seldom attempted, in drawing such analogies as that between the bones and blood vessels of the human body and the mountains and rivers of the earth, to demonstrate the overall congruence of various orders of reality. Instead, they generally presented correspondences as means of illuminating a certain philosophical principle or advancing a particular line of argument.

Lu Shi-yi (1611–1672), among early Qing scholars, most frequently invoked structural correlations between cosmic and human parts. In explaining his theory of solar and lunar eclipses, for example, he commented that "heaven's having paths and degrees is like the human body's having arteries and veins; the sun and moon having eclipses is like the limbs of the human body having sickness and pain."[54] In the same anatomical vein, Lu likened the pervasive cosmic pneuma to the pulse of the human body: "When the pulse is disordered, then the man dies; and when the pneuma is disordered, then the country is ruined."[55]

Lu also proposed an extended analogy between the Milky Way in the sky and the mountains and rivers on the earth, arguing that the same basic physical structure was common to both.[56] Each, moreover, was the ideal basis of cartographical order in its respective realm. Just as the stars should be grouped in keeping with the framework outlined by the Milky Way, so boundaries of earthly states should be made to conform to the contours of the mountains and rivers.[57] Inasmuch as these primary physical features of heaven and earth both lack the kind of symmetry favored by traditional cosmographers, Lu's suggestion that they be made the basis of cartographical order might not have been met with the approval of earlier systematizers.

At least one other well-known early Qing scholar, Fang Yi-zhi, proposed various types of anatomical analogies among celestial, terrestrial, and human parts. Fang, like Lu, compared the vascular structures of the human body with those of the earth, remarking that "the blood of the body is like the waters of the earth." According to Fang, the rising of the blood to the upper parts of the body, the head and the brains, might be understood by analogy to the apparent upward movement of the earth's waters to appear in mountain springs and pools. Just as the blood runs throughout the body, so "the seas are all absorbed in the earth's center wherein they circulate through the veins and arteries [of the earth] and rise upward, seeping to the mountaintops. . . From source to outflow and from outflow back to the source thus [forms] one cycle." But neither blood nor water really flows upward in the absolute sense, since "the earth in the midst of the heavens is a sphere with four quarters and six directions in which everyone takes what he walks upon to be 'down' and where his head stands to be 'up'; the pneuma vibrates to make it seem like this. [But in view of the] gradual slope of the [earth's] turn, man, like an ant, is not aware of this."[58] Fang thus proceeded from the relation of a simple structural correspondence to a general natural-philosophical conclusion.

Fang followed this same procedure in other instances to illustrate different principles. To demonstrate the pattern of plentitude in the cosmos, Fang asked, rhetorically, why it was that the human body had so many discrete parts, including four sense organs, four limbs, and 360 joints. Why not just a heart or mind? He answered this query by recalling that the heavens also contain many distinct entities: "Can [it] be said that heaven ought only to have the sky and not the sun, moon, and stars?" The languages of China follow the same pattern; for the dialects of Wu, Chu, and the Central Plain are all different. From this set of analogical illustrations,

Fang concluded that there is a cosmic propensity toward plentitude or differentiation that resists the consolidation of distinct entities.[59] In contrast, the traditional correlative thinker, when presented with such data, might well have attempted to pair particular celestial objects with specific geographical regions or parts of the human body, as the *Huainanzi* and the *Chunqiu Fanlu*, in fact, did do.

SURVIVALS AND REVIVALS OF CORRELATIVE COSMOLOGY

In sum, a few major early Qing savants, including Lu Shi-yi and Fang Yi-zhi, persisted in expounding certain aspects of correlative cosmology, albeit rather sporadically. A greater number of relatively minor and obscure scholars in the late Ming and early Qing composed treatises developing various numerological and divinatory schemata based ultimately on correlative modes of thought, as is evident from the reviews in the "Arts of Calculation" section of the *Siku Quanshu Zongmu* (General Catalogue to the Complete Library in Four Treasuries). Yet the significance of an intellectual body count based on such a comprehensive bibliographical catalogue as the *Siku* should not be overrated. The number of astrological works composed by twentieth-century Western authors is probably greater than the count for sixteenth-century writers, but one could not say, for that reason, that the intellectual influence of astrology is as great in the twentieth-century West as it was in the sixteenth. On the contrary, astrology in the contemporary West, like several of the divinatory arts in eighteenth-century China, seems to be in general disrepute, particularly among the intelligentsia.

But did the criticisms which elite scholars directed at the perennial cosmology influence the life and thought of the common man? Did the cosmological reformation of the early Qing lead to the undermining of folk belief in such divinatory arts as geomancy, chronomancy, and physiognomy? There is little evidence that the cosmological criticisms articulated by major scholars of this era were widely disseminated among the common people. But a few of the more popular divinatory arts, especially geomancy, were objects of more or less popular criticism in the mid- and late-Qing eras. As Paul Ropp has pointed out, both the principles and practitioners of geomancy were ridiculed in the popular eighteenth-century vernacular novel, *Rulin Waishi* (An Unofficial History of the Scholars), as well as in other writings of that era.[60] Moreover, Hui-chen Wang Liu's study of clan rules in thirty Chinese clan genealogies dating from the 1912–1936 era presents evidence that more rules opposed geomantic practice on various grounds than favored them.[61] One of the reasons for such grassroots opposition to geomancy in prerevolutionary China, as Sidney Gamble's study of a group of North China villages in the 1930s has established, is that they contradicted the classical rule of *zhaomu* according to which the positions of graves were to be alternated with each generation of the dead.[62] Obviously, one could not follow this rule while allowing geomancers to site graves according to the principles of their art.

Perhaps the most common charge raised against geomancy in the prerevolutionary literature was, however, that it was mere superstition, not to be taken seriously by thoughtful people. This is one additional indication of the general decline of correlative cosmology. For a tenet comes to be regarded as *mere* superstition only after the larger cosmological framework which once informed it is no longer recognized or understood. The planting of garden vegetables according to the phases of the moon, as is still done in my native East Tennessee, may well seem silly to one who does not comprehend the correlative cosmology in which this practice is ultimately grounded. Thus my grandfather, who took no notice of this larger framework, was fond of remarking that he planted his garden seed in the ground, not in the moon. Such comments might well be quite common among skeptical folk dealing with the decontextualized vestiges of a cosmology transformed into superstition.

As its cosmological foundations crumbled away, Chinese geomancy was also subjected to ridicule, even while geomancers' services remained in demand. Thus the relative popularity of a particular divinatory art is not an indication that the cosmology on which it was based was also flourishing. Indeed Ming and Qing geomancers' success in exploiting their art commercially may well have helped to discredit the yin-yang–*wuxing* cosmology in which it was grounded, as C.T. Hsia has suggested.[63]

However, the obituary of correlative cosmology in China, even so far as high intellectual history is concerned, could hardly have been written as early as the end of the seventeenth century. For a number of prominent mid- and late-Qing scholars rehabilitated certain aspects of correlative thought. Ironically, one of the chief bases of seventeenth-century cosmological criticism, the revival of classicism, also contributed to the mid-Qing renewal of correlative ideas. For when eminent eighteenth-century historians and classicists reexamined ancient literature carefully, they discovered that anticipations of certain ideas associated with correlative cosmology, especially the notion of resonant interaction between astronomical and political entities, were embedded even in the earliest stratum of the classics. These ideas may well have been distorted and misused by later commentators, especially in the Han; but one could not deny, said the eminent eighteenth-century historian Zhao Yi (1727–1814), that the *Spring and Autumn Annals* poses forms of intercommunication between heaven and man, for "If [heaven] really has no contact with man, then why would the sage [Confucius] have wasted so much ink [in relating such matters]?"[64] Even the editors of the *Four Treasuries*, while criticizing the cosmological constructions devised by later systematizers at almost every opportunity, occasionally acknowledged that anticipations of some of the divinatory arts might be found in classical literature. These ideas had later been woefully misinterpreted; "yet one cannot say that in antiquity there were no such theories."[65] In view of the great prestige of the classics in eighteenth-century scholarship, this admission suggested that not all aspects of correlative thought were to be unreservedly condemned.

The eighteenth-century, especially its middle decades, was the period in which the school of Han Learning (Hanxue) dominated classical studies and scholarship. This suggests a second possible reason for the cosmological recidivism of the mid-Qing: inasmuch as some of the Han commentators to whom eighteenth-century Han Learning scholars looked for authoritative interpretations of the classics were also responsible for the establishment of correlative cosmology, the latter gained new prestige. Thus even Hui Tong (1697–1758), the purported inventor of the term "Han Learning," endorsed the *najia* system which systematically correlated the trigrams of the *Change* with the phases of the moon and the denary and duodenary cyclical characters. Hui even supposed that the trigrams were really invented in the manner depicted in later versions of the *najia* schema by abstracting the physical images that the moon presented in its various phases.[66] Hui's studies on the classical Ming Tang also gave full play to the cosmographical fantasies with which Han commentators had imbued that structure.

Finally, a striking late-Qing revival of a form of correlative cosmology appears in the late nineteenth-century development of the new-text (jinwen) school of classical scholarship. Late-Qing commentators in the new-text tradition did not, of course, expressly aim at rehabilitating correlative thought. Their major concerns included the revelation of the true Confucius through a study of such texts as the *Gongyang* commentary to the

Spring and Autumn Annals and the promotion of institutional reforms. In the late nineteenth century, however, a leading new-text scholar and publicist, Kang You-wei (1858–1927), melded various elements inherited from earlier traditions into the comprehensive interpretation of the classics and history that has come to be associated with new-text scholarship.[67]

Kang's theory of historical development, his conception of the three ages (sanshi), was based in part on the ideas of such Han cosmologists as Dong Zhong-shu (c. 179–c. 104 B.C.) and He Xiu (A.D. 129–182). So it is not surprising that it assumed the form of a system of correspondence, albeit one set on a progressive historical scale. Kang characterized his three ages, the eras of great peace (taiping), approaching peace (shengping), and disorder (juluan), by correlating each of them with a specific moral virtue, social ideal, and political form. For example, Kang predicted that the virtue of humanity (ren), the way of great harmony (datong), and a democratic form of government (minzhu) would prevail in the final age of the great peace. On the other hand, men of the age of approaching peace must be governed through the virtue of propriety (li), the way of small tranquility (xiaokang), and the institution of a monarchy.[68] One of Kang You-wei's major disciples in the tradition of new-text learning, Liang Qi-chao (1873–1929), further developed Kang's correlative interpretation of the canonical three ages. With the age of disorder Liang paired the political system of feudalism, the rule of force, the philosophical doctrine that human nature is evil, and the teachings of Xunzi. And with the coming utopian era, the age of great peace, Liang correlated political democracy, the rule of intellect, the philosophical doctrine that human nature is good, and the teachings of Mencius.[69]

Both Kang and Liang subdivided each of the three ages in a way that is reminiscent of the three-based numerological cosmos constructed by the Han cosmologist Yang Xiong. Dividing by three, Kang maintained that each of the three major ages incorporates three corresponding lesser ages. For example, within the age of approaching peace, there are disorderly, approaching-peace, and great-peace stages. But even each of these nine lesser ages, Kang continued, might be subdivided, producing eighty-one divisions, and so on ad infinitum.[70] Kang occasionally invoked subsidiary ages to explain such empirical phenomena as the persistence of comparatively backward subcultures within more advanced civilizations. For example, the cultures of the Miao, Yao, Tong, and Li aboriginal peoples in the south of China, said Kang, correspond to the disorderly (juluan) subphase within the larger era of approaching peace (sheng ping) that held sway over most of imperial China.[71] But inasmuch as Kang cited such empirical illustrations only sporadically, they appear to have been afterthoughts not applied until the larger numerological system was constructed.

One reason why Kang You-wei's theory of historical development assumed the form of a correlative system is that he relied much on the work of prominent Han cosmologists, as noted above. However, Kang drew from a wide array of sources, both classical Chinese and modern Western, in formulating his theory. He took the idea of three stages of historical development, those of "disorder," "approaching peace," and "great peace," from the *Gongyang* commentary to the *Spring and Autumn Annals*, and the concepts of the "small tranquility" and "great harmony" from the *Record of Rites*.[72] Moreover, Kang apparently drew the virtues of humanity and propriety from the *Analects*, and the ideas of monarchy, democracy, and other political forms from Western political theory. From such a diverse array of ideas, Kang built the system of correspondence sketched above. Thus Kang You-wei's syncretic approach to political and social ideas inclined him to correlative thinking.

Chinese political thinkers after Kang You-wei continued to develop correlative schemata based on the notion of the three ages. According to Lu Bao-qian, republican revolutionaries' conception of the three political stages of the Chinese revolution was influenced by Kang's three ages.[73] The image of Kang's three ages might also be seen in the strange historical theory, widely discussed in the Chinese press during the late 1960s, by which the three major figures in world Communist tradition were correlated with the three paradigmatic revolutions in the Communist experience: Marx with the 1871 rising of the Paris Commune, Lenin with the October Revolution, and Mao with the Chinese Cultural Revolution of the 1960s.[74] The first of these three pairings, that of Marx with the Paris Commune, might even be interpreted as a "forced fit," for Marx is not known to have assumed either ideological or tactical direction of the 1871 rising. Yet Marx, a highly important figure in the Communist tradition, obviously had to be paired with *some* great revolutionary engagement in order to complete the correlative set.

The revival of a form of correlative thought in the high intellectual tradition of late-Qing China, particularly in new-text scholarship, might be compared with similar movements in Western cultural and intellectual history of the same era. The most celebrated such movement, and the one which harbored the most conspicuous revival of correlative cosmology, was Romanticism. As Paul Reiff has pointed out, the Neoplatonic philosopher and premier correlative thinker of late antiquity, Plotinus (A.D. 205–270), is the "key" to early Romanticism, especially to the thought of such German philosophers as Fichte (1762–1814), Novalis (1772–1801), Schlegel (1772–1829), and Schellling (1775–1854).[75] Moreover, Renaissance Neoplatonic philosophers of cosmic unity such as Giordano Bruno (1548–1600) and Jacob Boehme (1575–1624) also influenced several famous Romantic figures, particularly Coleridge and Hegel.[76]

Of these, the author who presents the clearest illustrations of correlative thought in the Neoplatonic tradition is probably Novalis (Friedrich von Hardenberg). But though he drew correspondences among the various realms of man and nature in an orthodox fashion, Novalis departed from Neoplatonism in suggesting that the yearning to ascend the ladder of souls is the major source of sin and sickness in the cosmos:

> The system of morality must become the system of Nature. All sickness is like sin in the sense that it is a transcendency. Our sicknesses are all phenomena of a heightened sensation that is seeking to pass over into higher powers. When man tried to become God, he sinned. Sickness of plants are animalizations, sicknesses of animals are rationalizations, sicknesses of stones are vegetizations. Should not each stone and animal correspond to a particular plant? Plants are dead stones, animals are dead plants.[77]

Novalis' disquisitions on correspondences may bear only a vague resemblance to the metahistorical speculations of nineteenth-century Chinese new-text scholars. Yet both Western Romantic and Chinese new-text revivals of correlative cosmology seem to have been motivated in part by a desire to restore a sense of grandeur to the cosmos and history, to rehabilitate a holistic vision largely lost in the course of the Scientific Revolution in seventeenth-century Europe and the cosmological reformation in early Qing China. Even while nineteenth-century new-text scholars built on the achievements of seventeenth- and eighteenth-century philology, they sometimes denigrated the type of concentrated exegetical study in which early- and mid-Qing classicists had excelled. Liao Ping (1852–1932) and Kang You-wei, in particular, were drawn instead to the grander theories of historical and cosmic evolution propounded by such Han commentators as Dong Zhong-shu and He Xiu. The early European Romantics likewise deplored the triumph of what they regarded as the intellectually and aesthetically impoverished mechanical philosophy. They were much more attracted by the "Renaissance vitalism" which "had envisioned an integral universe without absolute divisions, in which everything is interrelated by a system of correspondences."[78]

Yet, ironically, notable advances in the physical sciences as late as the mid-nineteenth century appear to have been influenced by vestiges of correlative thinking. One example is the so-called "law of octaves" formulated by J.A.R. Newlands (1837–1898), one of Mendeleyev's distinguished predecessors in the framing of the periodic table of the elements. According to Newlands, the chemical elements, when ordered by their atomic weights, constitute a series which resembles the keyboard of a piano; "the fifty-six elements so arranged . . . forms the compass of eight octaves."[79] Newlands went so far as to assert that "members of the same group [of chemical elements] stand to each other in the same relation as the extremities of one or more octaves in music."[80] Though this suggestion drew ridicule from his English audience, Newlands' Russian contemporary Mendeleyev (1834–1907), who also believed in a "general reign of order in nature,"[81] if not literally in a "law of octaves," performed the labor necessary to establish the periodicity of the elements. Thus the formulation of the periodic table, like Kepler's development of his planetary laws more than two centuries earlier, seems to have been mediated by correlative thought.

After the end of the Romantic era, however, correlative cosmology was relegated to increasingly idiosyncratic and isolated subcultures. Analogical and symbolic modes of thought continue to be quite important in many forms of human culture. But the idea that systematic proportional relationships exist among such diverse realms as the astronomical heavens, the human body, musical scales, political structures, and celestial beings is not widely accepted by educated people in the twentieth-century West. In fact, the densest concentrations of correlative thinkers in the contemporary West might well be found in mental hospitals, especially among schizophrenics, a possibility which suggests a link between adherence to defunct cosmologies and insanity as defined in our culture. The plausibility of such a connection is supported by Michel Foucault's demonstration that definitions of madness often change in times of cosmological transition.[82] It is also illustrated, though hardly proven, by Karl Jasper's suggestion that Emanuel Swedenborg's (1688–1772) universal system of correspondence between the natural and spiritual worlds, as outlined in his *Arcana Coelestia*, is the product of a schizophrenic imagination.[83]

Correlative cosmology has also occasionally reappeared in aesthetic and literary currents in the post-Romantic West, such as "Symbolism" in late nineteenth-century French poetry. Not only did such Symbolist poets as Baudelaire and Rimbaud systematically correlate sounds and colors, even cultivating a sort of colored hearing, but Baudelaire went so far as to adapt Swedenborg's theory of correspondences.[84] Moreover, poetic metaphor in general, even as used by contemporary poets, preserves vestiges of correlative cosmology. For example, "the expression 'sweet melody,' " as James F. Anderson has pointed out, "implies the 'metaphorical proportionality' that melody is to auricular sensation as something saccharine is to palatal sensation (sweetness)."[85] Inasmuch as correlative thinkers of earlier ages systematically matched flavors with sounds, "sweet melody" might be interpreted as decontextualized fragment of a larger system of correspondence.[86]

But correlative thinking has not survived in modern Western culture only in the form of fragments and vestiges. Several of the major figures in the history of modern social theory applied forms of correlative thought in their analysis of man and society. Auguste Comte, for example, likened the individual to the social organism, characterizing the family as a social cell, social forces as social tissues, and cities as social organs. Herbert Spencer also posed such analogies, though he denied that there was any real identity between individual and social organisms. A more obscure nineteenth-century social theorist, Johann Casper Bluntschli, however, emphatically asserted such an identity, specifically comparing sixteen parts of the human body with sixteen organs of the body politic. "He also determined the sex of the social organism, stating that it was scientifically demonstrable that the state was masculine and the church feminine."[87]

Sigmund Freud also developed forms of correlative thought, though not in such a traditional fashion as did Comte, Spencer, and Bluntschli. His ontogeny-recapitulates- phylogeny dictum is reminiscent of correlative cosmological schemata in positing the real existence of systematic correspondences between the development of the individual (microcosm) and that of the race as a whole (macrocosm). Thus Freud remarked that "the animistic phase [of human intellectual development] corresponds in time as well as in content with narcissism, the religious phases corresponds to that stage of object finding which is characterized by dependence on the parents, while the scientific stage has its full counterpart in the individual's state of maturity."[88] Freudian interpretations of dreams, as well as of art and culture, might also be regarded as modern adaptations of correlative thinking. Thus correlative thought perhaps helped to mediate the birth of modern psychology, as well as modern astronomy, modern mathematics, and modern chemistry.

Contemporary anthropologists have also employed forms or adaptations of correlative thought. Claude Lévi-Strauss, for example, apparently based his general theory of society and culture on the notion that there exists a systematic correspondence between the structure of social organization, the structure of myth, and the structure of the mind. This correspondence, as Lévi-Strauss suggests, is not merely fortuitous; mental structures are objectified in both mythical narratives and social organizations. For example, the mental propensity to polarize experience is reflected in the tendency to pair mythical ideas into such dichotomies as "raw" and "cooked," as well as in the organization of social units into moieties.[89]

Marxist interpretations of history and society also frequently apply forms of correlative thought, especially in analyzing the various stages of historical development. Those who are accused of being "vulgar" Marxists have a particular tendency to mechanically correlate artistic, literary, political, and religious forms with basic modes of economic and social organization, even to the extent of practically ignoring the functional relationships between Marxist substructure and superstructure. Such theorists sometimes seem to proceed from the basic cosmological assumption that there exists a natural, systematic correspondence among those various products of human endeavor which are synchronic, such as capitalism, the romantic novel, evangelical religion, and parliaments. A belief in the correspondence of basic orders of reality, mind, nature, and history is implicit even in Friedrich Engels' *Dialectics of Nature.* For "the dialectics of the brain," Engels wrote, "is only the reflection of the forms of motion of the real world, both of nature and of history."[90]

It is fashionable to dismiss such social and psychological theories—Comtean, Freudian, Marxist, and Lévi-Straussian—as merely "reductionist" rather than adaptations of earlier cosmological ideas. Is it not possible, however, that many of those theories generally labeled "reductionist," and perhaps even reductionism itself, may stem from mutant forms of correlative cosmology that have survived and flourished in modern times? After all, the intellectual genealogy of Lévi-Strauss has been plausibly traced back to the French Symbolists of the late-nineteenth century,[91] who in turn drew on the theories of such correlative thinkers as Swedenborg.

The Hegelian dialectic (and its Marxist transformation), like so much of the German Romantic philosophy, may also be linked to cosmological antecedents.[92]

That such ideas continue to attract contemporary minds is not surprising, especially in view of the human propensity, noted by Bacon, "to suppose the existence of more order and regularity in the world than it finds."[93] However, long-term attempts to operate within a mental universe based on correlative modes of thought may lead to intellectual stultification and even ridicule, as indicated by the experience of late-medieval allegorists, Song Chinese numerologists, and modern Marxists and Freudians. Witness the review by Alexis Tolstoy, a Soviet writer of the 1940s, of Shostakovich's Fifth Symphony:

> Here we have the "Symphony of Socialism." It begins with the Largo of the masses working underground, an accelerando corresponds to the subway system; the Allegro in its turn symbolizes gigantic factory machinery and its victory over nature. The Adagio represents the synthesis of Soviet culture, science, and art. The Scherzo reflects the athletic life of the happy inhabitants of the Union. As for the Finale, it is the image of the gratitude and the enthusiasm of the masses.[94]

It may be that only the arms of NATO and the laboratory mice of the behaviorists stand between us and a truly massive retrogression in world intellectual history.

Chapter Eight

Criticisms of
Geometrical Cosmology
In Late-Traditional China

Geometrical cosmology was less pervasive in both Chinese and European civilizations of premodern times than was correlative cosmology. It ramified into fewer areas of high culture in either civilization and seems to have affected popular life and thought only slightly. Hence the decline of geometrical cosmography did not have such broad effects as those set in motion by the decline of correlative cosmology.

Nevertheless, at least one aspect of geometrical cosmography, that which attributed perfect circularity to the heavenly bodies, did meet its end with some fanfare in seventeenth-century Europe. Some of the most celebrated figures in the history of seventeenth-century thought, particularly Galileo, Kepler, and Bacon, made a special point of puncturing the Aristotelian axiom that all superlunary bodies were shaped like perfect spheres and moved in perfect circles. Bacon's disquisition on the "Idols of the Tribe" condemned his scholastic predecessors for their belief in "the fiction that all celestial bodies move in perfect circles."[1] The first of Kepler's three planetary laws, the one which states that the planets move in elliptical orbits around the sun, furnished a scientific basis for abandoning this axiom. Finally, one of the most celebrated of Galileo's telescopic discoveries, described in his *Starry Messenger* of 1610, was "that the surface of the moon is not smooth, uniform, and precisely spherical as a great number of philosophers believe it (and the other heavenly bodies) to be, but is uneven, rough, and full of cavities and prominences, being not unlike the face of the earth."[2] This, as well as the Galilean discoveries of the sunspots and the rings of Saturn, graphically illustrated the imperfections of the heavenly bodies, thus confuting the key Aristotelian cosmological distinction between sublunary and superlunary realms.

The Renaissance supercession of circular forms had ramifications not only in astronomy, but also in art, as Lynn White has stated. Remarking that "fixation on the circle was almost complete in ancient culture," White notes that "As late as the fifteenth century, artists could not draw a picture of the Colosseum which showed it oval." But "Michelangelo and his successors during the next fifty years created an atmosphere in which ovoid forms became respectable, until finally Baroque art was dominated by the oval." This development, White speculates, "prepared the way for Kepler's astronomical breakthrough."[3] It also apparently contributed to the replacement of circular by oval forms in sacred cosmography, as well as in astronomy. Whereas Pico represented the form of the All by a circle, his seventeenth-century follower Athanasius Kircher distorted this figure into a form approaching an ellipse, "which is labeled 'the circle of worlds' and which flames with divine fire."[4] Kircher's near contemporary, the Elizabethan magus John Dee (1527–1608), also stretched the Hermetic circle into an oval form, though perhaps not deliberately.[5]

Like the Renaissance repudiation of circularity, the late-traditional Chinese critique of nonary cosmography ramified into several areas of culture. Since early Chinese cosmographers had used nonary figures, especially the 3 × 3 grid, to order such diverse forms of space as agrarian, political, and architectural, it is not surprising that the decline of geometrical cosmography affected all those fields, though some only marginally. However, the majority of the nonary cosmograms conceived by traditional Chinese cosmologists were supposed to be applied not in ethereal astronomical and artistic realms, as were their circular European counterparts, but in concrete geographical space. Hence, the physical science that most stimulated cosmographical criticism in late-traditional China was not astronomy, as was the case in Europe, but geography. For geographical studies highlighted better than any other branch of learning widely cultivated in premodern China the gap between geometrical ideality and the physiographical irregularity of the surface of the earth.

CRITICISMS OF THE WELL-FIELD SYSTEM

The best-known of the traditional cosmograms, the well-field (jingtian) schema, supposedly used by ancient sagely rulers for apportioning agrarian space into a neat array of squares, had been criticized long before the Qing. Agrarian reformers who suggested its implementation frequently encountered articulate opposition. By the Song era, opponents of the perennial proposal to reinstitute the well-field schema had formulated systematic arguments against this plan. But few of these objections took much note of physiographical circumstances, emphasizing instead the social and economic obstacles to applying the well-field model. Ma Duan-lin, for example, stressed the social dislocations that would arise, predicting that "it would only invite resentment and bitterness."[6]

Song advocates, as well as opponents, of the well-field plan seldom focused on the purely physical barriers to implementing the system. The Neo-Confucian philosopher Zhang Zai (1021–1077), for example, commented that the well-field reformer had only to mark off the lines of the grid and distribute a square to all who were eligible.[7] Zhang, apparently, did not foresee that any technical difficulties would block the consummation of this enterprise.

In contrast to most of their major Song and Yuan predecessors, early Qing commentators on the well field were most concerned with the disjunction between the ideal geometry of the grid and the physiographical irregularity of much of the land in the realm. A consciousness of this discrepancy led Lu Long-qi (1630–1693) to conclude that the well-field system was meant to be applied only in those limited areas where the topography was suitable.[8] In an extended discussion of the agrarian systems instituted under the three ancient dynasties, the Xia, Shang, and Zhou, Lu added that the former kings adapted the standard measurements for agricultural fields to suit varying geographical and demographical circumstances. Unlike such self-styled reformers as Wang Mang (r. A.D. 9–23) and Wang An-shi (1021–1086), the sage kings of antiquity, said Lu, did not attempt to force the entire realm into one rigid mold:

The earth has both wide and narrow [places], the population has both concentrations and diffusions, and the force of circumstances may be convenient or not. For this reason, the former kings could not have forcibly made [the land system] uniform [throughout the realm]. But if one takes all of the agricultural fields in the world and exhaustively [measures them off] into units of fifty *mou*, seventy *mou*, or a hundred *mou*, then there will necessarily be obstructions... Thus the fifty-*mou* [units used by] the Xia Dynasty, the seventy-*mou* [units used by] the Shang, and the hundred-*mou* [units used by] the Zhou only refer to the broad outline [of the agrarian systems implemented by these dynasties]. For how could the world of those eras have possibly been so uniform?[9]

Huang Zong-xi (1610–1695), among other scholars of the day, also suggested that the agrarian mensural schemata devised by the ancients were meant to be flexible and of limited applicability. He indicated that Mencius intended his endorsement of the well-field grid to apply only to a limited area rather than to the realm as a whole.[10] Contrary to Zhu Xi, Huang maintained that a study of the classical significance of the well-field system should begin with the *Mencius*, a "free text" by Karlgren's definition, rather than with the *Zhouli* (Rites of Zhou), the bible for totalistic agrarian and bureaucratic reform in imperial Chinese history.

Even the early Qing proponents of the well-field arrangement generally focused their attention on the physical aspects of the system. Some of them even proposed the imposition of the well-field grid primarily as an instrument for topographical realignment rather than as a vehicle for utopian economic reform. Gu Yan-wu, for example, argued that one of the chief advantages of the ancient ditched well fields was that they furnished physical barriers against the depredations of invading armies, especially those equipped with war chariots. By thus making long walls and great armies unnecessary, they facilitated the maintenance of local autonomy in ancient China. The Great Wall, Gu contended, had to be constructed only after the old agrarian regime with is built-in impediments to cavalry attack had vanished.[11]

Gu's contemporary Lu Shi-yi (1611–1672) also conceived the well-field schema almost entirely in physiographical terms. The ancients, Lu contended, physically ordered the surface of the earth according to the lines of the well-field grid, circumventing only high mountains and great rivers which could not easily have been removed. In contrast to the latter-day cartographers, whose creations, especially lines of latitude and longitude, existed only on paper, the physiographers of antiquity imposed a rectilinear mold on the face of the land. They thus accomplished the unification of the cartographical and physiographical orders, even to the extent that topographical features, especially ditches and other barriers, conformed to parallels and meridians on the map. But from the end of the three dynasties and the fall from high antiquity, Lu lamented, actual boundaries increasingly failed to conform to the lines of the cartographical grid, as rivers, fields, and hills with rounded edges and borders began to appear. In later times, such irregularities proliferated to the point that the oblique and the curvilinear became the rule. Even worse, odd units of land appeared in the irregular interstices between geographical features. Finally, the unregulated construction of all sorts of structures on the surface of the earth, especially houses and graves, made restoration of the antique physiographical order even more difficult. But perhaps, Lu concluded, circumstances would arise that would make possible the gradual reimposition of the ancient grid and the elimination of the insidious irregularities that had come to deface the surface of the earth.[12]

Thus even Lu Shi-yi, probably the most enthusiastic advocate among major early Qing scholars of a well-field restoration, admitted the existence of a tremendous gap between the geometrical ideality of the system and physiographical reality. Lu did, of course, attempt to mitigate this discrepancy through his strange theory that the ancients managed to mold topographical features to fit the pattern of their ideal schema. Although Lu raised the possibility of reversing the mensural fall from high antiquity, he acknowledged that the irregular surfaces and edges of terrestrial space would make any such enterprise very difficult to accomplish.

CRITICISMS OF THE NINE-PROVINCES SCHEMA

A second nonary cosmographical conception critically examined by Qing scholars was the nine-provinces (jiuzhou) schema supposedly outlined by Yu the Great. Like a number of the other cosmograms we have considered, the nine provinces, as described in the "Tribute to Yu" chapter of the *Documents Classic*, was not classically conceived as a tidy array of squares. Rather, each province was generally marked off by physical features or natural boundaries. However, as explained earlier, commentators in the Han and later epochs tended to slight the topographical basis of the ancient *jiuzhou* and to discuss it in terms of political geometry or numerology.

Several Qing commentators on the "Tribute of Yu" and other geographically oriented sections of the canon, however, reiterated the topographical nature of the classical boundaries. Yan Ruo-ju (1636–1704) emphasized that "Yu fixed the frontiers of the nine provinces by mountains and rivers."[13] The late-Qing savant Chen Li (1810–1882) contrasted the geography of the ancient sage kings, which "took mountains and rivers as being primary," with that of later ages, which concentrated on the bounding of political units.[14]

Qing commentators were not the first scholars to do this. The great Song encyclopedist Zheng Qiao (1108–1166) and the major Neo-Confucian philosopher Zhu Xi also argued that interpretations of the nine provinces in terms of political geometry were inventions of later commentators and that the ancient states and regions were bounded by mountains and rivers.[15] Zhu Xi remarked that "the system of marking off the borders of states [by straight lines] was only a method of calculation laid down by Han scholars. The reality was not like this. In establishing a state, it is necessary to proceed according to the terrain. There is no pattern that can be clearly marked off into squares."[16] Zhu Xi, a cosmological conservative in many respects, thus anticipated Qing criticisms of Han political geometry.

At least one major early Qing scholar, Mao Qi-ling (1623–1716), challenged numerological as well as geometrical interpretations of the nine provinces and related arrangements. According to Mao, the ancients, in naming geographical features such as mountains, marshes, rivers and regions by "nines," did not necessarily mean that there were nine and only nine of each. The numerical prefix was only a manner of speaking, not a means of enumeration. Thus "Taihu is only one lake and yet it is named the 'Five Lakes'. 'Zhaoyuqi' is only one marsh and yet it is named the 'Nine Marshes.' " Yet Han commentators, taking such numerical prefixes too literally, attempted to enumerate *the* nine rivers, *the* nine provinces, *the* nine mountains, and *the* nine marshes. In doing so, they necessarily omitted those that could not be fit into nonary sets. Thus "Zhen marsh is presently known by the name 'marsh.' But it is not counted among the nine marshes. How does one explain this?"[17]

In the view of some early Qing commentators, postclassical interpretations of the nine provinces were open to question not only because of their lack of canonical support, but also because of the vast historical and geographical changes that had occurred since antiquity. Of all major seventeenth-century scholars, Gu Yan-wu was perhaps most conscious of the extent to which the physical geography of the empire, especially of the once flourishing Northwest, had changed since antiquity. Gu, in fact, blamed the progressive depopulation of large areas of the Northwest partly on one version of the *jiuzhou* conception itself, arguing that it left a sector of this territory outside the bounds of the empire, thus facilitating the transfer of the center of cosmic gravity from the Northwest to the Southeast.[18] As a means of recovering this territory, of restoring politically and ecologically lost lands in the far Northwest and Northeast, Gu proposed extensive reclamation projects in these areas. He suggested a change in geographical nomenclature to facilitate the projected northward expansion.

Gu's meditations on the inadequacy of ancient *jiuzhou* conception and his concern for the Northwest prefigured a significant theme in Qing intellectual history. For later geographical thinkers, such as Liu Xian-ting (1648–1695), pursued studies which they hoped would facilitate the reconstruction of irrigation works in that area.[19] Even in the late-Qing and Republican periods, such famous reformers and scholars as Tan Si-tong (1865–1898) and Gu Jie-gang continued to lament the decline of the North-west and the narrow limits that the classical nine-provinces conception had allegedly set on China's territorial expansion.[20]

CRITICISMS OF THE FENYE
(FIELD ALLOCATION) SYSTEM

In contrast to other aspects of cosmographical criticism in late-traditional China, the early Qing critique of the astrological field allocation (fenye) schema may well have been significantly influenced by the scientific writings of the Jesuit missionaries in late-Ming China. In fact, one of these missionaries, Giulio Aleni (1582–1649), systematically attacked the *fenye* system in one of his Chinese works, the *Xifang Dawen* (Questions and Answers on the West). Aleni argued that matching the fields of the heavens with the regions of only one country, China, was unjustified, since "all countries in the whole world are covered by the same sky." Moreover, in view of the diurnal rotation of the heavens around the earth, "how can we say that a certain star belongs to one particular region?"[21]

The points raised by Aleni were repeated by such seventeenth-century commentators as Fang Yi-zhi (1611–1671), who had read widely in the natural-scientific literature published by the missionaries. This does not mean, however, that the Jesuits originated such arguments. Even before the first Jesuit missionaries set foot in China, Wang Ting-xiang (1474–1544) had already characterized as "biased" the assumption that unusual celestial phenomena were warnings directed only at the Chinese ruler. Just as a father loves all of his children equally, so heaven looks down upon all countries impartially.[22] But seventeenth-century critics of *fenye* did not, in any case, restrict themselves to repeating the points raised by Aleni or Wang Ting-xiang. They posed a variety of arguments, several of which reflect very clearly the general early Qing animus against an over-wrought symmetry and a gratuitous precision.

Probably the most comprehensive case was the posed by Fang Yi-zhi in his encyclopedic work, the *Dongya* (Comprehensive Refinement). Fang raised at least four objections to *fenye*. First, he argued, "the heavens constantly revolve while the earth, once established, has not moved. To harmonize the ultimate of movement [the heavens] with the ultimate of quiescence [the earth] is not easily arranged." Second, the two supposedly corresponding realms, the heavens and the earth, were incommensurate on other points as well, chiefly that the heavens are so much vaster than the earth. Third, Fang pointed out that while the geographical area of the southerly Yangzhou region in the *fenye* schema comprises about half of China's territory, it was allotted only three of the twenty-eight lunar lodges in the heavens, another glaring instance of the system's having paired incommensurable entities. But in this instance, "the earthly [region] is broad while the [supposedly corresponding] heavenly [region] is narrow." Finally, Fang remarked that the *fenye* arrangement failed to take into account the far southerly regions of the heavens not visible in China.[23]

Like Fang Yi-zhi, the early Qing classicist Yan Ruo-ju was particularly concerned with the failure of correspondence and the lack of symmetry in the *fenye*. But Yan, following the great astronomers of the Tang era, maintained that these problems were not so much inherent in the original nature of the system as they were products of secular changes in the configurations of corresponding heavenly and earthly territories. In the celestial realm, such movements as the annual difference (suicha) had altered the relative positions of the celestial markers used by the ancients. And the terrestrial units used in the system, particularly the nine provinces supposedly demarcated by Yu the Great, had changed even more radically. If the idea of *fenye* was to be salvaged at all, it would clearly have to be based on less ephemeral units, particularly physiographical ones.[24]

Other Qing critics of *fenye* focused their attention on the gratuitous precision that was particularly evident in the latter refinement of the schema. They observed that the original *fenye* was much less exact than were its postclassical elaborations. According to Huang Zong-xi, *fenye* was at first intended only as a rough outline, and was not geared for the degree of astrological precision later demanded of it.[25] Huang's younger contemporary Lu Long-qi denied that the ancients ever conceived *fenye* to be a system at all. Instead, it was built up gradually and haphazardly, in a purely empirical manner:

> If a certain star had a [portentous] change which was verified constantly in a certain state, then [this star] was subsequently established as the allotted asterism of that particular state. Doubtless the system could not have been established by one person or in one era. Too, its principles basically cannot be explained. It may be called a case of the stars and the earth being connected

through the refined pneuma; but it has nothing to do with boundaries.[26]

The eighteenth century editors of the *Siku Quanshu* (Complete Libraries in Four Treasuries) continued the early Qing critique of the gratuitous precision and systematization that postclassical cosmologists had introduced into the *fenye* schema. While rejecting, at the outset, the supposition that vast celestial spaces could somehow be paired with the limited territories of the Middle Kingdom, the editors were particularly skeptical of the refinements that such later scholars as Liu Ji (1311–1375) had devised. Liu, not being content with pairing the regions of China with the nine celestial fields or the twenty-eight lunar lodges, had gone on to correlate degrees of the celestial sphere with countries of the empire. This innovation, the editors said, was even more arbitrary than occultists' theories, not least because it lacked any observational basis. It also demonstrated that even a scholar of Liu Ji's caliber could not rationalize the system or rid it of its absurdities.[27]

A few major Qing scholars who thus repudiated traditional forms of the *fenye* compensated for this cosmographical loss by abstracting a sort of ersatz *fenye* from the new cartography introduced by Westerners. Specifically, as both Fang Yi-zhi and Dai Zhen (1724–1777) indicated, the 360 degrees of the celestial and terrestrial spheres corresponded, and even resonated (xiangyin) with one another.[28] According to Dai Zhen, one could "borrow" the degrees of the heavens to measure the terrestrial sphere; a one-to-one correspondence could thus be established. Though neither Fang nor Dai proposed that this correspondence had any astrological import, the prospect of reestablishing a mensural symmetry between the heavens and the earth apparently attracted them. Thus they proceeded to draw a cosmographical conclusion from the cosmologically arid cartographical standards of the new mathematical astronomy.

CRITICISMS OF THE MING TANG (LUMINOUS HALL)

Qing criticisms of cosmological interpretations of the Ming Tang were generally based on textual and historical arguments rather than geographical ones. Such criticisms frequently took note of the differences between classical and Han interpretations of this institution. Mao Qi-ling, for example, pointed out the disjunction between the classical twelve-chambered version of the Ming Tang and the nonary "nine palace" (jiugong) schema most favored by Han cosmologists.[29] Wang Fu-zhi (1619–1692), moreover, likened Han commentators' interpretations of the Ming Tang, particularly those which endowed it with such features as a round roof (resembling the heavens) a square base (resembling the earth), and nine rooms (resembling the nine provinces of the realm), to children's games. Such a structure, Wang pointed out, was not only based on heterodox theories but also architecturally impractical.[30]

Wang Fu-zhi's contemporary, Lu Shi-yi also faulted cosmographical constructions on the Ming Tang, particularly the *Yueling* (Monthly Ordinances) figure as interpreted by Zhu Xi, as serious distortions of the classical institution. Lu's main objection to the form of the Ming Tang described in the *Yueling* was that this plan failed to accord with the proper ritual function of the institution:

> Now what the ancients called the "Ming Tang" was meant only for regulating [affairs] by facing the light. It was only for facilitating the courtly reception of the feudal lords. But according to the "Monthly Ordinances," the Son of Heaven during the three winter months ought to reside in the Dark Hall (xuantang), the Great Ancestral Temple (taimiao), and the [adjacent chambers to the] left and right [on the north side of the structure]. [But] in this season, the north wind is strong. [Thus if] the Son of Heaven opens the door directly to the north, I fear that this would greatly contravene the idea of guarding and regulating in accordance with the season. Moreover, when the Son of Heaven advances and halts, all of the officials follow suit. But if he resides on the left or the right sides [of the structure], then the slant [of such a position] is awkward and also not in accordance with the rite of the lord looking down on his subordinates from on high. I fear that the ancients could not have been so inflexible or pedantic as this.[31]

Although such eighteenth-century classicists as Hui Tong (1697–1758) refurbished Han cosmologists' constructions on the Ming Tang, a later scholar, Jiang Fan (1761–1831), continued the early Qing critique. Like Wang Fu-zhi, Jiang asserted that Han commentators, especially those who were active in the reign of the Emperor Guangwu (r. A.D 25–57) of the Later Han, had distorted the classical Ming Tang by adulterating it with apocryphal and occultist interpretations. Even the *Yueling* version, said Jiang on the authority of the Han scholiast Zheng Xuan (A.D. 127–200), was based not on the Ming Tang of the ancients but on that outlined in the *Lüshi Chunqiu* (Master Lü's Spring and Autumn Annals), a deliberately syncretic text compiled around 240 B.C. Jiang traced the cosmographical and correlative constructions on the Ming Tang that arose in the Later Han, the ones by which it was furnished with a round roof, a square base, twelve halls, nine rooms, and the like, to the influence of heterodox learning.[32]

CRITICISMS OF THE HETU (YELLOW RIVER CHART) AND LUOSHU (LUO RIVER WRITING)

The final nonary cosmogram critically reviewed by Qing scholars, a figure which some commentators regarded as the historical source or cosmological key to all the others, was the Luoshu (Luo River Writing). This schema, unlike the other four considered in this chapter, was not intended to be used for ordering any form of physical space. Nevertheless, Han and Song interpretations of the Luoshu and of its cosmographical complement, the Hetu (Yellow River Chart), elicited more critical commentary from major Qing scholars than did any of the other four cosmograms.

Early Qing commentators were not the first to have critically examined the standard cosmological versions of the Hetu and Luoshu. Several fourteenth-century Confucian scholars, including Wang Wei (1323–1374), Chen Ying-run, and Song Lian (1310–1381), pointed out the heterodox origins of the Song Neo-Confucian versions of these figures and particularly questioned the association of classical references to either the Hetu or the Luoshu with the "nine palaces."[33] Song Lian contended that no classical reference to either the Hetu or the Luoshu, including those that appear in the *Analects*, the *Documents*, and the "Great Commentary" to the *Change*, associated these figures with any particular numbers. All numerological disquisitions on the Hetu and Luoshu thus were the inventions of later commentators.

Late-Ming and early-Qing commentators on the Hetu and Luoshu did not, however, merely reaffirm the points made by earlier scholars. First, their examinations of the classical sources and historical development of these figures were much more meticulous than those of their predecessors. Second, the later commentators did not merely impugn the cosmological interpretations of the Hetu and Luoshu for their unclassical provenance. They criticized geometrical and numerological aspects of these figures on a priori grounds, arguing that they were too rigid to represent the true texture of reality. These critics regarded with particular suspicion the identification of the Luoshu with the nonary plan also associated with the well-field, nine-province, *fenye*, and Ming Tang schemata.

As with a number of the other nonary cosmograms, extended critiques of the geometrical and numerological associations of the Hetu and Luoshu seem to date from the mid- or late-Ming. Apart from Wang Ting-xiang, the most notable sixteenth- century critic of these figures was Gui You-guan (1507–1571), a literatus more celebrated in Ming literary history than in the history of Neo-Confucian philosophy. Like his fourteenth-century predecessors, Gui argued that the established versions of the Hetu and Luoshu had no classical sanction and were the inventions of later cosmographers who formulated them by conflating names and figures drawn from various early texts. But Gui also faulted the Han and Song versions of these diagrams for their excessive symmetry. Citing the statement in the "Great Commentary" to the *Change* that "the divine has no locus and the *Change* has no substantial form," Gui argued that a preoccupation with rounded and squared figures necessarily gives rise to distortions. In fact, any precise graphic or numerological depiction of the Hetu and Luoshu misrepresented their true meaning. For these figures were really ubiquitous under heaven, immanent in every form and space. They could never be precisely defined. How much the less could the particular diagrams devised by such historical cosmographers as Kong An-guo, Yang Xiong, Liu Xin, Ban Gu, and Zhu Xi ever adequately represent the full significance of the Hetu and Luoshu?[34]

Gui did single out the nonary version of the Luoshu for special criticism, faulting the Han commentator Kong An-guo for having arbitrarily identified the Luoshu of the *Change* with the "nine categories" (jiuzhou) of the "Great Plan" chapter of the *Documents*. Such associations, Gui maintained, significantly distorted the meaning of the classical texts thus conflated, particularly of the *Change* and the "Great Plan." Although "the Way of the *Change* is abundantly clear, the scholars confused it by [their disquisitions on] the Hetu. And though the meaning of the 'Great Plan' is abundantly clear, the scholars confused it by [their disquisitions on] the Luoshu. This [confusion] first arose with the apocrypha, and has lately issued from the hygienists."[35]

The early Qing classical scholar Mao Qi-ling also specially criticized the nonary interpretation of the Luoshu. Like Gui You-guan, he traced the formulation of this cosmographical construction to Han commentators' having arbitrarily identified the Luoshu, the chief *locus classicus* of which is the "Great Commentary" to the *Change*, with the "nine categories" mentioned in the "Great Plan" chapter of the *Documents*. The association, Mao remarked, could not be substantiated, not least because the *Spring and Autumn Apocrypha* associated the Luoshu with six instead of nine. Moreover, even the nine categories mentioned in the "Great Plan" were unrelated to the nine-squared grid later associated with the Luoshu. This particular geometrical form, rather, originated with the Ming Tang as described in the *Ming Tang* chapter of the *Dadai Liji* (The Elder Dai's Record of Rites).[36] Thus the Han and Song cosmographers, particularly Kong An-guo, Liu Xin, Ban Gu, Shao Yong (1011–1077), and Cai Yuan-ding (1135–1198), who identified the Luoshu with the nonary grid were doubly mistaken. They erred in arbitrarily associating the Luoshu with the nine categories of the "Great Plan," and they blundered in equating the nine categories with the nine-squared form of the Ming Tang. In sum, they created a new cosmographical figure by arbitrarily conflating at least three unconnected references in the ancient literature.

The most renowned early Qing commentators on the Hetu and Luoshu, and in general on the diagrams and numerologies associated with the *Change* are Huang Zong-xi and Hu Wei (1633–1714). Both of these scholars composed special studies on the figures, Huang the *Yixue Xiang-shu Lun* (Discussion of the Images and Numerologies Associated with the Study of the *Change*) and Hu Wei the *Yitu Mingbian* (Clarifying Critique of the Diagrams Associated with the *Change*). The latter work is the more substantial of the two and is generally regarded as a landmark in the history of Qing scholarship. Joseph Needham, indeed, credits it with having "placed the history of . . . what might be called para-scientific thought on a sound critical basis," calling it, moreover, "essential for the study of the development of Chinese thought."[37]

While Hu Wei admitted that the original forms of the Hetu and Luoshu were lost in antiquity, his criticism of the standard cosmological interpretations was milder than were those of either Gui You-guan or Mao Qi-ling. He did refer to Liu Xin's pairing of the Hetu and Luoshu with each other and with the eight trigrams and nine categories, respectively, as an instance of "drawing a snake and adding feet." On the other hand, Hu embraced some aspects of nonary cosmography. He argued, for example, that the systems or institutions fashioned by the ancients, from the macrocosmic nine provinces to the microcosmic well fields, and including the Ming Tang though not the Hetu, were generally based on the "rule of nine."[38]

Huang Zong-xi was generally more critical of nonary cosmography and was especially skeptical of Han cosmologists' imposition of the nonary form on the Hetu and Luoshu. He remarked that while "the earth has nine provinces and the heavens have nine fields, it was declared that the Hetu and Luoshu were each of nine units. But how can one borrow numbers in this fashion?" Huang concurred with Hu Wei's opinion that the original forms of the Hetu and Luoshu were lost in high antiquity. In contrast to Hu, Huang had definite ideas on their basic character and functions, even if he could not reproduce the forms exactly. According to Huang, the Hetu and Luoshu were not anciently cosmograms, not schematic representations of some essential aspect of the world, but geographical charts and registers. Specifically, the Hetu were topographical maps and the Luoshu economic geographies, both of which were used by the court of the Western Zhou for administrative and tax purposes. They were called by the names "He and Luo" because these rivers were located near the center of the Zhou realm, signifying that the charts and registers were to be submitted from the outlying regions to the Center. However, "in the time of Confucius, the world no longer revered the Zhou house; so each of the various states had possession of its own land and people, and thus the Hetu and Luoshu were not forwarded [to the Zhou capital]." The only genuine notices of the original Hetu and Luoshu preserved were the brief elliptical references in the *Analects*, the *Record of Rites*, the *Documents*, and the *Change*.[39]

Mao Qi-ling entertained a similar belief, as did Huang Zong-yan (1616–1686), who remarked that "the Hetu and Luoshu were geographical records which recorded the contours of mountains and rivers and the rates of the land tax."[40] Hu Wei, however, expressly opposed this idea on the grounds that such elaborate administrative devices would have been ill-suited to the time of the ancient sage king, Fu Xi: "When customs and manners were simple and sincere, how could there have been topographical maps? When [the realm was] governed by knotted cords, how could there have been registers of households and of strategic places and positions."[41] In any case, the mere appearance of the idea that the Hetu and Luoshu were originally not cosmograms subverted traditional cosmological conceptions. For by reducing them to the level of practical administrative tools, Qing critics trivialized the figures that, in the view of Han and Song systematizers, quintessentially manifested cosmic geometry and numerology. To relegate these figures to such a position was almost tantamount to denying the possibility of cosmography in the traditional mode.

Several more conservative early Qing scholars, however, recoiled before such an unsettling prospect. While generally admitting that the antique forms of the Hetu and Luoshu were lost practically beyond recall and that the current versions were mostly spurious, these scholars yet devised a historical means of access to these founts of cosmographical inspiration.

They did this by invoking the theory, for which a statement by Confucius in the *Analects* provides some support, that the Hetu and Luoshu were historically recurrent phenomena.[42] According to Yan Ruo-ju, the Hetu appeared not only in the time of the sage king Fu Xi but also during the reigns of the Yellow Sovereign, Yao, Shun, Yu the Great, and the Duke of Zhou. It even figured in mundane historical epochs, having appeared as recently as the twelfth century on the occasion of Zhu Xi's announcing his commentary on the Four Books.[43] He Wei also postulated the repeated historical appearance of the Hetu and Luoshu, remarking that "moral sovereigns throughout history have all received the Hetu and Luoshu; they did not appear only in the times of Fu Xi and Yu." But Hu went on to note that the Hetu and Luoshu do not necessarily assume the forms of the eight trigrams and the nine units, and that they were not known to have appeared in recent historical epochs.[44]

Several scholars associated with the school of Song Learning, including Lu Shi-yi, Lu Long-qi, and Lu Guang-di (1642–1718), went so far as to endorse the established cosmological interpretations of the Hetu and Luoshu. Since much of Song cosmology rested on these cosmograms, early Qing advocates of the Cheng-Zhu school could hardly have abandoned them without compromising an important aspect of the scholastic tradition to which they adhered. Thus Lu Shi-yi affirmed the established Song view of the Hetu as the original source of the eight trigrams and the Luoshu as the chief inspiration for the nine categories, adding that the patterns of the entire cosmos were immanent in these figures.[45] Lu Long-qi also espoused the standard Song interpretations of the Hetu and Luoshu, and even credited Shao Yong with having rediscovered their true forms hidden away in the recesses of heterodox studies.[46] Li Guang-di upheld the Song versions of the Hetu and Luoshu and embraced Song Neo-Confucianism in general, even those numerological systems of correspondence based on the five phases and the figures of the *Change*. For example, in his commentary on the *Zhengmeng* (Correcting Youthful Ignorance) of Zhang Cai, Li remarked that "forms have five colors, sounds have five tones, and odors and flavors also all have five. Thus warmth and coolness have the pneuma of the five phases; and movement and rest have the nature of five phases. There is nothing that is not completed in fives."[47]

None of Li Guang-di's major contemporaries were nearly so consistent in their cosmological conservatism. Both Lu Shi-yi and Lu Long-qi, as outlined above, generally criticized postclassical systematizers' interpretations of other nonary cosmograms and systems of correspondence. That they hesitated to fault the cosmological interpretations of the Hetu and Luoshu associated with Shao Yong and Zhu Xi may be attributed to the importance of these diagrams in Song Neo-Confucian thought rather than to the greater conservatism of seventeenth-century Song Learning scholars in general. In fact, the question of the origin and authenticity of the standard versions of the Hetu and Luoshu is one of the few cosmological issues in seventeenth-century thought on which there was a marked cleavage more or less along scholastic lines.

By the eighteenth century, even adherents of the Song school, such as Wang Mao-hong (1668–1741), were constrained to admit the heterodoxy of the versions of the Hetu and Luoshu attached to Zhu Xi's commentaries on the *Change*. Wang did attempt to exculpate Zhu by arguing that these diagrams were appended to Zhu Xi's *Zhouyi Benyi* (Basic Meaning of the *Zhou Change*) without his knowledge or consent.[48] In any case, so discredited were these figures by the end of the nineteenth century that Pi Xi-rui (1850–1908), the great late-Qing historian of classical studies, stated categorically that no one believed in the Hetu and Luoshu any longer.[49]

However, schematic cosmography, while definitely on the wane in Qing times on the level of high intellectual history, persisted at the popular level. Though apparently lacking a detailed knowledge of the nonary cosmograms discussed above, people were still concerned with maintaining a ritually correct spatial order, one that was in line with traditional cosmographical conceptions. Though many illustrations of the persistence of such traditional orientations among the common people could be cited, one related by George Kates, an American adventurer and aesthete who resided in Peking during the 1930s, comes most readily to mind. According to Kates, one of his Chinese servants, lamenting the dethronement of the last Qing emperor, once spoke as follows: "Yet even if he could be put back on his throne again, how could this any longer be made right? Is not the *Desheng Men*, the Gate of Triumphant Virtue, not ruined?"[50] It was, in other words, inconceivable that a restoration of order or sagely rule could proceed in unregulated, undemarcated space. On a more domestic level, Kates' servants insisted that the arrangement of bushes in the courtyard had to exhibit the same type of symmetry that was manifest in the plan of the old imperial capital.[51]

Qing cosmographical critics looked askance at the kind of rectilinearity and symmetry which Kates' servants and other common people favored even in domestic situations. But they were still quite concerned with the ordering of space, as well as of time. So having repudiated the cosmography established by the Han and Song systematizers, they proceeded to devise a new kind of world picture, one that recognized, even celebrated, the sinuous and the anomalous.

Chapter Nine

Qing Scholars'
Anticosmological
World View

CONGRUENT IRREGULARITIES IN SEVENTEENTH-CENTURY
ART, COSMOLOGY, AND MORAL PHILOSOPHY

One of the major criticisms that late-Ming and Qing scholars directed against Song Neo-Confucian cosmology, it will be recalled, was that it presumed the existence of more regularity and symmetry than was manifest in the world. Wang Ting-xiang, for example, faulted Shao Yong's numerological cosmology on the grounds that it ignored the fact that "the transformations of the cosmic Way are uneven" and that "consequently numbers have odd and even variations." Huang Zong-xi similarly criticized Shao's calendrical cosmology for its neglect of remainders and incommensurables. And Zhang Hui-yan accused Zhu Xi of "not being aware that the ways of heaven and earth are invariably uneven and irregular," as illustrated by the irregular movements of the sun and moon through the heavens.[1]

Late-Ming and early-Qing landscape painters might well have criticized their Northern Song counterparts on similar grounds. For what Michael Sullivan has called the "almost painful distortions" in late-Ming landscapes and James Cahill the "somber landscapes and tortured forms" in early Qing "Individualist" art[2] contrast the order and symmetry evident in the great landscape paintings of the Northern Song.

Thus trends in cosmological thought and landscape art seem to have paralleled one another in both the eleventh and the seventeenth centuries. A particular illustration of this accord in the eleventh century is the famous painting attributed to Li Cheng, "A Solitary Temple amid Clearing Peaks." This work, in James Cahill's view, reveals the artist's "conviction of a coherence and order underlying surface appearances in nature, the same conviction that inspired Song philosophers to erect the vast and orderly structure of Neo-Confucian cosmology."[3] Another famous Northern Song landscape, Fan Kuan's "Traveling Among Streams and Mountains," Michael Freeman suggests, presents "a cosmological vision as grandiose and all-encompassing as that found in Shao Yong's charts." Both Fan Kuan's painting and Shao Yong's diagrams "testify to the common urge to render the world into a comprehensible whole."[4] Comparisons between eleventh-century landscape art and Neo-Confucian cosmology are implicit in the writings of Song commentators. Su Shi (1037–1101), for example, emphasized that the highest aim of the landscape painter is to grasp the constant pattern or order (changli) in the scene as a whole, and not simply to reproduce the outward physical forms (xing) of the particular objects in the landscape.[5]

Some well-known seventeenth century landscape paintings might also be related to the cosmological, or anticosmological, thought of that era. The "River Landscape, in the Manner of Ni Zan" of Wang Yuan-qi (1642–1715), with its "complex deviations and distortions," particularly "the intricate off-symmetrical arrangement and the fantastically mismatched horizons at the two sides of the picture,"[6] might well be taken as an artistic microcosm of the world as viewed by early Qing cosmological critics. It calls to mind Wang Fu-zhi's dictum that "the transformations of heaven and earth are subtle by dint of their irregularity and are balanced by dint of their irregularity."[7]

That movements in cosmological thought and landscape art accorded with each other should not seem too surprising, for early Chinese landscape paintings were frequently conceived as schematic depictions of the cosmos, complete with directional orientation, in which "a vertical stroke of three inches equals a height of several thousand feet, and a horizontal stroke of a few feet embodies an area of a hundred miles."[8] Even some later landscapes manifest "a tremendous effort to grasp the reality of nature within a highly schematic and intellectual format,"[9] to form a microcosm. Many Chinese landscape artists, in other words, were cosmologically oriented, even though they did not construct geometrical cosmograms. Thus their paintings often reflect patterns or ideas established by the prevailing cosmography. This point raises the question of whether or not seventeenth-century cosmological criticism affected the landscape painting of that era. A number of prominent Qing landscape artists were, after all, literati presumably well able to comprehend the works of early-Qing cosmological critics. Moreover, a few of these critics, such as Fang Yi-zhi,

Figure 10. Attributed to Li Cheng, "A Solitary Temple amid Clearing Peaks."
Hanging scroll, ink and slight color on silk. Courtesy of the Nelson-Atkins Museum
of Art, Kansas City, Missouri (Nelson Fund).

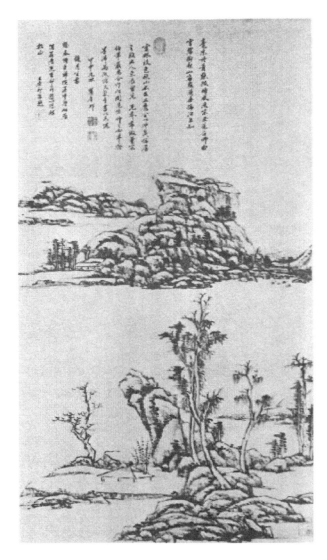

Figure 11. Wang Yuan-qi, "River Landscape, in the Manner of Ni Zan." Hanging scroll, ink and light colors on paper. Courtesy of the Freer Gallery of Art, Smithsonian Institution, Washington D.C.

were also painters of some repute. However, there is no evidence that seventeenth-century cosmological commentary actually influenced early- and mid-Qing artists' orientations toward the landscape.

The possibility remains, however, that a larger change in world outlook predisposed both landscape painters and cosmological critics to highlight asymmetry, irregularity, and incompleteness in their works. One possible inspiration for such a change, at least as far as the "individualist" or "eccentric" painters of the early Qing are concerned, was the Manchu conquest of 1644. That this political revolution influenced early Qing artistic style seems particularly plausible in the case of Gong Xian (c. 1620–1689), a Ming loyalist who "saw Nature as a vast battlefield strewn with sinister wreckage" and who "created a vision of blasted landscape that has no antecedents in Chinese tradition."[10] According to Chu-tsing Li, such disturbing images in Gong's art may be interpretted as artistic expressions of his "anguish over the loss of his country."[11] On the other hand, the tendency to "distort" or "torture" forms in landscape painting, to imbue the landscape with a "restless" or vitalistic quality, was pronounced even before the fall of the Ming, as was a cosmological criticism in the Confucian tradition. Thus it seems reasonable to interpret the irregular forms preferred by both landscape painters and cosmological commentators in the seventeenth century as outgrowths of some more deeply rooted trend in late-Ming thought and culture.

Such a tendency, which might well have hastened in the demise of the Northern Song view of both the natural landscape and the cosmos at large, did arise in the later history of Neo-Confucian thought, culminating in the seventeenth century. This is what William Theodore de Bary has called a trend toward "vitalism and a sense of the unfailing creativity (shengsheng) of Heaven-and-earth."[12] Indeed, the two most famous philosophers of the early- and mid-Qing, Wang Fu-zhi and Dai Zhen (1724–1777), are both noted for having celebrated the powers of generation and the constancy of change in both man and cosmos. Similarly, some of the more celebrated painters of the early- and mid-Qing, both "orthodox" and "individualist," imparted a special dynamic or vitalistic quality to their works and even seem to have attempted to portray organically processes of cosmic change. According to James Cahill, the "Man in a House Beneath a Cliff" of Dao Ji (1641–c. 1717) "is not so much depicting rocks as presenting to our senses the forces that mold and destroy rocks." Moreover, Cahill continues, "Dao Ji's leaf has even more of organic character than Zhu Da's; the lines that

Figure 12. Gong Xian, "A Thousand Peaks and Myriad Ravines." Hanging scroll, ink on paper. C.A. Drenowatz Collection. Courtesy of the Museum Rietberg, Zurich.

serve as contours and crevices of the rocks penetrate the forms as a vivifying network, like veins and arteries of a living thing."[13]

Is there, however, a necessary connection between cosmic creativity and vitality on the one hand, and irregularity, asymmetry, and imperfection on the other? Must cosmology based on the former conceptions lead one to recognize the generality of the latter conditions? It is possible to imagine how a vitalist cosmology might be reconciled with the idea that the universe is symmetrical in its various parts. But as matter of fact, life is intimately bound up with asymmetry and change with irregularity, as nineteenth-century biologists discovered. Thus Louis Pasteur concluded from his famous investigations on the molecular asymmetry of natural organic products that "the essential products of life are asymmetric and possess such asymmetry that they are not superposable on their images," and further speculated that "asymmetric forces exist at the moment of the elaboration of natural organic products."[14] More generally, Pasteur remarked on what Martin Gardner has called the "sharp conflict between the symmetry of nonlife and the asymmetry of life."[15]

Premodern philosophers, though lacking the biological perspectives of Pasteur and his successors, also seem to have generally associated change and growth with irregularity, if not necessarily life with asymmetry. Such a link seems implicit in such diverse ancient sources as the *Laozi* and Heraclitus, though it is much more evident with such European Romantics as Schlegel and Wordsworth.[16] Neo-Confucian thinkers, on occasion, also explicitly associated change with unevenness. Lu Xiang-shan (1139– 1193), for example, expressed such an idea in the context of a numerological discourse, commenting that "if numbers are even then they are regular, if odd then irregular. Only with irregularity is there change. Thus uneven numbers control change."[17]

Even from a more empirical perspective, however, one might expect that a world view based on an organic metaphor, or on the notion of the primacy of growth in the cosmos, should highlight the asymmetrical, the eccentric, and the incomplete. For the correspondence between life, growth, and asymmetry is apparent even to the naked eye, though the irregularity of forms affected by processes of degeneration is much more evident. Moreover, the emphasis in late-Ming and early-Qing cosmology on "pneuma" (qi) as opposed to "ultimate pattern or principle" (li) also predisposed seventeenth-century philosophers, and also perhaps landscape artists, to accent the irregularity in cosmic forms and processes. For the movements and workings of *qi* were usually conceived as uneven.

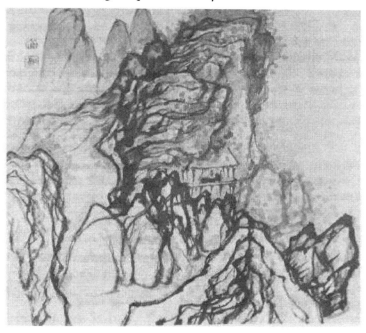

Figure 13. Dai Ji (Shitao), "Man in A House Beneath a Cliff." Album leaf, ink and light color on paper. By permission of Chi-Chien Wang Art Studio, New York.

In sum, the emergence of an anticosmological world view in early-Qing thought, though mediated by the seventeenth-century critique of correlative cosmology and geometrical cosmography, may also have been advanced by a vitalist, organicist strain in later Neo-Confucianism. The convergence of these two trends led some Qing thinkers not only to recognize and record cosmic asymmetries, irregularities, and imperfections but even to celebrate them.

In contrast, Song Neo-Confucians generally regarded irregularity, especially imbalances in the constitution of the *qi*, as the major cosmological source of evil in the world. Zhang Cai (1020–1077), for example, commented that "Man's strength, weakness, slowness, quickness, and talent or lack of talent [are due to] the one-sidedness of the *qi*. Heaven is originally harmonious and not one-sided. By cultivating one's *qi* and returning to its original nature without being one-sided, one can fully develop human nature and [be in harmony with] heaven."[18] Cheng Hao (1032–1085) similarly remarked that "What is called evil is not original evil. It is only through excess or deficiency [or deviation from the mean] that it is like this."[19]

On the other hand, the early-Qing philosopher Yan Yuan (1636–1704), regarded deviation from the mean or imbalance in the *qi* as a basis for good, though perhaps initially only partial good. To illustrate the point, Yan included in his *Cunxing Bian* (A Treatise on Preserving the Nature) a diagram of the various forms of human nature (xingtu). Throughout the circular confines of this chart, Yan drew dots of all shapes and sizes representing the kinds of human nature. The ideal position, for such a dot was, to be sure, in the very center of the circle, the locus of the *xingshan* or natural innate goodness. Dots located near each of the two horizontal and two vertical axes of the chart were also in a relatively moral position; for these dots adhered closely to one of the four Confucian virtues or four Mencian endowments or sprouts of virtue (siduan). Nevertheless, Yan argued, even unshapely dots in odd locations could be similarly developed into a state of sageliness. Take, for example, the dots in the upper left-hand quarter of the *xingtu*:

Of the several smaller dots in the corners [of the diagram], some are large, some are small, some square, some round, some uniform, some pointed, some sparse, some dense, some at the hub, some inaccessible, some near the center, some near the [vertical and horizontal] axes, some near the diagonals,

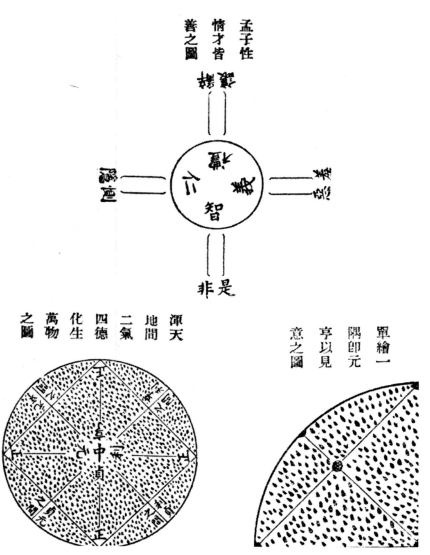

Figure 14. Diagrammatic depictions of Yan Yuan's theory of human nature. The upper chart locates the four Confucian virtues within the circle. Each virtue is linked with one of the four Mencian endowments. The lower left-hand chart fills in the blank spaces between each of the Mencian axes with dots representing various forms of human nature, most of which have apparently deviated from the axial loci of the Confucian and Mencian Virtues. The lower right-hand corner is an enlargement of the upper left quadrant of the second diagram. It is the subject of the long quotation from the *Cunxing Bian* translated herein. Source: Yan Yuan's *Cunxing Bian* in *Sicun Bian* (Taipei: Shijie Shuju, 1966), p. 24, 29, 30.

some near the left horizontal axis, some near the top vertical axis. But all, by dint of having one or two virtues, generally contain the pneuma and pattern of all the four virtues [humanity, wisdom, propriety, and righteousness] and thus reside in a center [of some kind]. [This is] what is known as "man obtaining the centrality of the cosmos at birth." Thus although open and obstructed, straight and bent all have their differences, the pneuma and pattern which fills the universe is the same everywhere. If one will do his utmost to practice his natural compassion without cruelty and convey his sense of respect without being arrogant, then he can become a Huang [Xian], a Fan [Ying], a Yan [Hui], a [Gong-]xi Hua, an Yi [Yin], or a Zhou-[gong]. Therefore it is said that "all men can become a Yao or a Shun."[20]

From one point of view, Yan Yuan may only have been reaffirming, in a particularly meticulous and graphic fashion, Mencius' teaching on the essential goodness of human nature. But he proceeded in such a way as to contravene the established Song Neo-Confucian assumption that deviation from the mean is the major source of evil in the world.

REAFFIRMATION OF COSOMOGRAPHICAL IRREGULARITIES

The like of Yan Yuan's graphical depiction of irregularities in human nature does not appear in the works of other prominent early Qing scholars. Most of the latter focused on asymmetry in the physical world, particularly on the astronomical and geographical planes. The form of the earth itself, so some seventeenth-century scholars contended, was not even approximately spherical, as the Jesuits in late-Ming China maintained, but rather rough and uneven. Lu Shi-yi (1611–1672), for example, suggested that the mottlings visible on the surface of the moon reflected the form of the earth, which would have made the latter irregularly shaped indeed.[21] Wang Fu-zhi, though denying that the image of the earth is reflected on the moon's face, also rejected the Western theory of the round earth: "Since it is in some places level, in others steep, in some places recessed and in others convex, then wherein lies its sphericity? . . . Thus from the earth's inclines, irregu-larities, heights, depths, and vastness, it is clear that it has no definite form."[22] The theory of the round earth had its defenders in Qing China, but even some of them acknowledged that the world was not wholly spherical and that its surface was marked with many rises and recesses.[23]

For most early Qing cosmographers, however, the prime loci of physical unevenness in the cosmos were the contours and boundaries of the earth rather than its overall shape. The Qing critique of the well-field, nine-province, and field-allocation schemata outlined in the preceding chapter illustrates this orientation. Wang Fu-zhi, an inveterate opponent of all such forms of political and administrative geometry, argued more generally for the demarcation of the physical world along natural topographical divides. In the course of expanding this idea, Wang sketched quite clearly the outlines of the new cosmography for the bounding of terrestrial space.

Wang's discussions on the art of geographical demarcation are scattered throughout several of his major exegetical and historical works. In his commentary on the *Record of Rites*, he contended that "in ordering a state, it is necessary to proceed according to the natural forms of mountains and rivers. One cannot scale mountains and straddle waters in seeking to insure that the boundaries are squared."[24] In one of his chief historical works, the *Du Tongjian Lun* (Discussion of the *Comprehensive Mirror* [of Sima Guang]), Wang emphasized that the empire as a whole must also be delimited by physiographical barriers and not defined by a terrestrial geometry. Thus "whatever is wound around by rivers and coiled about by mountains is combined to form one territory, and the spirits of the people are [who live in this territory] are thereby mutually responsive." Wang argued, on this basis, that Vietnam, which had been independent for several centuries, should be reincorporated into China.[25] But in the same volume Wang condemned historical Chinese conquests which overstepped the natural boundaries of China. In censuring the westerly ventures of Zhang Qian (fl. 140–126 B.C.), Wang remarked that "west of the Jade Gate, the rivers flow toward the West; consequently, [this region] cannot be combined with China... But Zhang Qian by relying on his own powers forcibly went through [natural boundaries]. He thus upset the cosmic order."[26]

In his philosophical commentary on the *Classic of Change*, Wang stated that the demarcation of boundaries on the basis of physical limits was a natural, universal pattern that was general throughout the biological world and not just confined to humankind. Thus "whatever has form and substance can demarcate limits or borders on the basis of its territorial confines, preventing admixture with other [kinds of things] for all ages."[27] Wang did not maintain that such limits are static or fixed; nor did he hold that such borders could be demarcated with much precision. They were instead determined in a spontaneous fashion by members of each group congregating with their fellows within the natural territorial expanse most appropriate for them.

Seventeenth-century scholars also favored naturally irregular lines of demarcation in astronomy. They generally insisted that divisions of astronomical space and calendrical time have some natural or physical basis. This led many of them to reject Western standards of celestial cartography introduced into late-Ming China by the Jesuits. One of the preeminent Chinese mathematical astronomers of the seventeenth century, Wang Xi-shan (1628–1682), contended that the Western division of the celestial sphere into 360 degrees was an unnatural schema that only served to facilitate calculation.[28] Wang, like Fang Yi-zhi (1611–1671) and Wang Fu-zhi, seemed to prefer the traditional Chinese system whereby one degree was measured by the extent of the sun's daily movement along the ecliptic, even though it yielded the unwieldy sum of approximately 365¼ degrees.[29] As Wang Fu-zhi argued, the sun and not some artificial calculatory standard was the true determinant of seasonal changes, the natural measure of celestial time and space. The use off solar measure might involve arithmetical difficulties. But doing away with such irregularities through the imposition of a system having easily manipulable units was as ridiculous, said Wang, as subtracting a period form the Zhou era and adding it to the Qin era in order to produce historical units of uniform duration:

> The sun's having day and night is like man's having life and death and historical periods' having dynastic changes. For the arrangement of historical periods it suffices to take one ruler [to correspond with] one era, and one family name [to correspond with] one dynasty. But if one were to pare the long duration of the Zhou to supplement the short duration of the Qin in seeking to insure equality and regularity without surplus or deficiency, then how could this not create confusion? The Westerners' carrying calculatory exactitude to the point of exaggeration is in general like this.[30]

Qing commentators posed the same general criticisms of the Western solar calendar, arguing that its divisions were unnatural and too artificially uniform. Both of the leading Chinese mathematical astronomers of the seventeenth century, Mei Wen-ding (1633–1721) and Wang Xi-shan, opposed the adoption of a Western-style calendar on the grounds that its months did not correspond to lunations but were merely conventional division of the solar year. And both favored the Chinese lunisolar calendar, the twelve divisions of which did correspond with lunations. Since there are only about 354 days in twelve lunar months, use of the lunisolar calendar left a ten- or eleven-day remainder at the end of the year. But dealing with such a problem was preferable to adopting a calendar with purely artificial divisions.[31]

The Jesuit missionaries in seventeenth-century China were not the first figures in Chinese history to have proposed the use of a solar calendar. The idea had been broached as early as the eleventh century by the great Northern Song polymath, Shen Gua (1031–1095), who pointed out that the substitution of twelve equal divisions of the solar year for the lunar months would eliminate, in one stroke, the perennial problem of Chinese calendrical astronomy, intercalation.[32] Shen's idea, however, seems not to have been accepted by any major astronomer before the nineteenth century. Ruan Yuan (1764–1849) criticized it as impractical, unnatural, and "not in accord with the purport of the classics."[33] Another Qing commentator, Zhang Wen-hu, opposed Shen's proposal on similar grounds, arguing that lunar and solar periods, having been established separately by the sages, should be kept distinct.

> The twelve months make up the lunar year, following the moon, while the twenty-four solar divisions make up the solar year, following the sun. The *Offices of Zhou* (Zhouguan) rectified the lunar and solar years as a way of properly ordering affairs. Each having what is appropriate, they proceed conjointly without conflict. What [Shen Gua] discusses is the intercalary day system [used in the] Muslim and Western [calendars]. But could it be promulgated in China?[34]

Of course, the Chinese predilection for natural divisions was not new. As Henri Maspero pointed out in his classic study of ancient Chinese astronomy, Chinese astronomers as early as Han times measured celestial degrees by the daily movements of the sun instead of by the division of the circumference of the celestial sphere into abstract units.[35] Even Shen Gua, while proposing the adoption of a solar calendar, did not advocate that astronomical or calendrical units be generally equalized. Like his astronomical predecessors, he defined degrees of celestial space by the sun's movements and even defended the uneven division of the lunar zodiac into twenty-eight lunar lodges by arguing that each of the lodges required physical markers, stars, to serve as referents.[36] Thus seventeenth-century critics of Western celestial cartography and the Western solar calendar were only drawing out proclivities that were indigenous to ancient and medieval Chinese astronomy.

Even those Qing scholars who accepted aspects of the Western system felt the need to establish that Western cartographical standards were not simply arbitrary conventions designed to facilitate calculation. Mei Wen-ding, for example, argued that the pre-Tychonic Western celestial coordinate system based on the ecliptic had some real basis in that the pole of the ecliptic was the axis of rotation for the precession of the equinoxes.[37] It was not, in other words, simply an ideal geometrical point chosen to facilitate calculation, even though no star marked its place in the heavens. Even in Western astronomy, Mei felt, there had to be some correspondence between celestial cartography and the natural structure of the heavens.

CRITIQUE OF DEFINITE DEMARCATIONS

Predilections for naturally formed boundaries were only one aspect of the world picture outlined by late-Ming and early-Qing scholars. A second more radical feature of this new cosmographical order was that in some cases it ruled out the demarcation of sharply defined boundaries of any sort, especially temporal ones.

Seventeenth-century scholars' critiques of marked division of time was not, however wholly unprecedented. The *Classic of Change* and its appendices stress the continuous nature of change as well as the importance of identifying the subtle germs of transformation at their earliest incipience (ji).[38] However, the cosmocalendrical systems that Han and Song cosmologists constructed partly on the basis of the *Change* often delineate temporal limits quite sharply. Shao Yong, for example, calculated the exact number of years in particular cosmic aeons, and even determined the precise date when the world began. By the sixteenth century, however, several prominent scholars in the Neo-Confucian tradition had come to visualize both cosmic and calendrical time in quite a different light.

One of the earliest and most articulate of these scholars was the inveterate anticosmologist from the sixteenth-century, Wang Ting-xiang. According to Wang, change on almost every conceivable scale—cosmic, historical, and seasonal—was gradual and almost always imperceptible. Just as summer does not suddenly turn to winter, so an era of order does not immediately pass into one of chaos. Even within the scope of a single temporal movement, there may be reversals that complicate the picture and make tidy lines of demarcation difficult to establish. For example, the decline of a political order may be temporarily reversed through the intervention of a sage.[39] Similarly, though in general spring is the season of life and fall of death, there are anomalies, such as the death of a species of asparagus in the second lunar month and the planting of wheat in the ninth lunar month, that mitigate the overall regularity of the pattern.[40] Moreover, even in the dead of winter, the generative forces of yin and yang interact to create life, as manifested in the pneuma that concentrates in wells during that season as well as in the appearance of the phenomenon of "floating mist" (yema) in winter. "This," Wang concludes, "is sufficient to prove that the circulation of the two pneumas [the yin and yang] create life without cease; it is only the sun's being distant that gives rise to winter, thus causing things to live or die."[41]

Small wonder, then, that Wang Ting-xiang was particularly critical of Dong Zhong-shu's (c.179–c. 104 B.C.) division of the year into two finely demarcated units of yin and yang months. According to Wang, Dong's procedure was only to "extrapolate from the figures and numbers of the *Change* in order to establish his meaning. This is quite contrary to seeking [the truth] in the traces of the real patterns of yin and yang." Had Dong followed the latter course, then he would have discovered that "there was never a case of pure yin without yang or pure yang without yin."[42]

On the scale of cosmic time, Wang objected to the type of speculative cosmogony that dated such events as the unfolding of the heavens (tiankai), the opening of the earth (dipi), and the birth of man (rensheng) at specific moments corresponding with the cyclical signs of the twelve earthly branches. While admitting that "creation and transformation definitely has an order," Wang proceeded to ask "how numbers can be so inflexible as this and how so regular as this?" Wang supported his argument against the theory of discrete, well-defined stages of cosmic evolution by positing that the second and third of the three traditional stages, the opening of the earth and the birth of living things, occurred almost simultaneously:

When the earth opened up, living things were immediately born on it. On land [there appeared] dragons, fish, and turtles; man was also of this class [of living things], and was born along with everything else. Thus the transformation of the pneuma could not have been like [earlier cosmologists said it was]. For how could [cosmic evolution] have taken so long? From [the time of the sage king] Yao up to now is only a little more than three thousand years. But from today's viewpoint it is quite distant. [So how can] it be true that [only] after eighteen thousand years living things began to be born?[43]

The late-Ming Neo-Confucian scholar Lü Kun (1536–1618) also argued that clear-cut temporal divisions do not exist in the cosmos and that really abrupt changes seldom occur, though he did not apply this principle so imaginatively on so many different time scales as did Wang Ting-xiang. If changes and stages of development were really sudden or segmented, Lü pointed out, one would expect to see parents at the moment of death giving birth to children, or grain ripening immediately after having been planted.[44] Thus Lü, like Wang Ting-xiang, used biological illustrations in order to establish that change in the universe proceeds in a gradual and irregular fashion. Such examples, again, indicate that a vitalist strain in later Neo-Confucian thought, an emphasis on the continuous creative activity of heaven and earth, was a solvent of Han-Song cosmology.

Like Wang Ting-xiang, Jiang Yong (1681–1762), the prominent mid-Qing classicist, posited the indefiniteness of temporal divisions on a cosmic scale, explaining why a point of cosmic origin or "superior epoch" could never be calculated exactly. In the first place, Jiang argued, it was quite unlikely that heaven and earth could have suddenly sprung into existence at some given point. Rather, they must have existed in a prenatal state for a considerable time before, like men and beasts in embryo, birds and insects in eggs, and grasses and trees in seeds and roots. Thus, when asked if the cosmos really began at midnight on the winter solstice of *jiazi* year at the new moon when the five planets and the sun and moon were all arrayed in a line in the heavens, as Han cosmologists said it did, Jiang replied as follows:

> Not necessarily. The opening up of heaven and earth is like the birth of man [in that it] is categorized as postnatal. For at its beginning, it had already spent time in embryo. Thus the sun, moon, and five planets did not necessarily all begin from a *jiazi* year [the first year of the traditional sixty-year cycle]. How do those who consider the beginning to have been in a *jiazi* year know that [the cosmos] did not begin in some other year? How do those who consider the beginning to have been at the new moon of the eleventh month know that [the cosmos] did not begin at the full moon of the eleventh month? How do those who take the winter solstice as the beginning know that [the cosmos] did not begin at the vernal equinox? And those who take midnight of a *jiazi* [day] as the beginning [fail to consider that] times vary according to [east-west] location. . . Thus what place on the broad earth ought to be set as the privileged point [from which the beginning of time is calculated]?[45]

Further, Jiang reflected, if the cosmos really did begin at midnight on the winter solstice when the sun and moon were in line with one another, then

there would have been an eclipse of the sun at this point of cosmic inception. Finally, why must the planets have been arrayed in a line like a string
of pearls? Why couldn't they have been scattered throughout the heavens?
Thus, Jiang concluded, "the superior epoch cannot be calculated."[46]

Several late-Ming and early-Qing scholars criticized earlier cosmologists' clear-cut differentiation of cosmological categories, as well as of
temporal units. Wang Fu-zhi, for example, accused earlier commentators on
the *Change* of having taken too literally that text's distinction between
things "above form" (xing er shang) and things "below form" (xing er xia).
" 'Above' and 'below', " Wang explained, "are both labels; they have no limits
that can be demarcated."[47] Wang also challenged the neat and meticulous
apportionment of things into yin and yang categories,[48] as did Lü Kun.
According to Lü, Zhou Dun-yi's (1017–1073) diagram dividing the circle
representing the "Great Ultimate" into yin and yang sectors distorts the face
of reality, since "the world does not have such distinct transformations of
the pneumas."[49] Rather, the two complementary cosmological opposites, the
yin and yang, generally interact in a way that does not lend itself to
cosmological cartography.

The idea that cosmological opposites interpenetrate, while hardly new
in late-traditional Chinese thought, was invoked especially by seventeenth-century critics in order to confute the conception that cosmological
boundaries could be sharply delineated. Fang Yi-zhi followed this approach
in his discussion of another cosmological pair, heaven and earth, arguing
that the two were so intertwined that neither could exist without the other.
The heavens, he declared, only became such because there existed such
earthly entities as mountains, rivers, animals, and plants which needed to be
provided with such heavenly objects as the sun and moon and the wind and
rain. "If there were no earth, then how could there be a heaven?"[50]

The most prolific early Qing philosopher of cosmological interpenetra-
tion, however, was Wang Fu-zhi. For Wang, almost every important duality
in the Neo-Confucian cosmological lexicon, including heaven and earth,
pattern (li) and pneuma (qi), and yin and yang, was so internally entangled
as to preclude the possibility that any one of a pair could be clearly distinguished from the other. Even the five phases, or, as Wang frequently
characterized them, the five elements, were contained within one another:

Metal is also earth; if one smelts it, then it begins to become [such]. Fire is
concealed in wood; if one bores it, then it begins to manifest [itself]. Water

freezes to become ice, and thus hardens to be the same as metal. Wood rots
into soil, and thus is definitely equivalent to earth. One cannot distinguish or
differentiate among the five elements.[51]

According to Wang, the basic elements of the cosmos were, moreover,
innumerable and not limited to five.

The early Qing critique of established spatial, temporal, and cosmological boundaries seems to be a fertile field for speculation on possible
social or political origins of change in cosmological views. The blurring of
boundaries in seventeenth-century cosmological thought, for example,
might be interpreted as a reflection of the political upheavals and social
dislocations of that era. Faced with the spectacle of urban riots, tenant
revolts, eunuch power, imperial ineptitude, merchant pretense and prosper-
ity, and scholar-official demoralization, later Ming intellectuals, one might
suppose, were inspired sympathetically to fuzz the formerly distinct
boundaries among various cosmological categories. Moreover, scholars'
proposals that boundaries in various cosmographical spheres be resituated
along more natural lines of demarcation might be taken as an encoded or
sublimated plan for restructuring the social order along natural lines of
cleavage.

This possibility is worthy of serious consideration. But there appears to
be little evidence that the various upheavals of the seventeenth century
inspired the early-Qing critique of traditional cosmological cartography.
On the other hand, there is abundant evidence that such criticism developed from trends in the history of late-traditional Chinese scientific
thought and classical scholarship. In fact, the science most extensively
cultivated in early-Qing times, astronomy, provided an anchor for the new
vision of the cosmos articulated by major seventeenth-century scholars.
This new conception of the cosmos, or anticosmos, is better illustrated in
the astronomical thought of the era than in any other branch of learning.

INTERPRETATIONS OF ASTRONOMICAL
ANOMALIES AND IMPRECISION

A frequently reiterated theme in Qing astronomical thought, as in the
critique of boundaries, is that a certain indeterminacy is woven into the
fabric of the cosmos and a corresponding imprecision into man's knowledge of the world. No matter how painstaking the observations and precise
the calculations that underlie a given astronomical system, anomalies in

celestial motions would eventually produce discrepancies between prediction and event. The formulation of a perpetual astronomical system, it seemed, was a hope even more forlorn than that of a restoration of the mensural order supposedly established by the ancient sage kings.

The astronomical anomalies recognized by Qing cosmological commentators range from the mundane to the metaphysical. Those most often cited by Neo-Confucian students of astronomy include the familiar annual difference between the solar and sidereal years, inequalities of solar and lunar motion, and planetary advances and retrogradations. Some early 'Qing scholars, notably Fang Yi-zhi, Gu Yan-wu, and Wang Xi-shan, also noted various optical distortions, such as those arising from atmospheric refraction, that hindered the accurate measurement of celestial phenomena.[52] Wang Xi-shan identified subjective sources of error in observational astronomy as well, remarking that even with trained personnel and precise instruments, two observers using the same device might see the same object differently.[53]

It is hardly remarkable that early Qing students of astronomy acknowledged the existence of such anomalies and sources of observational and mathematical error. Most, indeed, had been discovered by ancient and medieval astronomers in both China and the West, and modern astronomers have detected many more besides. But what *are* remarkable, or at least worthy of note in a discussion of seventeenth-century thought, are the cosmological conclusions that early-Qing scholars drew from their study of astronomical irregularities. They might, after all, have confined themselves to admitting that there were certain complications in celestial movements and limitations in observational capacities that had to be taken into account.

But in fact Qing scholar-astronomers did infer a cosmological point from astronomical anomalies and distortions, though one anticipated by Chinese mathematical astronomers over the course of the previous few hundred years. This was that no matter how advanced the astronomer's art, minute disjunctions between prediction and phenomenon will appear, eventually widening to the point where a general reform becomes necessary. As Wang Fu-zhi explained, "though the astronomical system may be precise, yet if one uses it for several hundred years, then there will necessarily be discrepancies." In such a case, "there cannot but be a reform."[54] Li Guang-po, the younger brother of Li Guang-di (1642–1718), similarly argued that "though the system is of the highest precision, how can one divide [spaces] smaller than a hairbreadth? Minute discrepancies accumulate over time [and finally] become apparent. Both cosmic patterns and the force of circumstance conduce toward this end. Thus in regulating an astronomical system, one cannot avoid reform."[55]

The lack of accord between prediction and phenomenon was not solely a product of human limitations, for there were fundamental irregularities and imponderables in the astronomical heavens that precluded exact measurement. Lu Shi-yi took an almost animist view of these anomalies, remarking that since "heaven is a moving thing (or animated being), how can those who divine the heavens avoid errors completely?"[56] Fang Yi-zhi also seems to have regarded aspects of the cosmos as fundamentally immeasurable. Both sound and light, said Fang, had an anomalous tendency to capriciously expand or "brim over," thus precluding accurate calculation.[57] Moreover, the constancy of change in the cosmos, Fang remarked, insured that no schema, astronomical or otherwise, could for long pass unmodified and still be of service. Thus "if one is unaware that differences constantly change and as a consequence clings to [the conception of] constancy, then there will be cases in which the *Ceremonial Rituals* of the Duke of Zhou cannot be used to order the world and cases in which the *Herbal* of Shen Nong can be relied upon to kill people [instead of curing them]."[58]

Later Qing scholars were generally not quite so imaginative in their accounts of various astronomical anomalies, irregularities, and imponderables. But they did draw the same sort of cosmological conclusions as did their seventeenth-century predecessors. Jiang Yong, for example, citing such apparently irregular celestial movements as the historical diminution in the obliquity of the ecliptic with respect to the celestial equator, as well as the change in the radius of the sun's orbit, concluded that "these two anomalies fall outside of [the scope of] constant [or predictable] patterns . . . and cannot be governed by rules." The only way to deal with them is to "periodically precisely measure [the phenomena] and change the tables [accordingly] in order to mesh them with celestial movements."[59] The late-eighteenth-century editors of the *Siku Quanshu* (Complete Library in Four Treasuries) also cited the historical shift in the obliquity of the ecliptic as "something that cannot be determined through skillful calculation. Thus one must periodically [undertake] precise measurements in order to harmonize [one's predictions] with celestial movements."[60]

A number of Qing scholars of various scholastic affiliations thus identified several of the astronomical deviations known to them as basically indeterminate, frequently drawing the conclusion that the patterns of the cosmos in general shifted in an irregular and even capricious fashion. They even regarded anomalies not so much as departures from a predictable order as themselves constitutive of the fundamental order, or disorder, of the cosmos. This view, of course, ran contrary to the world view established by Han and Song cosmologists, though it was anticipated by mathematical astronomers in medieval times. However, even earlier astronomers, or at least the authors of the introductory sections to the treatises on mathematical astronomy in some of the standard dynastic histories, occasionally proposed that a perpetual astronomical system, one free of significant error, could be created. Thus the editors of the "Treatise on Astronomy" in the *Yuan History* identified the "Season Granting" (Shoushi) system of that era as one which was in such complete and fundamental accord with the patterns of the heavens that it would never have to be reformed. The *Shoushi*, they maintained, was so accurate that it could be used to calculate the ephemerides of both the distant past and the far future. It could be used "perpetually without error; it is not accurate just for the present."[61]

Wang Xi-shan and Mei Wen-ding, the two most celebrated Chinese astronomers of the seventeenth century, were not so optimistic. Wang, for example, remarked that "reform is of the utmost importance in mathematical astronomy. Thus, there has never been an astronomical system that was not reformed after several hundred years."[62] Even the *Shoushi* system, the epitome of the traditional astronomer's art, could not, said Wang, have been completely without flaws, even though it had been in continuous use for some three hundred years. The Western system, too, could not be used perpetually without modification, despite its proven excellence.[63] In sum, Wang commented, "we see that celestial movements are profound but that human knowledge is superficial. The longer one studies [these movements], the more one knows that one cannot attain [complete understanding of them]. The more deeply we go [into these studies], the more fully we understand that they are difficult to fathom. Even if we were really able to surpass the men of former times, that still would not entitle us to claim that we 'know heaven.'"[64]

Mei Wen-ding adopted a slightly more sanguine view of the progress of astronomical science over the previous two millennia. But even Mei did not predict that such progressive development would eventually produce a perfectly precise and comprehensive astronomical system. Without access to accurate observational records encompassing hundreds of years, Mei maintained, even such important irregularities in celestial motions as the annual difference between the solar and sidereal years might never be detected, much less precisely measured. Such irregularities "have both subtle and obvious [manifestations]. Unless they accumulate to the point of being obvious, even a sage cannot be aware of them."[65] Once they have been properly recorded and measured, however, such anomalies might be satisfactorily accounted for within the framework of an astronomical system. For example, the Western model of the precession of the equinoxes elegantly explained both the annual difference and the apparent longitudinal displacement of the fixed stars, assimilating them to a more general conception of order within which they were no longer anomalous.

Few of Mei Wen-ding's Chinese contemporaries, however, subsumed such anomalies within a larger order. Instead, they generally assumed that anomalies (cha) and irregularities (buqi), far from merely complicating the world picture, were actually basic to the structure of the cosmos. Indeed, some Ming and Qing commentators seem to have imbued the words *cha* and *buqi* with the kind of metaphysical aura formerly reserved for such terms as "ultimate principle" (li) and "pneuma" (qi). This metaphysical metamorphosis of *cha* and *buqi* is perhaps best illustrated in the works of a pair of Ming philosophers, Huang Dao-zhou (1585–1646) and Wang Ting-xiang, along with two Qing scholars, Jiang Yong and Zhang Xue-cheng (1738–1801). Thee four figures, with the possible exception of Zhang Xue-cheng, were serious students of astronomy, as well as notable figures in the history of Ming and Qing thought. Hence they were well situated to extrapolate from astronomical studies, particularly form their recognition of *cha* and *buqi* in celestial motions, to other areas of learning. In the course of doing this, they practically apotheosized these ideas, building a general conception of nature or of history around them.

Huang Dao-zhou occupies a curious position in the history of seventeenth-century cosmological thought. While he was one of the last great Neo-Confucian cosmologists in the tradition of Shao Yong and Cai Yuan-ding, he admitted the generality of anomalies in the cosmos to an extent that might well have scandalized his Song predecessors. Like the astronomers discussed above, Huang recognized such established irregularities as the inequalities of solar and lunar motion, planetary advances, and retrogradations, and the annual difference, deviations that many earlier Chinese cosmologists had either ignored or explained away. Huang asserted, moreover, that the precise measure of these anomalies could never be calculated. Since even such relatively determinate phenomena as solar and lunar eclipses could not be predicted with great accuracy, then how, he asked, could one hope to trace the anomalous motions of the five planets?[66]

Huang's astronomical works treat anomalies as obstacles to a complete comprehension of the patterns of the heavens. Yet, paradoxically, Huang identified anomaly in a more philosophical sense as a principal source of human knowledge of the universe. Indeed, if "discrepancies" (cha), or more broadly, differentiation, did not exist then there would be little basis for acquiring knowledge in some fields. In government, for example, one identified the correct way by examining the excesses and deficiencies of previous rulers. And in astronomy, one used the discrepancies in the orbital periods of the sun, moon, and planets as a basis for calculation. Differentiation existed even in the world of Confucian learning. For one could not rely solely on one standard as a guide to conduct and cognition. If this were not the case, Huang remarked, then "learning would stop with the *Doctrine of the Mean* and the handling of affairs would be exhausted with the *Analects*, and the *Songs Classic*, the *Documents Classic*, the *Record of Rites*, the *Record of Music*, and the *Spring and Autumn Annals* all need not have been composed . . . and the histories all need not be read."[67]

Wang Ting-xiang, unlike Huang Dao-zhou, did not propose that anomaly or differentiation in general had any sort of epistemological value. But he did posit that irregularities were immanent in the structure of the cosmos. Offering a simple (anti)numerological illustration of this principle, Wang pointed out that while there is just one great ultimate (taiji), there are two of yin and yang, heaven and earth, male and female, and day and night, three powers (cai), namely heaven, earth, and man, four seasons, five phases, and so on. In sum, "the irregularities of things are in the nature of things."[68]

Jiang Yong, unlike Huang Dao-zhou and Wang Ting-xiang, seldom discussed purely cosmological topics at length. Nevertheless, he did induce from his studies in astronomy the conclusion that irregularity and differentiation, not similitude and correspondence, were immanent in the structure of the universe and even necessary for the maintenance of cosmic order. If, for example, there were no distinctions between equator and ecliptic, if the sun's annual course followed the celestial equator, then there would be no seasons. In that case, "how could [the sun] give birth to the myriad things?"[69] Similarly, the general movement of the planets in a direction opposite to the diurnal motion of the heavens illustrates the indispensability of contraries (ni) for setting off regularities (shun). Having no contraries in the cosmos, Jiang speculated, "would be like rivers having no bends and mountains no turns." In such a case, "there would be no place to concentrate the vessels of the earth or to shelter humankind."[70] Indeed, it is apparent that a regular, uniform terrestrial surface corresponding to that envisaged by literal-minded Chinese well-field reformers and such Old Testament prophets as Isaiah could not be easily turned to such ends. If every valley were exalted and every mountain and hill made low, then whence would the milk and honey flow?

Zhang Xue-cheng, another eighteenth-century scholar who applied the notion of astronomical anomaly to other fields, presented his argument more systematically in an essay entitled, "Analogy of Heaven" (Tianyu). In this work, Zhang compared the processes by which astronomical systems and political-moral orders degenerate and are reformed:

> The human heart and social customs cannot endure for a long time without corruption, just as the [astronomical] systems of the *xihe* [astronomical officials who served under the legendary sage king Yao] and the *baozhang* [chief astronomer of the Zhou court] could not have lasted long without discrepancies. [Thus it was necessary to] take account of corruption and carry out a rectification just as astronomers take account of discrepancies and discuss a reform. [Further, just as] the discrepancies in astronomical systems are on the side of either excess or deficiency, so the corruption of customs tends toward either gravity or frivolity. [In cases where there are] biases toward gravity or frivolity, or excess or deficiency, if one does not go to extremes to reverse them, one cannot attain the mean that is appropriate.[71]

Zhang cited several examples of reforms in morality and learning, particularly those inspired by Confucius, Mencius, Han Yu, Cheng Yi, and Zhu Xi, which he regarded as analogous to calendrical reforms. But none of these reforms, moral or calendrical, Zhang emphasized, approximated "Heaven" or "the heavens," no matter how well they might have succeeded in temporarily correcting deviations. For heaven in itself is "undifferentiated and indistinct." All classifications are artificial devices imposed by reformers attempting to rectify a particular situation. Hence, since no ordering can ever be in objective accord with heaven (or the heavens), then no order can be eternal, or really more than an appropriate response to a special set of historical (or astronomical) circumstances.[72]

TRANSCENDENCE OF ANOMALY IN
EARLY MODERN WESTERN SCIENCE

The extent to which the Ming and Qing commentators discussed above metaphysically transmuted astronomical anomalies, even constructing a general conception of nature or history around them, is remarkable. Yet these commentators' conception that the exact measure of such anomalies was indeterminate is hardly unique in world intellectual history. The fourteenth-century European scholastic Nicole Oresme also posited the existence of a "kind of basic numerical indeterminacy which even the best astronomical data cannot overcome."[73] Vestiges of the idea that the structure of nature is at bottom irregular may have survived with some of the great figures of seventeenth-century science. According to Dudley Shapere, even Galileo "sometimes . . . seems to hold that there is an inherent indeterminacy in nature which prevents a complete and precise scientific account even 'in principle.' "[74] But such a view, after all, was supported by high classical authority in the Western intellectual tradition. According to Plato, the "genuine astronomer" will never imagine that various astronomical periods and proportions can "go on forever without change or the slightest deviation," and thus will not "spend all his pains on trying to find exact truth in them."[75] He will focus, instead, on the Ideas, not on their imperfect manifestations in the visible universe.

By the end of the seventeenth century, however, major figures in the Scientific Revolution had managed to subsume anomalies within a larger conception of order. But the new order was hardly a cosmographical one. For unlike both the Platonic and Aristotelian world pictures, it was not primarily concerned with the proper arrangement of things in space and time, but rather with obedience to laws.[76] "Harmony," in this new scientific cosmos, "resides no longer in numbers which can be gained from arithmetic without observation. Harmony is no longer the property of the circle in higher measure than the ellipse. Harmony is present when a multitude of phenomena is regulated by the unity of a mathematical law which expresses a cosmic idea."[77] In Ernst Cassirer's words, "the totality of the scientific cosmos is a totality of laws, i.e. of relations and functions."[78] These laws, moreover, were regarded as perfectly determinate, at least in theory. As Kepler explained, "God wanted us to perceive them when he created us in His image in order that we may take part in His own thoughts. . . Our knowledge [of numbers and quantities] is of the same kind as God's, at least insofar as we can understand something of it in this mortal life."[79]

Investigators might well encounter discrepancies even in a determinate universe, as a number of European scientific revolutionaries recognized. But "For the science of the seventeenth century, every deviation from the behavior specified by a scientific law can in principle be explained in terms of counterforces which themselves obey precise laws."[80] As for those "anomalous facts" which appear irreconcilable with any theory, one could, according to J.F.W. Herschel, an eminent nineteenth-century philosopher of science, only "record them as curiosities awaiting explanation."[81]

Imperfections in nature were treated with considerably more attention and respect in eighteenth-century biological thought, as well as in the works of some of the Romantic natural philosophers. Yet in the early eighteenth century, the conception of a higher harmony or lawful order transcending apparent anomalies was articulated by both the leading philosopher and the most eminent English poet of the era. According to Leibniz, "There are doubtless a thousand irregularities, a thousand disorders, in particulars. But it is impossible that there should be any in the whole, or even in each Monad, because each Monad is a living mirror of the Universe, according to its own point of view."[82] The poetic expression of this idea, by Alexander Pope in his *Essay on Man* (1733), is far more famous:

> All nature is but art, unknown to thee;
> All chance, direction, which though canst not see;
> All discord, harmony not understood;
> All partial evil, universal good:
> And, spite of pride, in erring reason's spite,
> One truth is clear, "Whatever is, is RIGHT."[83]

The uncannily benign view of the operation of nature's laws expressed in these lines was one of the major casualties of the great Lisbon earthquake of 1755, the publication of *Candide*, and of subsequent disasters. But a belief in an orderly, lawful cosmos, in which "discord" and "chance" are only local or apparent, survived in several of the natural sciences through most of the next century.

In Qing China, in contrast, commentators had so reified, even apotheosized, irregularities and indeterminates that the conception of a lawful universe had little chance of becoming established. From the standpoint of the type of scientific development that occurred in early modern Europe, early Qing cosmological critics thus did their work too well. They confuted the dominant intellectual modes of the prescientific stage of world intellectual development, particularly correlative thought and geometrical cosmography. But their critique of traditional cosmology went so far as to deny that a uniform world order of any kind was accessible to human intelligence or even immanent in the cosmos. Thus Ruan Yuan praised ancient Chinese astronomers for having realized that the ways of the heavens are "profound and subtle, and are not such that human power can fathom." Unlike their less judicious Western counterparts, these astronomers "only spoke of the phenomena and did not go on to forcibly inquire of the reasons why [they are as they are]."[84] In Wang Fu-zhi's view, even so simple a calculation as the Western measurement of the earth's circumference by the latitudinal variation of the equatorial pole above the earth's horizon could not be trusted. For there were too many sources of distortion, such as man's limited vision and the uneven contours of the earth's surface, that precluded accurate calculation of the pole's height at any latitude.[85]

Wang, as well as many other Qing scholars, thus rejected the metaphysical presuppositions of both late-traditional Chinese cosmology and early modern Western science, presuppositions that seemed to be in mutual accord in positing the existence of a uniform, determinate order in the physical world and in the cosmos in general. And neither apparently recognized such subtle variations in cosmic processes as could not be assimilated to measure or system. Thus the character of the early-Qing rejection of traditional cosmology might well have inhibited the development of modern science in China, for there were evidently no late-traditional Chinese equivalents of Kepler, Newton, Leibniz, or Newlands, transitional figures whose grounding in correlative cosmology helped to prepare the way for the rise of modern science.

A FEW SUGGESTIONS FOR FURTHER STUDY

Inasmuch as this book considers a broad subject over a long span of history, it has not been possible to give a complete account of the development and decline of Chinese cosmology. Even were the historiography in this field much more developed than it is, it is doubtful that a comprehensive examination of such an extensive topic could be compressed within the limits of a single volume. Nevertheless, I hope that this study has identified some general patterns in the history of Chinese cosmological thought that are worthy of further investigation.

Along what lines might such investigation proceed? The most obvious and perhaps important requirement is for more concentrated studies of the primary sources of Chinese cosmological thought. Although recent scholars have devoted studies to important cosmological texts of the Han era, similar works form the late-traditional period deserve closer attention as well. Second, the possible political and social relationships of Chinese cosmology could bear further scrutiny. It would be difficult to establish that political or social developments or structures inspired the formulation of Chinese cosmological ideas in general; but studies of the larger milieus might help to explain how some of these ideas were transmitted or transformed, or why they were accepted or rejected. Third, in view of the wide distribution and pervasive influence of correlative cosmology in several distinct historical civilizations, particularly the Indian, Arabic, and Mesoamerican, as well as the European, Chinese, and Japanese, comparative studies in the historical development of this mode of thought might well yield valuable insights. For example, they might further clarify why correlative cosmology and geometrical cosmography generally flourished in the postclassical but premodern phases in the history of most civilizations.

Finally, a more intensive examination of anthropological and psychological literature concerned with such topics as classification, ritual, anthropomorphism, analogical thinking, play, and dreams, might help to explain when and why correlative modes of thought first arose and how they developed. If, for example, anthropomorphism can be shown to have a neurological basis,[86] then one might expect schemata based on man-cosmos correspondences to have been the earliest and most basic mode of correlative thought. And if analogical thinking is really a product of the evolution of language, then might some forms of correlative thought have arisen from linguistic developments?[87] With respect to the rejection of correlative cosmology, studies of how and why most children abandon symbolic play by about age twelve might be illuminating.[88] For this type of play is based in part on the notion of correspondence between a microcosmic play world and some aspect of the larger adult world. Finally, perhaps the historical evolution of dreamwork and its interpretation influenced the development and decline of cosmological thought. [89] Inasmuch as the closest approaches to systems of correspondence that appear in the literature of the ancient Near East are contained in accounts of dreams, it is possible that memories and interpretations of such dreams contributed to the rise of correlative cosmology.

The extensive ramifications and wide distribution of correlative modes of thought make the issue of its development and decline important in human thought and culture in general. Several of the sciences of man have something to contribute to an understanding of this subject. Further studies of correlative cosmology by sinologists might well take advantage of the perspectives developed in such nonsinological disciplines as comparative history, historical linguistics, cultural anthropology, and developmental psychology.

Notes

Full citations are given in the notes only for those items not included in the bibliography. For an account of the criteria I used for selecting works to be included therein, see the explanatory note to the bibliography.

Introduction

1. Matila Ghyka, *The Geometry of Art and Life*, p. 112. For a brief account of the history of the Greek root of "cosmos," see Clarence J. Glacken, *Traces on the Rhodian Shore*, pp. 16–17. According to Plutarch's *Moralia*, "Pythagoras was the first philosopher that gave the name of *kosmos* to the world, from the order and beauty of it; for so that word signifies." See *Plutarch's Morals*, trans. William W. Goodwin (Boston: Little, Brown, 1871), 3:132.

2. Examples of recent studies devoted to such topics include Charles Yvon Le Blanc, "The Idea of Resonance"; John S. Major, "Myth, Cosmology, and the Origins of Chinese Science"; Schuyler Cammann, "The Magic Square of Three."

3. A few recent scholars, however, have noted that by late-traditional times in China, established cosmological ideas and presuppositions had been progressively challenged in such special fields as mathematical astronomy (Nathan Sivin), moral philosophy (H.G. Lamont), historiography (Hsu Dau-lin), medicine (Helen Dunstan), law (Derk Bodde), vernacular literature (C.T. Hsia), and mathematical harmonics (Derk Bodde and Kenneth G. Robinson).

1. Correlative Thought in Early China

1. Of these three forms, allegory, which is "based on parallels between two levels of being that correspond to each other," bears the closest relationship to correlative modes of thought. This characterization of allegory appears in Angus Fletcher, *Allegory: The Theory of a Symbolic Mode* (Ithaca: Cornell University Press, 1964), p. 113.

2. See Wendy D. O'Flaherty, ed. and trans., *The Rig Veda: An Anthology* (Harmondsworth, Eng.: Penguin, 1981), pp. 29–32; E.M.W. Tillyard, *The Elizabethan World Picture*, pp. 91–92.

3. *Shijing* 1.1.6; *Lunyu*, bk. 2, chap. 1.

4. *Huainanzi* 3.16a–16b.

5. Ibid., 7.2a.

6. For a synopsis of man-cosmos correspondences in the *Baihu Tongyi*, see Tjan Tjoe Som, "Introduction" to Tjan, trans., *Po Hu T'ung: Comprehensive Discussions*, 1:109.

7. See, for example, Rolf Homann, trans., *Pai Wen P'ian or the Hundred Questions: A Dialogue between Two Taoists on the Macrocosmic and Microcosmic Correspondences*, Nisaba Religious Texts Translation Series, vol. 4 (Leiden: E. J. Brill, 1976), p. 32. The idea of the purified Daoist body as a microcosm of both the physical world and the imperial government is explored in Kristofer Schipper, "The Taoist Body."

8. *Chunqiu Fanlu* 11.186, 188 (chap. 45).

9. Ibid. 13.206 (chap. 56). My translation of these two passages is based upon those given in Wing-tsit Chan, *A Source Book in Chinese Philosophy,* p. 282.

10. *Chunqiu Fanlu* 13.205 (chap. 56). In the same way, the institution of marriage is exalted in the Christian church even today by dint of the correspondence between the union of husband and wife and that of Christ and his church.

11. *Lüshi Chunqiu* 2.6b; *Zhongyong,* chap. 30; *Lunyu,* bk. 8, chap. 19.

12. *Baihu Tongde Lun* 3.18b.

13. *Huainanzi* 3.4b; *Chunqiu Fanlu* 7.118–121 (chap. 24); Nakayama Shigeru, "Characteristics of Chinese Astrology," p. 593.

14. *Chunqiu Fanlu* 11.182 (chap. 43).

15. *Baihu Tong* 8.14a, 3.1a–1b.

16. Sarah Allan, "Sons of Suns," p. 321.

17. David N. Keightley, "The Religious Commitment," p. 216.

18. Arthur P. Wolf, "Gods, Ghosts, and Ancestors," in Wolf, ed., *Religion and Ritual in Chinese Society* (Stanford: Stanford University Press, 1974), p. 144; Alvin P. Cohen, "Coercing the Rain Deities in Ancient China," *History of Religions* (February–May 1978), 17:256.

19. Juliet Bredon and Igor Mitrophanow, *The Moon Year: A Record of Chinese Customs and Festivals* (Shanghai: Kelly and Walsh, 1927; reprint ed., Taipei: Ch'eng-wen, 1972), p. 443.

20. Marcel Granet, *Danses et légendes de la Chine ancienne* (Paris: Libaririe Félix Alcan, 1926), 1:10, 2:617–18.

21. John Major has recently argued that "the five are drived from the five visible planets," though he advances this hypothesis to explain the origin of the conception rather than its triumph over rival numerological orders. See John S. Major, "Myth, Cosmology, and the Origins of Chinese Science," pp. 11–12.

22. There is considerable disagreement among scholars regarding the date of composition of the *Hongfan.* According to Joseph Needham, "the five-element theory" was not incorporated into the text until the early years of the second century B.C.; *Science and Civilisation in China,* 2:247.

23. Bernhard Karlgren, trans., *The Book of Documents,* p. 30. That the *wuxing* were originally conceived as material substances has been affirmed by several modern sinologists. See, for example, Henri Maspero, *China in Antiquity,* trans. Frank A. Kierman, Jr. (Amherst: University of Massachusetts Press, 1978), p. 278; Hsü Fu-kuan, *Lianghan Sixiang Shi,* 2:18. Apart from the passage in the "Great Plan" chapter of the *Documents,* a reference to the *wuxing* in the *Guoyu* (Conversations of the States) (SBBY ed.) 4.7b, also seems to support this interpretation.

24. Karlgren, *Documents,* p. 30.

25. Ibid., pp. 9, 30.

26. Vitaly A. Rubin, "The Concepts of Wu-Hsing and Yin-Yang," p. 134.

27. Manfred Porkert, *The Theoretical Foundations of Chinese Medicine,* p. 45.

28. *Lüshi ChunQiu,* 13.4a.

29. For a discussion of the various orders and sequences into which late-classical cosmologists arranged the five phases, see Needham, *Science and Civilisation,* 2:253–65. Needham's analysis is based in part on the more comprehensive treatment included in Wolfram Eberhard, "Beiträge zu kosmologischen Spekulation Chinas in der Han Zeit," pp. 41 ff. On the mutual production and mutual conquest orders, see also Michael Loewe, *Chinese Ideas of Life and Death: Faith, Myth, and Reason in the Han Period (202 BC–AD 220)* (London: Allen and Unwin, 1982), pp. 40–41.

30. *Baihu Tong* 3.17b; Tjan, 2:442.

31. Tjan, 2:603. This particular passage does not appear in the *Sibu Congkan* edition of

the *Baihu Tong.*

32. *Xinjiao Shiji Sanjia Zhu* 74 (*Fengshan Shu* 6). 1381–82, 1402. The relevant passages from the *Shiji* are translated in Burton Watson, *Records of the Grand Historian of China* (New York: Columbia University Press, 1961), 2:34, 66–67.

33. W. Allyn Rickett, *Kuan-tzu*, pp. 180–83. Guo Mo-ruo's brief discussion of the *Yuguan* or *Xuangong* (Dark Palace) seasonal chart may be found in his *Guanzi Jijiao*, p. 105. Guo's reconstruction of the chart itself appears in a foldout following p. 142 of the same text. Guo notes earlier commentators' identification of this chart with the Ming Tang (Luminous Hall), a classical ceremonial structure which Han cosmologists developed into an architectural microcosm, as related in chapter 2.

34. *Baihu Tong* 3.15a; Tjan, 2:439.

35. Xu Fu-guan, *Lianghan*, p. 253; Fung Yu-lan, *Zhongguo Zhexue Shi*, p. 500; *Chunqiu Fanlu* 10.172 (chap. 38).

36. Xu Fu-guan, *Liang-Han*, p. 17.

37. *Baihu Tong* 3.15a.

38. Xu Fu-guan, *Liang-Han*, p. 17.

39. Porkert, *Theoretical Foundations*, p. 51.

40. *Weishu* 107A, *Lülizhi* A (Wei History, Treatise on Astronomy and Harmonics), in *Lidai Tianwen Lüli Deng Zhi Huibian*, 6:1801.

41. Bernhard Karlgren, "Legends and Cults in Ancient China," p. 241.

42. Pierre Huard and Ming Wong, *Chinese Medicine*, trans. Bernard Fielding (New York: McGraw-Hill, 1968), p. 38.

43. Li Ding-zhuo, comp., *Zhouyi Jijie Zuanshu* 9.814.

44. S.K. Heninger, Jr., *The Cosmological Glass*, p. 138.

45. Frances A. Yates, *The Art of Memory*, pp. 148–9.

46. Nathan Sivin, Review of John Blofeld, trans., *The Book of Change, Harvard Journal of Asiatic Studies* (1966), 26:293.

47. Chapell Brown, "The Tetrahedron as an Archetype for the Concept of Change in the I Ching," *Journal of Chinese Philosophy* (June 1982), 9:159.

48. *Zhouyi Zhushu* 9.4b (chap. 11 of *shuoguazhuan*).

49. Ibid. 7.9a (chap. 6 of *shangzhuan*). This translation is a slightly modified version of that given in William J. Peterson, "Making Connections," p. 90.

50. Peterson, "Making Connections," p. 85.

51. *Zhouyi Zhushu* 7.1b (chap. 1 of *shangzhuan*). The translation is that of Peterson in "Making Connections," p. 86.

52. For a diagrammatic representation of such correlations, see the chart in Needham, *Science and Civilisation*, 2:313.

53. Luo Guang, *Zhongguo Zhexue Sixiang Shi, Liang-Han Nanbeichao Pian*, pp. 6, 469–71, 479.

54. Ibid., p. 480; Hsu Fu-kuan, *Liang-Han*, pp. 51–52, 341–42. Luo Guang also briefly describes two other solutions to the problem of correlating the number of lines in the hexagrams with the number of days in the year.

55. Luo Guang, *Zhongguo Zhexue Sixiang Shi*, p. 482; E.G. Pulleyblank, "The Chinese Cyclical Signs as Phonograms," p. 24.

56. Luo Guang, *Zhongguo Zhexue Sixiang Shi*, p. 482, 484, 485, 488, 490, 512–13. For a chart depicting the correlation of the trigrams with the phases of the moon according to the *najia* schema, see Liu Ts'un-yan, "Taoist Self-Cultivation in Ming Thought," pp. 302–3.

57. *Zhouyi Zhushu* 7.17a (chap. 11 of *shangzhuan*).

58. Li Ding-zhuo, *Zhouyi Jijie Zuanshu* 8.788, 792–93.

59. *Qinshu* 17, *Lülizhi* B (Qin History, Treatise on Astronomy and Harmonics), in *Lidai Tianwen*, 5:1584.

60. Li Ding-zhuo, *Zhouyi Jijie Zhuanshu* 9.830.

61. A much more complex example of such a numerological derivation of astronomical constants, translated from the "Treatise on Astronomy and Harmonics" of the *Han History*, is given in Nathan Sivin, "Cosmos and Computation," pp. 8–9.

62. Zhang Yachu and Liu Yu have recently speculated that the origins of Yang Xiong's system may be traced to Shang (1766–1122 B.C.) antecedents. Based on their comparison of the forms of the *shou* in Yang's schema with the figures appearing in some Shang inscriptions, the authors conclude that "the system [of the *Tai Xuan Jing*] could not have been a creation of Yang Xiong's imagination; the two systems must have a definite developmental relationship." See Zhang Yachu and Liu Yu, "Some Observations about Milfoil Divination Based on Shang and Zhou *bagua* Numerical Symbols," trans. Edward Shaughnessy, *Early China* (1981–82), 7:53.

63. Willy Hartner notes that the *huangzhong*, the tonic pitchpipe, "is reported to have measured nine inches." See Hartner, "Some Notes on Chinese Musical Art," in Nathan Sivin, ed., *Science and Technology in East Asia* (New York: Science History Publications, 1977), p. 35.

64. For a brief discussion of this discrepancy in Yang Xiong's cosmocalendrical system, see Luo Guang, *Zhongguo Zhexue Sixiang Shi*, p. 219.

65. Such an explication of a classical term through a linguistic pun may be found in *Zhouli Zhengzhu* 28.4b, an interpretation of which appears in Derk Bodde, *Festivals in Classical China*, p. 79.

66. Hsü Dau-lin, "Crime and Cosmic Order," p. 113.

67. For a brief account of the two major theories proposed by Han scholiasts to explain the origins of the *Yueling*, see William G. Boltz, "Philological Footnotes to the Han New Year Rites," pp. 425–26.

68. Bodde, *Festivals*, p. 15. On the *Xia Xiaozheng*, see also Rickett, *Kuan-tzu* [Guanzi], p. 189. The text in question is included in chapter 2 of the *Dadai Liji* (The Elder Dai's Record of Rites).

69. Rickett, *Kuan-tzu*, p. 188.

70. *Lüshi Chunqiu* 1.1a. This translation is a slightly modified version of that given in Wm. Theodore de Bary et al., *Sources of Chinese Tradition*, 1:208.

71. *Lüshi Chunqiu* 1.1b–2a; de Bary, 1:208.

72. *Lüshi Chunqiu* 1.3b; de Bary, 1:210.

73. Bodde, *Festivals*, p. 16.

74. Ibid., pp. 191–92, 199–200.

75. Charles Yvon Le Blanc, "The Idea of Resonance," p. 224.

76. See, for example, *Chunqiu Fanlu* 13.206–7 (chap. 57).

77. *Han-shu* 21A, *Lüli Zhi* A (Han History, Treatise on Astronomy and Harmonics), in *Lidai Tianwen*, 5:1385.

78. Bodde, *Festivals*, p. 178. Bodde adds that descriptions of this ritual may be found in the "Treatise on Astronomy and Harmonics" in the *Later Han History* and in the apocrypha to the *Change*, among other works.

79. *Zhouli Zhenzhu* 22.6a–6b.

80. Max Kaltenmark, "The Ideology of the T'ai-p'ing ching [Taiping Jing]," p. 44.

81. Hsü Dau-lin, "Crime and Cosmic Order," p. 115.

82. *Chunqiu Fanlu* 4.51 (chap. 6), also translated in Chan, *Source Book*, p. 285.

83. *Huainanzi* 3.2a–2b. My translation of this passage is based on that given in John S.

Major, "Astrology in the *Huai-nan-tzu* and Some Related Texts," p. 20.

84. See, for example, *Luo Guang, Zhongguo Zhexue Sixiang Shi*, p. 146.

85. Karlgren, *Documents*, p. 33.

86. Jean Piaget, *The Child's Conception of Physical Causality*, pp. 61, 73, 260–1.

87. Of all the proposed English translations of *qi*, "pneuma" seems to be the most satisfactory. For the "pneuma" as conceptualized by the Stoic philosophers resembles the Han cosmological interpretation of *qi* by virtue of its subtlety, pervasiveness, association with breath or air, and dynamic internal tension. For a brief account of the pneuma of the Stoics, see G.E.R. Lloyd, *Greek Science After Aristotle*, pp. 28–31.

88. My colleague Stephen Farmer may be credited with this idea.

89. Luo Guang, *Zhongguo Zhexue Sixiang Shi*, p. 312.

90. Piaget, *Child's Conception*, p. 268.

91. Karlgren, *Documents*, p. 74

92. Pseudo-Dionysius, *The Divine Names*, chap. 4, trans. C.E. Rolt, in Herman Shapiro, ed., *Medieval Philosophy: Selected Readings from Augustine to Buridan*, Modern Library (New York: Random House, 1964), pp. 54–55.

93. See, for example, *Xinjiao Hanshu Jizhu* 27A (*Wuxing Zhi* 7A).1339, 1346.

94. Lien-sheng Yang, "The Concept of 'Pao' as a Basis for Social Relations in China," pp. 297, 302.

95. *Lunyu*, bk. 8, chap. 2, trans. in D.C. Lau, *The Analects*, p. 92.

96. Emile Durkheim and Marcel Mauss, *Primitive Classification*, pp. 73–4.

97. Ernst Cassirer, *The Philosophy of Symbolic Forms*, 2:87.

98. Paul Wheatley, *The Pivot of the Four Quarters*, pp. 414–15.

99. Much of the argument in this paragraph is based on Jack Goody, *The Domestication of the Savage Mind*.

100. Clifford Geertz, "Thick Description: Toward an Interpretive Theory of Culture," in *The Interpretation of Cultures: Selected Essays by Clifford Geertz* (New York: Basic Books, 1973), p. 24.

101. Goody, *Domestication*, pp. 102–6.

102. Jack Goody, "Introduction" to Goody, ed., *Literacy*, pp. 17–18.

103. Benjamin I. Schwartz, "On the Absence of Reductionism in Chinese Thought," p. 32; H.G. Creel, "Comments on Harmony and Conflict," *Journal of Chinese Philosophy* (October 1977), 4:274.

104. A curious parallel exists between this propensity to trace the origins of numerological cosmology in China to Zou Yan and the "Naturalists" and the tendency of both Helenistic commentators and modern Western historians of Greek thought to identify the Pythagoreans as the inventors of numerological cosmology in the Western tradition. For a recent estimate of the originality and significance of Pythagorean cosmology, see W.T. Jones, *The Classical Mind: A History of Western Philosophy*, 2d ed. (New York: Harcourt Brace Jovanovich, 1970), pp. 38–9.

105. Nathan Sivin has pointed out that evidence for the existence of such a school is both late and suspect (personal communication). Ironically, the theory that there was such a school may itself be a product of Han scholastics' correlative thinking. One could argue, for example, that Ban Gu, in pairing the various schools of Zhou philosophy with departments of the ancient political administration, seized on the *yinyangjia* as a convenient correlate to the ancient office concerned with astronomy and the calendar, the *Xihe Zhiguan*, see *Han-shu* 30 (*Yiwenzhi* 10). 1734–5.

106. *Shiji* 74 (Liezhuan 14).2344. The *Lüshi Chunqiu* 13.4a also explains the rise and fall of these ancient dynasties by the theory of the succession of the five phases, though it does

not directly attribute the theory to Zou Yan.

107. For an English translation of Ma Guo-han's collection of the extant fragments from the works of Zhou Yan, see Needham, *Science and Civilisation*, 2:236–38.

108. Luo Guang, *Zhongguo Zhexue Sixiang Shi*, pp. 53–4; Feng Yu-lan, *Zhongguo Zhexue Shi*, pp. 200–2.

109. Representative statements of this position may be found in Luo Guang, *Zhongguo Zhexue Sixiang Shi*, pp. 3, 13, 53.

110. John S. Major, "Research Priorities in the Study of Ch'u [Chu] Religion," p. 231.

111. Heninger, *Cosmographical Glass*, pp. 179–80.

112. *Laozi* A.14b (chap. 25).

113. *Zhouyi Zhushu* 8.3a (chap. 2 of *xiazhuan*).

114. For a brief discussion of Confucius' use of analogy in his teaching on moral cultivation, see D.C. Lau's "Introduction" to his translation of the *Analects*, p. 51.

115. *Lunyu*, bk. 2, chap. 1.

116. The *locus classicus* for such hierarchical pairings is the *wen-yan* appendix to the *kun* (earth) hexagram of the *Change* (Zhouyi Zhushu 1.16a).

117. Dong Zhong-shu, quoted in *Han-shu* 22 (Liyuezhi 2). 1031.

118. William G. Boltz, "Kung Kung and the Flood," p. 147.

119. Karlgren, "Legends and Cults," p. 345.

120. Ibid.

121. Bernhard Karlgren, "Some Sacrifices in Chou China," p. 2; Karlgren, "Legends and Cults," p. 356.

122. Karlgren, "Legends and Cults," p. 201; *Shiji* (Records of the Historian) (Peking: Zhonghua shuju) 130.3319–20. I have followed the translation of this passage, given in David Johnson, "Epic and History in Early China," *Journal of Asiatic Studies* (1981), 40:270. I use the word "syncretic" here to refer to attempts to reconcile or coordinate elements or tenets of diverse classical texts, philosophical schools, or religious or scientific traditions. This use of the term accords with the primary definiation of "syncretism" given in the *Oxford English Dictionary*.

123. John Major relates the extension of a similar numerological series, one based on eight, by a Later Han commentator on the *Huainanzi*, Gao Yu (fl. A.D. 205–212), who paired the eight winds with the eight trigrams and the eight musical instruments. See Major, "Notes on the Nomenclature of Winds and Directions in the Early Han," pp. 77, 79.

124. For an interpretation of how yin-yang and *wuxing* were first related to one another, purportedly by Zou Yan, see Rubin, "Concepts of Wu-Hsing and Yin-Yang."

125. *Baihu Tong* 3.10a. On the Han synthesis of the yin-yang and five-phase sequences, see also Michael Loewe, *Ways to Paradise*, p. 6.

126. Zhang Zai, *Zhangzi Zhengmeng Zhu* 1.41. As Wang Fu-zhi notes in his commentary, the character for "ice" has been mistakenly substituted for "water" in this passage.

127. Arthur Wright, *Buddhism in Chinese History* (Stanford: Stanford University Press, 1971), pp. 37–8.

128. Raoul Birnbaum, "Introduction to the Study of T'ang Buddhist Astrology," pp. 12 ff.

129. Judith A. Berling, *The Syncretic Religion of Lin Chao-en*, p. 207.

130. Karlgren, "Legends and Cults," p. 201.

131. Harry Austryn Wolfson, *Philo: Foundations of Religious Philosophy in Judaism, Christianity, and Islam* (Cambridge: Harvard University Press, 1947), 1:102.

132. Marcel Simon, *Jewish Sects at the Time of Jesus*, trans. James H. Farley (Philadelphia: Fortress Press, 1967), p. 22.

133. Heninger, *Cosmographical Glass*, p. 90.

134. Ibid., pp. 191–92.

135. Ibid., p. 91.

136. Luo Guang, *Zhongguo Zhexue Sixiang Shi*, p. 223.

137. Berling, *Syncretic Religion*, p. 205. Karlgren's "Legends and Cults," pp. 344–45, also lists other devices through which later "systematizers" sought to work up the classical literary legacy into a consistent whole.

138. John Skorupski, *Symbol and Theory A Philosophical Study of Religion in Social Anthropology* (Cambridge: Cambridge University Press, 1976), p. 199.

139. Karlgren, "Some Sacrifices," p. 10. A serious challenge to the rigidity of Karlgren's initial distinction between "free texts" and "systematizing texts" appears in Sven Broman, "Studies on the Chou Li [Zhouli]." Although Broman does not directly contradict Karlgren, he does conclude that the *Zhouli* (Rites of Zhou), a late-classical work identified by Karlgren as a systematizing text, "depicts a governing system which, in all essentials, prevailed in middle and late feudal Chou in the various states and has its roots in the system pertaining to late Yin and early Chou" (p. 73).

140. Karlgren, "Some Sacrifices," pp. 8, 15.

141. Ibid., p. 15; "Legends and Cults," p. 242.

142. Karlgren, "Legends and Cults," pp. 263–64; Bernhard Karlgren, "Glosses on the Book of Documents," p. 49.

143. Derk Bodde, "Myths of Ancient China," in Samuel Noah Kramer, ed., *Mythologies of the Ancient World* (Garden City, NY: Doubleday, Anchor, 1961), p. 396.

144. Han Yu, "Yuan Gui" (On Ghosts), in *Han Changli Quanji* 11.9b.

145. Burton Watson, *Early Chinese Literature* (New York: Columbia University Press, 1962), pp. 68, 133.

146. John H. Finley, Jr., *Four Stages of Greek Thought* (Stanford: Stanford University Press, 1966), p. 71.

147. *Huangdi Neijing Suwen Wang Bing Zhu* 3.6b.

148. *Yunqi Lun* (A Discussion of the Revolutions of the Pneumas), excerpted in Wang Ying-lin, *Liujing Tianwen Bian* A.37. The preceding very summary discussion of systems of correspondence in Chinese medicine is based largely on my reading of excerpts from the *Huangdi Neijing Suwen* and on Ilza Veith, trans., *Huang ti nei ching su wen: The Yellow Emperor's Classic of Internal Medicine*, new ed. (Berkeley: University of California Press, 1972). I have also consulted Manfred Porkert's *Theoretical Foundations of Chinese Medicine*, as well as Ulrike Unschuld's "Traditional Chinese Pharmacology."

149. Nathan Sivin, "Chinese Alchemy and the Manipulation of Time," pp. 114–15.

150. Berling, *Syncretic Religion*, p. 96.

151. Henri Maspero, *Taoism and Chinese Religion*, p. 352.

152. On the subject of alchemy as a syncretic science, see Wayne Shumaker, *The Occult Sciences in the Renaissance*, p. 169.

153. Nathan Sivin, "Discovery of Spagyrical Invention," pp. 222–23.

154. *Huangdi Zhai Jing* (The Yellow Sovereign's Site Classic) B.6b, trans. in Steven J. Bennett, "Patterns of Sky and Earth," pp. 13, 21.

155. Ibid., p. 18; Xu Di-shan, "Daojia Sixiang yu Daojiao," p. 199.

156. Jeffrey F. Meyer, "Feng-shui of the Chinese City," pp. 149–50.

157. Nathan Sivin makes a similar point in "Science in China's Past," p. 22.

158. Liu Xie, *Wenxin Diaolong* (The Literary Mind and the Carving of Dragons) (SBBY ed.) 6.5a–5b. I have followed the translation of this passage from Pauline Yu, *The Poetry of Wang Wei*, p. 4.

159. Yu, *Wang Wei*, pp. 4–5.

160. Heninger, *Cosmographical Glass*, p. 119.

161. According to Erich Auerbach, "the Homeric poems conceal nothing, they contain no teaching and no secret second meaning... Later allegorizing trends have tried their arts of interpretation upon him, but to no avail." See his *Mimesis: The Representation of Reality in Western Literature*, trans. Willard R. Trask (Princeton: Princeton University Press, 1953), p. 13.

162. Hans H. Frankel, *The Flowering Plum and the Palace Lady*, p. 16; Jeremy H.C.S. Davidson, "Images of Ecstasy: A Vietnamese Response to Nature," in George B. Milner, ed., *Natural Symbols in South East Asia* (London: University of London School of Oriental and African Studies, 1978), pp. 300, 37–39, 51.

163. Sir Edward Dyer, "My Mind to Me a Kingdom Is," in *Immortal Poems of the English Language*, ed. Oscar Williams (New York: Washington Square Press, 1952), p. 36; Han Yu, "Encountering Spring in the Eastern Capital," trans. in Frankel, *Flowering Plum*, p. 41.

164. Hans Frankel implies as much when he writes of Han Yu's poem that "Change in the poet's own life is associated with the change of seasons: youth is spring, old age . . . is winter" (*Flowering Plum*, p. 43).

165. This characterization of the Elizabethan mind appears in Rosemond Tuve, *Elizabethan and Metaphysical Imagery: Renaissance Poetic and Twentieth-Century Critics* (Chicago: University of Chicago Press, 1947), pp. 160–61.

166. Derk Bodde, "Types of Chinese Categorical Thinking," p. 207.

167. A valuable discussion on "law and cosmic harmony" in traditional China may be found in Derk Bodde and Clarence Morris, *Law in Imperial China*, pp. 43–48, 561–62.

168. The discussion of the cosmological facets of Sang Hong-yang's economic theory is based largely on my reading of J.L. Kroll, "Toward a Study of the Economic Views of Sang Hung-yang," pp. 11–12. Sang Hong-yang did, however, recognize that there was metal in the East even though the wood element dominated that quarter and that there was correspondingly wood in the West even though metal was paramount there. *Yantie Lun* (Discourses on Salt and Iron) (Shanghai: Renmin Chuban She, 1974) 1.7 (chap. 3).

169. C.K. Yang, *Religion in Chinese Society*, p. 17.

170. Examples of cosmological correspondences in contemporary folk medicine may be found in Marjorie Topley, "Cosmic Antagonisms: A Mother-Child Syndrome," in Arthur P. Wolf, ed., *Religion and Ritual in Chinese Society* (Stanford: Stanford University Press, 1974), pp. 235–37; and Arthur Kleinman, *Patients and Healers in the Context of Culture: An Exploration of the Borderland between Anthropology, Medicine, and Psychiatry*, Comparative Studies of Health Systems and Medical Care, no. 3 (Berkeley: University of California Press, 1980), pp. 7, 126.

171. Kwang-chih Chang, "Ancient China," in Chang, ed., *Food in Chinese Culture*, pp. 46–48; Ying-shih Yu, "Han," in ibid., p. 68; Frederick W. Mote, "Yuan and Ming," in ibid., pp. 225, 233.

172. H. Dubois, *Monographie des Betsiléo* (Paris: Institut d'Ethnologie, 1938), p. 953, quoted and translated in Maurice Bloch, "Astrology and Writing in Madagascar," in Goody, ed., *Literacy*, p. 297.

173. Of course, not all peasants in traditional China were illiterate. For a discussion of literacy rates in the late-traditional era, see Evelyn Rawski, *Education and Popular Literacy in Ch'ing* [Qing] *China* (Ann Arbor: University of Michigan Press, 1979), esp. p. 23.

174. Much of the following discussion is inspired by conversations with my colleague, Stephen Farmer, who is presently completing a study of the "nine hundred theses" of Pico della Mirandola, a work crucial to the understanding of syncretic and correlative thought in the Renaissance.

175. Moses I. Finley, *The World of Odysseus*, 2d. ed. (Harmondsworth, Eng.: Penguin Books, 1978), p. 132.

176. Clarence J. Glacken, *Traces on the Rhodian Shore*, p. 10.

177. Plato, *Republic*, 8, 9, in Frances M. Cornford, trans., *The Republic of Plato* (Oxford: Oxford Unversity Press, 1941), pp. 267, 306.

178. Robin R. Schlunk, *The Homeric Scholia and the Aeneid: A Study of the Influence of Ancient Homeric Literary Criticism on Vergil* (Ann Arbor: University of Michigan Press, 1974), pp. 33–34; Rudolf Pfeiffer, *History of Classical Scholarship from the Beginning to the End of the Hellenistic Age* (Oxford: Oxford University Press, 1968), p. 240. However, Theagenes of Rhegium, who flourished in the sixth century B.C., was "the first scholar known to have applied the allegorical method of interpretation to Homer." Kathleen Freeman, *Ancila to the Pre-Socratic Philosphers*, p. 15.

179. Yates, *Art of Memory*, p. 15.

180. Lloyd, *Greek Science*, p. 140.

181. Seyyed Hossein Nasr, *Science and Civilisation in Islam* (New York: New American Library, 1970), pp. 223–24.

182. Heninger, *Cosmographical Glass*, p. 158.

183. Yates, *Art of Memory*, p. 110.

184. Heninger, *Cosmographical Glass*, p. 116–18, 122.

185. Pico della Mirandola, *Heptaplus*, p. 77.

186. Saint Bonaventura, *The Mind's Road to God*, trans. George Boas, The Library of Liberal Arts (Indianapolis: Bobbs-Merrill, 1953), p. 20.

2. Geometrical Cosmography in Early China

1. Matila Ghyka, *The Geometry of Art and Life*, p. 142 and illustration p. 145.

2. Kwang-chih Chang, *The Archeology of Ancient China*, p. 251.

3. Wolfram Eberhard, for example, has argued that Chinese cities were "well-planned, being quadrangular, with straight streets, high walls, and at least four gates" because they came into being as garrisons and administrative centers. See Eberhard, *Chinese Festivals* (New York: Henry Schuman, 1952), p. 121.

4. Plato, *Timaeus*, trans. Benjamin Jowett, The Library of Liberal Arts (Indianapolis: Bobbs-Merrill, 1949), p. 16; Aristotle, *De Caelo*, excerpted in W.D. Ross, ed., *Aristotle Selections* (New York: Scribner's, 1927), p. 126.

5. Samuel Sambursky, "Harmony and Wholeness in Greek Scientific Thought," p. 445.

6. Plato, *Laws* 5, in Benjamin Jowett, trans., *The Dialogues of Plato*, 2:511.

7. Empedocles, trans. in Kathleen Freeman, *Ancilla to the Pre-Socratic Philosophers*, p. 56.

8. Pico della Mirandola, *Heptaplus*, p. 118.

9. Michael Sullivan, *The Arts of China*, rev. ed. (Berkeley: University of California Press, 1977), p. 19.

10. Chang, *Archeology*, p. 251.

11. David N. Keightley, "The Religious Commitment," p. 221.

12. *Huainanzi*, 3.9a.

13. Marcel Granet, *La Pensée Chinoise*, p. 90. Granet's reference is apparently to *Shanhai Jing* 12.4a (in SBBY ed.).

14. Schuyler Cammann, "The Magic Square of the Three in Old Chinese Philosophy and Religion," p. 44. Other explanations for the ancient Chinese propensity for ordering things in sets of nine may be found in William Edward Soothill, *The Hall of Light*, p. 36; and Edward H. Schafer, *Pacing the Void*, p. 78.

238 Notes

15. *Mencius*, bk. 3, pt. 1, chap. 3.

16. *Lüshi Chunqiu* 13.1a; *Huainanzi* 4.1a.

17. *Zhouli Zhengzhu* 41.14b, 17a.

18. *Huangdi Neijing Suwen Wang Bing Zhu* 3.4a–4b (chap. 9), 6.10a (chap. 20).

19. Cai Chen, *Hongfan Huangji Neipian* 67.13b–14a.

20. Wu Ch'i-ch'ang, "The Chinese Land System before the Ch'in [Qin] Dynasty," in E-tu Zen Sun and John DeFrancis, eds., *Chinese Social History*, p. 67.

21. Cho-yun Hsü, *Ancient China in Transition: An Analysis of Social Mobility, 722–222 B.C.* (Stanford: Stanford University Press, 1971), p. 112.

22. Wolfram Eberhard, *Conquerors and Rulers: Social Forces in Medieval China*, 2d rev. ed. (Leiden: E.J. Brill, 1965), pp. 34–36.

23. *Zhouli* 42.1b; *Mencius*, bk. 3, pt. 1, chap. 3.

24. Paul Wheatley, *The Pivot of the Four Quarters*, p. 176.

25. Hsü Chung-shu, "The Well-Field System in Shang and Chou [Zhou]," in Sun and DeFrancis, *Chinese Social History*, p. 16.

26. This definition by Gao Yu (fl. A.D. 205–212) appears in his commentary on the *Huainanzi* (SBBY ed.) 4.9b.

27. *Xinjiao Shiji Sanjia Zhu* 74 (liezhuan 14). 2344.

28. Cammann, "Magic Square of Three," p. 67.

29. *Huainanzi* 4.3b; *Liji Zhengzhu* 4.2a.

30. *Zhouli* 33.8b–9a.

31. John W. Hall, *Japan from Prehistory to Modern Times* (New York: Dell, 1970), p. 276.

32. Wm. Theodore de Bary et al., comps., *Sources of Chinese Tradition*, 2:66.

33. Plato, *Laws* 5, in *Dialogues*, 2:511–12.

34. *Xinjiao Hanshu Jizhu* 27 (Wuxing Zhi 7).1517.

35. Clarence J. Glacken, *Traces on the Rhodian Shore*, pp. 112–13. A brief notice of the Babylonian theory of astrological resonance between celestial and terrestrial regions may be found in H. and H.A. Frankfort, "Introduction," in Henri Frankfort et. al., *Before Philosophy: The Intellectual Adventure of Ancient Man* (Balitmore: Penguin, 1949), p. 30.

36. Hashimoto Masukichi, *Shina kōdai rekiho shi kenkyū*, pp. 515–17. On the origins of the *fenye*, see also Kiyosi Yabuuti, "Chinese Astronomy," p. 92.

37. *Lüshi Chunqiu* 13.1a–1b; *Zhouli* 26.9b.

38. Ho Peng-yoke, *The Astronomical Chapters of the Chin-shu*, p. 113.

39. Ho Peng-yoke, "The Astronomical Bureau in Ming China," p. 144.

40. Schafer, *Pacing*, pp. 75, 78.

41. *Jiu Tangshu* 36, *Tianwen Zhi* B (Old Tang History, Treatise on Astrology), in *Lidai Tianwen Luli Deng Zhi Huibian*, 3:637. See also Schafer, *Pacing*, p. 78.

42. *Xin Tangshu* 31, *Tianwen Zhi* B (Old Tang History, Treatise on Astrology), in *Lidai Tianwen*, 3:718–19, 722.

43. *Zhouli* 41.14b.

44. Wheatley, *Pivot*, p. 425. K.C. Chang, however, has pointed out that no city wall has yet been discovered at Anyang, though Zhengzhou, an earlier Shang capital, was surrounded by a wall which formed a "roughly square enclosure." See Chang's *Shang Civilization*, pp. 134, 268.

45. Arthur F. Wright, "The Cosmology of the Chinese City," pp. 42–3.

46. Jeffrey F. Meyer, *Peking as a Sacred City*, p. 53.

47. *Zhouli* 41.14b.

48. Wheatley, *Pivot*, p. 414.

49. Jeffrey Meyer speculates that the main reason why the relatively simple canonical

prescriptions for the construction of the ideal city were never completely applied in the construction of any historical Chinese capital was because "they conflicted with the requirements of *feng-shui*" or geomancy. See Meyer, "*Feng-shui* of the Chinese City," pp. 140–41.

50. Ping-ti Ho, "Lo-yang, A.D. 495–534: A Study of Physical and Socio-Economic Planning of a Metropolitan Area," *Harvard Journal of Asiatic Studies* (1966), 26:77–79.

51. Wheatley, *Pivot*, p. 414.

52. See Meyer, *Peking*, p. 202.

53. Wheatley, *Pivot*, p. 423.

54. Meyer, *Peking*, pp. 172, 189.

55. For English translations of the very brief accounts of the Ming Tang in the *Mencius* and *Zuozhuan*, see Laurence Sickman and Alexander Soper, *The Art and Architecture of China*, p. 212. For a general account of references to the Ming Tang in Zhou literature, see Henri Maspero, "Le *Ming-tang* et al crise religieuse Chinoise avant les Han," pp. 44–46.

56. Sickman and Soper, *Art and Architecture*, pp. 212, 214.

57. Cai Yong, "Ming Tang Yüeling Lun" 10.1a. The modern historian Hsü Fu-kuan has most recently reaffirmed this interpretation in his *Lianghan Sixiang Shi*, 2:21–22. Such an interpretation might plausibly be read into the early references to the Ming Tang in the *Zuozhuan* and *Mencius*.

58. Luo Guang, *Zhongguo Zhexue Sixiang Shi, Lianghan Nanbeichao Pian*, p. 108.

59. Maspero, "Le *Ming-t'ang*," pp. 66–67; Sickman and Soper, *Art and Architecture*, p. 214.

60. Eugene Cooper, "The Potlatch in Ancient China: Parallels in the Socio-Political Structure of the Ancient Chinese and the American Indians of the Northwest Coast," *History of Religions* (November 1982), 22:115.

61. See, for example, *Zhouli Zhengzhu* 41.15a–16a; K'ang Yu-wei, *Dadai Liji Buzhu*, p. 147; Luo Guang, *Zhongguo Zhexue Sixiang Shi*, p. 108. The Han scholastics Cai Yong, Zheng Xuan, and Ying Shao (c. A.D. 140–c. 206) followed a similar procedure in devising a respectable pedigree for the Han new year festival and sacrifice, spuriously identifying the *La* of the Han Dynasty with the *Jia* of the Zhou, the *Qingsi* of the Yin, and the *Jiaping* of the Xia. See Derk Bodde, *Festivals in Classical China*, p. 68.

62. Wright, "Cosmology of the Chinese City," p. 49.

63. Pi Xi-rui, *Jingxue Tonglun* 3.76.

64. The various numerological interpretations of the Ming Tang are not, however, perfectly distinct in Han sources. Some such sources, especially Cai Yong's "Ming Tang Yueling Lun," are numerologically quite eclectic. To speak of the "nonary" and "quinary" models of the Ming Tang is to refer essentially to its floor plan, not to its overall structure.

65. Maspero, "Le *Ming-t'ang*," p. 50–51.

66. *Zhouli Zhengzhu* 41.15a–16b.

67. Maspero, "Le *Ming-t'ang*," pp. 24, 26, 36–37.

68. Luo Guang, *Zhongguo Zhexue Sixiang Shi*, p. 110.

69. Cai Yong, "Ming Tang Yueling Lun," pp. 6a–6b. I have checked my translation of this passage with that given by Maspero in "Le *Ming-t'ang*," pp. 30–31.

70. Zhu Xi, "Ming Tang Shuo" (A Discourse on the Luminous Hall), in *Zhuzi Dachuan* 68.11a; Kang You-wei, *Dadai Liji Buzhu*, pp. 144–45.

71. Marcel Granet emphasizes this point in his *Pensée Chinoise*, p. 178. Another interpretation of the ruler's ritual circumambulation through the divisions of the Ming Tang is that he "was following the [annual] circuit of the handle of the Dipper, or Bushel, as it is called in Chinese," through the heavens; Soothill, *Hall of Light*, p. 93.

72. *Shiji* 28 (Fengshan Shu 6).1401.

73. Sickman and Soper, *Art and Architecture*, p. 226.

74. Wright, "Cosmology and the Chinese City," p. 51.

75. Sickman and Soper, *Art and Architecture*, p. 226; Maspero, "Le *Ming-t'ang*," pp. 7–10. A brief account of the archeological remains of the later Han Ming Tang built in A.D. 56 may be found in Wang Zhongshu, *Han Civilization*, trans., K.C. Chang et al. (New Haven: Yale University Press, 1982), p. 39.

76. A brief account of some of these structures may be found in Sickman and Soper, *Art and Architecture*, p. 227.

77. Maspero, "Le *Ming-t'ang*," p. 16.

78. Sickman and Soper, *Art and Architecture*, p. 239. A brief account of the Ming Tang in Tang times also appears in Schafer, *Pacing*, pp. 16–19.

79. James T.C. Liu, "The Sung [Song] Emperors and the Ming-t'ang or Hall of Enlightenment," pp. 54–55.

80. Meyer, *Peking*, pp. 103–4.

81. Ibid., p. 109.

82. Michael Saso, "What is the Ho-t'u [Hetu]?" p. 403; Cammann, "Magic Square," p. 51.

83. Cai Yuan-ding, excerpted in Zhu Xi, *Yixue Qimeng* 1.7.

84. Bernhard Karlgren, "Legends and Cults in Ancient China," p. 273.

85. *Zhuangzi* 5.19b (Tianyun chap.).

86. Sun Xing-yan, "Hetu Luoshu Kao," 110.17a. Sources in Han literature for these identifications include *Hanshu* 27A (Wuxing Zhi 7A).1315; *Shangshu Kongzhuan* 7.1b; and Li Ding-zhuo, comp., *Zhouyi Jijie Zuanshu* 9.793.

87. *Hanshu* 27A (Wuxing Zhi 7A).1315.

88. For an explication of the relevant passage from the *Qianzuo Du*, see Cammann, "Magic Square of Three," pp. 61–64. Cammann also associates the nonary Ming Tang figure outlined in the *Dadai Liji* with the Luoshu (ibid., pp. 43–44). However, neither of these texts specifically identifies the Luoshu with the nine-squared form, though the *Qianzuo Du* does mention both. Thus the Qing cosmological critic Zhang Hui-yan (1761–1802) dated the association of the Luoshu with the "nine palaces" form not from the Han but from the Eastern Qin era (A.D. 317–420). See Zhang Hui-yan, *Yitu Tiaobian*, p. 3b.

89. See, for example, Hu Wei, *Yitu Mingbian* 2.116; and Pi Xi-rui, *Jingxue Lishi*, p. 213.

3. Medieval Criticisms and Extensions of Correlative Cosmology

1. For some examples of politically oriented cosmological theories and rites which were either deemphasized or discontinued following the fall of the Han, see Derk Bodde, *Festivals in Classical China*, pp. 214–15; and Luo Guang, *Zhongguo Zhexue Sixiang Shi*, pp. 96, 99.

2. Edward H. Schafer, "T'ang," in Kwang-chih Chang, ed., *Food in Chinese Culture*, p. 130.

3. Mao Qi-ling, *Shangshu Guangting Lu* 2.13b.

4. E.MW. Tillyard, *The Elizabethan World Picture*, p. 99. On the effects of geographical expansion on cosmographical conceptions in the Hellenistic Age, see Clarence J. Glacken, *Traces on the Rhodian Shore*, p. 105.

5. Joseph Needham comments that "the more elaborate and fanciful the symbolic correlations became, the further away from the observation of Nature the whole system tended"; Needham, *Science and Civilisation*, 2:266.

6. Lü Kun, *Shenyin Yu* 4.177.

7. Tillyard, *World Picture*, p. 26.

8. Glacken, *Traces*, p. 440.

9. These examples appear in *Zhuangzi* 1.18a–18b (Qiwu chapter).

10. Ibid., 7.26a (Zhi Beiyu chapter), 6.15a (Qiushui chapter).

11. Ibid., 9.6a (Waiwu chapter). My discussion of uses of analogy in classical Daoism and Buddhism has benefited from a reading of Shu-hsien Liu, "The Use of Analogy and Symbolism in Traditional Chinese Philosophy."

12. Liu, "Use of Analogy," p. 324.

13. Philip B. Yampolsky, trans., *The Platform Sutra of the Sixth Patriarch*, p. 130.

14. Ibid., p. 132.

15. Wang Chong, *Lunheng* 17.273–74. This idea that the course of nature is unaffected by a ruler's personal virtues or vices recalls the statement in the *Tianlun* chapter of the *Xunzi* that "Heavenly ways have a constancy; they are neither preserved by a Yao nor ruined by a Jie."

16. Wang Chong, *Lunheng* 17.274.

17. Ibid. 5.75, 77, 78, 80; 24.369–70.

18. Luo Guang, *Zhongguo Zhexue Sixiang Shi*, p. 264.

19. Wang Chong, *Lunheng* 3.49. I have consulted the translation of this passage given in Needham, *Science and Civilisation*, 2:266.

20. Wang Chong, *Lunheng* 18.281.

21. Ibid., 3.47.

22. Ibid., 18.277.

23. Ibid., 11.176.

24. Ibid., 5.80, 19.278. On Wang's view of omens, see also Rafe de Crespigny, "Politics and Philosophy under the Government of Emperor Huan 159–168 A.D.," *T'oung Pao* n.s. (1980), 66:62; and Donald Leslie, "Contribution to a New Translation of the Lun Heng," *T'oung Pao* n.s. (1956), 44.140.

25. *Lunheng* 11.167–68.

26. Needham, *Science and Civilisation*, 2:386–87.

27. Edward H. Schafer, *Pacing the Void*, p. 63.

28. Chi-yün Chen, *Hsün Yüeh* [Xun Yue]: *The Life and Reflections of an Early Medieval Confucian* (Cambridge: Cambridge University Press, 1975), pp. 106, 139, 145. For Xun Yue's statement on physiognomy, see Chi-yün Chen, *Hsün Yüeh* [Xun Yue] *and the Mind of Late Han China: A Translation of the Shen-chien with Introduction and Annotations* (Princeton: Princeton University Press, 1980), p. 154.

29. Luo Guang, *Zhongguo Zhexue Sixiang Shi*, pp. 317–19; Itano Chohachi, "The *T'u-ch'en* Prophetic Books and the Establishment of Confucianism," *Memoirs of the Research Department of the Tōyō Bunkō* (1976), 34:53.

30. Luo Guang, *Zhongguo Zhexue Sixiang Shi*, pp. 77, 331–33.

31. Walter Liebenthal's "Translator's Forward" to T'ang Yung-t'ung, "Wang Pi's New Interpretation of the *I Ching* and *Lun-yü*," p. 125.

32. *Zhouyi Zhushu* 4.12a (chap. 9 of *shang zhuan*).

33. Mou Zong-san, *Caixing yu Xuanli*, pp. 109–110, 112–13. The commentary by Wang Bi on this passage in the "Great Commentary" appears in *Zhouyi Wang Han Zhu* 7.48–49.

34. *Zhouyi Wang Han Zhu* 10.65. I have checked my translation of this passage with Liebenthal's in T'ang Yung-t'ung, "Wang Pi's New Interpretation," p. 143. The correlation of the *qian* trigram with a horse and the *kun* trigram with a cow appears in *Zhouyi Zhushu* 9.4a (chap. 8 of *shuogua zhuan*).

35. Niu Seng-ru, trans. in H.G. Lamont, "An Early Ninth Century Debate on Heaven," p. 199.

36. Liu Zong-yuan, "Shiling Lun" (A Discussion of the "Seasonal Ordinances"), in *Liu*

He-dong Chuanji 3.12b–13a. A brief account of this essay by Liu appears in Lamont, "Ninth Century Debate," p. 205–6.

37. Liu Zong yuan, "Duanxing Lun" (A Discussion on Assessing Penalties), in *Liu He-dong Chuanji* 3.15a.

38. *Tianwen Tiandui Zhu*, pp. 4–6.

39. Ouyang Xiu, *Yitong Ziwen* (A Child's Queries on the *Change*) 1.2b, in *Ouyang Wenzhong Ji* 76.2b.

40. Ibid., 3.1a, 3a (78.1a, 3a).

41. Ouyang Xiu, "Yi Huowen Sanshou" (Queries in Three Parts on the *Change*), in *Ouyang Wenzhong* 18.1a–1b.

42. Ouyang Xiu, "Zhengtong Lun Sanshou" (A Discussion in Three Parts on the Legitimate Line of Succession), in *Ouyang Wenzhong* 16.3a.

43. H.G. Lamont draws a similar conclusion regarding Liu Zong-yuan's cosmological criticism, particularly his "anti-phenomenalism," in "Ninth Century Debate, Part 2," p. 64.

44. Hsü Dau-lin, "Crime and Cosmic Order," pp. 116–17.

45. Su Xun, "Taixuan Lun" (A Discussion of [Yang Xiong's] *Great Mystery*), in *Su Xun Ji* 7.67.

46. Ibid., 7.61–62.

47. Sima Guang, "Zang Lun" 13.7a–7b.

48. Shen Gua, *Mengqi Bitan Jiaozheng* 8.330, 7.315, 327. For a well-informed account of Shen's scientific investigations and achievements, as well as a complete bibliography of primary and secondary sources for the study of Shen Gua, see Nathan Sivin, "Shen Kua."

49. Hok-lam Chan, "'Comprehensiveness' (*T'ung*) and 'Change' (*Pien*) in Ma Tuan-lin's Historical Thought," in Chan and Wm. Theodore de Bary, eds., *Yuan Thought: Chinese Thought and Religion Under the Mongols* (New York: Columbia University Press, 1982), pp. 44–45.

50. Nathan Sivin, "Cosmos and Computation in Early Chinese Mathematical Astronomy," esp. pp. 3–4 and 65.

51. *Xu Hanshu, Luli Zhi* C (Later Han History, Treatise on Astronomy and Harmonics), in *Lidai Tianwen Luli deng zhi Huibian*, 5:1482. My translations of this and other short excerpts from the astronomical treatises in the standard histories have benefited from a comparison with Nathan Sivin's translations of some of the same passages in his unpublished paper on "The Limits of Scientific Knowledge in Traditional China."

52. *Jinshu* 18, *Luli Zhi* C (Jin History, Treatise on Astronomy and Harmonics), in *Lidai Tianwen,*, 5:1645–46.

53. Ibid., p. 1645.

54. This translation of *suicha*, suggested by Nathan Sivin, is a more accurate rendering than "precession of the equinoxes."

55. Schafer, *Pacing*, p. 14; Henri Maspero, "L'Astronomie dans la Chine ancienne: Histoire des instruments et des découvertes," in *Mélanges posthumes sur les religions et l'histoire de la Chine*, vol. 3, *Etudes historiques* (Paris: Presses Universitaires de France, 1967), p. 34.

56. On the discovery, in China, of these astronomical anomalies, the lunar inequality by Liu Hong in the Later Han era and the annual inequality in the sun's motion by Zhang Zi-xin in the sixth century, see Kiyosi Yabuuti, "Astronomical Tables in China from the Han to the Tang Dynasties," in Yabuuti, ed., *Chūguoku chūsei kagaku gijutsu shi no kenkyū*, pp. 461–62, 467–68.

57. *Songshu*, 13, *Luli Zhi* C ([Liu] Song History, Treatise on Astronomy and Harmonics), in *Lidai Tianwen*, 6:1768. Dai's reference is to *Mencius*, bk. 4, pt. 2, chap. 26; James Legge, *The*

Works of Mencius (New York: Dover, 1970), p. 331.

58. *Xin Tangshu* 27A, *Lizhi* 3A (New Tang History, Treatise on Astronomy), in *Lidai Tianwen*, 7:2177, 2188, 2196.

59. *Songshi* 68, *Luli Zhi* 1 (Song History, Treatise on Astronomy and Harmonics), in *Lidai Tianwen*, 8:2442.

60. *Yuanshi* 52, *Lizhi* (Yuan History, Treatise on Astronomy), in *Lidai Tianwen*, 9:3299.

61. Kiyosi Yabuuti, "Chinese Astronomy," p. 96.

62. *Songshu* 11, *Luli Zhi* A, in *Lidai Tianwen*, 6:1661–63.

63. *Songshu* 13, *Luli Zhi* C, in *Lidai Tianwen*, 6:1768.

64. *Xin Tangshu* 25, *Lizhi* 1, in *Lidai Tianwen*, 7:2117.

65. See, for example, *Xin Tangshu* 27A, *Lizhi* 3A, in *Lidai Tianwen*, 7:2170 ff.

66. Qian Bao-zong, "Cong Chunqiu Dao Mingmo de Lifa Yange," p. 59; *Xin Tangshu* 27B, *Lizhi* 3B, in *Lidai Tianwen*, 7:2207.

67. *Xin Tangshu* 27B, *Lizhi* 3B, in *Lidai Tianwen*, 7:2214.

68. *Xin Tangshu* 27B, *Lizhi* 3B, in *Lidai Tianwen*, 7:2208.

69. *Xin Tangshu* 27B, *Lizhi* 3B, in *Lidai Tianwen*, 7:2207.

4. Correlative Cosmology in the Neo-Confucian Tradition

1. Tang Jun-yi, *Zhongguo Zhexue Yuanlun: Yuanjiao Pian*, pp. 12, 23–24, 26; Qian Mu, *Song- Ming Lixue Gaishu*, p. 28.

2. Michael D. Freeman, "From Adept to Worthy," pp. 482, 484.

3. This partial list of things that Shao Yong enumerated by fours is based upon that given in Wing-tsit Chan, comp., *A Source Book in Chinese Philosophy*, p. 481.

4. Cai Yuan-ding, excerpted in Shao Yong, *Huangji Jingshi Shu* A.12b of front matter. See also *Huangji Jingshi Shu* 6.15a.

5. Shao Yong, *Huangji Jingshi Shu* 5.2a. See also Chan, *Source Book*, pp. 484–86.

6. Shao Yong, *Huangji Jingshi Shu* 5.9a. The fourteenth-century scholar Wang Wei (1323– 1374) developed a similar correlative schema in a more comprehensible fashion, matching the five classics with the Confucian four books, a set of mental principles, and an array of concrete social applications. For a brief explanation of this schema, see John W. Dardess, *Confucianism and Autocracy*, pp. 26–27.

7. Freeman, "From Adept to Worthy," p. 484.

8. Shao Yong, *Huangji Jingshi Shu* 1.3a.

9. See, for example, *Ercheng Yulu* 17.275; Huang Dao-zhou, "Song Lishu" (Song Books on Astronomy), in *Chongding Bowu Tianhui* 1.28b; Pi Xi-rui, *Jingxue Lishi*, p. 214, n. 11.

10. Freeman, "From Adept to Worthy," p. 477.

11. See, for example, Cai Yuan-ting, "Yixiang Yiyan" 62.13b.

12. Cai Yuan-ding, *Fawei Lun*, pp. 8a–8b.

13. Ibid., p. 10b.

14. Cai Yuan-ding, excerpted in Wang Ying-lin, *Liujing Tianwen Pian* A.56.

15. The *Taiji Tushuo* may be found in the *Song-Yuan Xue'an* 12.1b, among many other sources.

16. Shao Yong, quoted in Zhu Xi, *Yixue Qimeng* 1.5–6.

17. Hoyt Cleveland Tillman, "The Idea and the Reality of the 'Thing' During the Song: Philosophical Attitudes Toward *Wu*," *Bulletin of Sung and Yuan Studies* (1978), 14:71; A.C. Graham, *Two Chinese Philosophers*, p. 75.

18. Zhang Zai, *Zhangzi Zhengmeng Zhu* 3.85.

19. Zhang Li-xiang, *Duyi Biji* (Reading Notes on the *Change*), in *Chongding Yangyuan Xiansheng Chuanji* 29.19a.

20. Gao Pan-long in Huang Zong-xi, comp., *Mingru Xue'an* 11.79 (zhuan 58).

21. Sherman E. Lee, *Chinese Landscape Painting*, p. 78.

22. *Er Cheng Yulu* 8.88.

23. Zhu Xi, quoted in Zhou Da-tong, *Zhu Xi*, p. 23.

24. Hu Ju-ren, *Juye Lu* 6.73–74.

25. Zhang Zai, "Yishuo" (Explications on the *Change*), in *Zhangzi Quanshu* 11.6a–6b. Zhang Zai's reference is to chapter 5 of *Laozi* (A.3b in SBBY ed.).

26. Zhu Xi, "Can Tong Qi Shuo" (Explications on the *Homology of the Triad* [of Wei Bo-yang]), in *Zhuzi Dachuan* 67.25a; Zhu Xi, "Yixiang Shuo" Explications on the Images of the *Change*), in *Zhuzi Dachuan* 67.1b.

27. Zhu Xi, *Zhuzi Yulei* 1.2. These four Confucian norms, to which is sometimes added a fifth, "belief" or "trust" (xin), do not appear as a set anywhere in the *Analects*.

28. Zhu Xi, "Shenglu Bian" (An Analysis of the Tones and the Pitchpipes), in *Zhuzi Dachuan* 72.2b–3a.

29. Wang Ying-lin, *Kunxue Jiwen* 9.18a–18b.

30. Wang Ying-lin, *Liujing Tianwen Bian* A.45.

31. Cheng Yi, *Henan Chengshi Yishu* 9.1a. As Wing-tsit Chan points out, the last character in this quotation, *xing* (human nature), is obviously a misprint and should read *xin* (belief or trust). For Chan's annotation on this passage, see Wing-tsit Chan, *Reflections on Things at Hand*, p. 30, n. 125.

32. Graham, *Two Chinese Philosophers*, p. 55.

33. Emily B. Lyle, "Dumezil's Three Functions and Indo-European Cosmic Structure," *History of Religions* (August 1982), 22:35–36.

34. Wang Yang-ming, "Qi-Hou Tuxu" (Preface to the Diagram of the *qi* and *hou* [Divisions of Time]), in *Yangming Quanshu* (Complete Works of [Wang] Yang-ming) (SBBY ed.) 12.3b–4a.

35. Lu Xiang-shan, "Sanwu Yibian Cuozong Qishu" (The Numbers 3 and 5 are Irregular by Virtue of Being Associated with *Change*), in *Xiang-shan Quanji* 21.4a. Lu's reference is to *Laozi*, chap. 42 (B.5a in SBBY ed.).

36. Lu Xiang-shan, "Sanwu Yibain Cuozong Qishu," p. 46b; Lu Xiang-shan, "Yishu" (The Numbers of the *Change*), in *Xiang-shan Quanji* 21.3a.

37. Lu Xiang-shan, "Yishu," p. 2a.

38. On the subject of various occult arts and beliefs current in the early and mid Ming, see Liu Cun-yan, "The Penetration of Taoism into the Ming Neo-Confucianist Elite," esp. pp. 74, 76 and 82.

39. Ibid., p. 74; Yun-yi Ho, "Ideological Implications of Major Sacrifices in Early Ming," *Ming Studies* (Spring 1978), 6:65.

40. Dardess, *Confucianism and Autocracy*, pp. 170–71.

41. *Siku Quanshu Zongmu* 107.2127, 110.2179.

42. Liu Zong-zhou, "Du Yitu Shuo" (Explications of the Diagrams Assoicated with the *Change*), in *Liuzi Quanshu* 2.209, 210, 212.

43. Ibid., 2.207.

44. Huang Dao-zhou, *Bowu Tianhui* 1.24a–b, 27b–28a, 30b–32a.

45. Sun Qi-feng, *Sun Xia-feng Xiansheng Yulu*, pp. 153–54.

46. Lu Kun, *Shenyin Yu*, 1.56, 4.179, 184, 187.

47. Liu Cun-yan comments in this connection that "in all of Chinese history Taoism," by which he apparently means various occult arts and beliefs, "was never more powerful or pervasive among all social strata than during [the Ming]." See Liu Cun-yan, "Taoist Self-Cultivation in Ming Thought," p. 291. Regarding syncretism, another fountainhead of

correlative thought, Judith Berling comments that "Never before or since in Chinese history did syncretism have so open and pervasive an impact on all levels of the religious imagination" as during the Ming. See Judith A. Berling, *The Syncretic Religion of Lin Chao-en*, p. 3.

48. Anthony C. Yu, trans. and ed., *The Journey to the West*, 1:67.

5. Early Qing Scholars and the Seventeenth-Century Intellectual Transition

1. Gu Yan-wu, "Yu Youren Lunxue Shu" (Letter to a Friend Discussing Learning), in *Gu Yan-wu Wen*, pp. 63–64. An English translation of part of this letter appears in Wm. Theodore de Bary et al., comps., *Sources of Chinese Tradition*, 1:553–55.

2. The first two biographies in Jiang Fan's *Hanxue Shicheng Ji* are of Yan Ruo-ju and Hu Wei. Similarly, the first and third biographies in the "transmitters of the Way" section of Tang Jian's *Qing Xue'an Xiaozhi* are of Lu Shi-yi and Lu Long-qi.

3. Pi Xi-rui was apparently the first major Chinese historian to have singled out these three figures as the "three great Confucian scholars" (san da ru) of the age. See Pi Xi-rui, *Qingxue Lishi*, pp. 281–82.

4. See the next note. On the other hand, at least two contemporary scholars, Willard J. Peterson and Benjamin Elman, have attempted to locate the moment of intellectual transition more precisely. Peterson, for example, dates "the point of departure of the new orientation in thought" from the 1630s; see *Bitter Gourd: Fang I-chih and the Impetus for Intellectual Change* (New Haven: Yale University Press, 1979), p. 2. And Elman, following Yamanoi Yu, argues that Qing savants' "turn away from moral cultivation to precise scholarship was a key element in the Chinese response to the Ming collapse." For Elman's discussion on this topic, see his "Ch'ing Dynasty 'Schools' of Scholarship," p. 6.

5. Wing-tsit Chan, "The *Hsing-li ching-i* and the Ch'eng-Chu [Cheng-Zhu] School of the Seventeenth Century," pp. 560–61.

6. Yu Ying-shi, "Cong Song-Ming Ruxue de Fazhan Lun Qingdai Sixiang Shi," pp. 33–34. Several of the studies in Wm. Theodore de Bary and the Conference on Seventeenth-Century Chinese Thought, *The Unfolding of Neo-Confucianism* follow a similar approachm, particularly Edward T. Ch'ien, "Chiao Hung and the Revolt against the Ch'eng-Chu Orthodoxy."

7. Yu Ying-shi, "Qingdai Sixiang Shi Di Yige Xin Jieshi," pp. 26–27, 33–34.

8. Tang Jun-yi, *Zhongguo Zhexue Yuanlun: Daolun Pian*, pp. 279, 332.

9. Gu Yan-wu, "Yu Youren Lunxue Shu," pp. 63–64.

10. Li Yan, *Zhongguo Suanxue Shi* (History of Chinese Mathematical Studies) (Taipei: Shangwu yinshuguan, 1972), p. 225. The other two were Mei Wen-ding and Wang Xi-shan.

11. For accounts of the position of Yan Ruo-ju and Hu Wei in the history of Qing scholarship and in the Qing school of Han Learning, see Jiang Fan, *Hanxue Shi Chengji* 1.4–14. On the same subject, see also Su Qing-pin, "Yan Ruo-zhu, Hu Wei, Cui Shu Sanjia Bianwei Fanfa Zhi Yanjiu." Thanks are due to Alison Black for calling this article to my attention.

12. Zhang Li-xiang, Lu Shi-yi, Lu Long qi, and Zhang Bo-xing (1652–1725) have generally been regarded as the four major early Qing representatives of the Cheng-Zhu school of Neo-Confucianism ever since they were designated as the four seventeenth-century "transmitters of the Way" by the orthodox nineteenth-century historian of Qing thought, Tang Jian, in his *Qing Xue'an Xiaozhi*.

13. The astronomical works of both Mei Wen-ding and Wang Xi-shan evoked high praise from several prominent mid- and late-Qing scholars, including Ruan Yuan, Jiao Xun, Zeng Guo-fan, Tang Jian, Liang Qi-chao, and the editors of the *Complete Library in Four Treasuries* (Siku Quanshu).

14. According to Nathan Sivin, Fang Yi-zhi's "comprehension of mathematics and computational astronomy was very limited, but he was among the few Chinese who responded to the Jesuits' scholastic meteorology, geology, and the like—obsolete as they were. Fang lacked the depth of technical knowledge to make important contributions to the scientific work of the time or to have any important influence on those who were doing that work." See Sivin, "Imperial China: Has Its Present Past a Future?" *Harvard Journal of Asiatic Studies* (December, 1978), 38:474.

15. For an account of Qing scholars' criticism and ridicule of geomancy and other divinatory sciences, see chapter 5 in Paul S. Ropp, *Dissent in Early Modern China*.

6. Intellectual Origins of Early Qing Cosmological Criticism

1. Marshall Clagett, *Greek Science in Antiquity* (New York: Collier Books, 1963), p. 166.

2. Frederick Copleston, *A History of Philosophy*, vol. 2, *Mediaeval Philosophy, Part 2: Albert the Great to Duns Scotus* (Garden City, N.Y.: Doubleday, Image, 1962), p. 32; David Knowles, *The Evolution of Medieval Thought* (New York: Random House, Vintage, 1962), p. 247.

3. E.J. Dijksterhuis, *The Mechanization of the World Picture*, trans. C. Dikshoorn (Oxford: Oxford University Press, 1961), pp. 128–29.

4. Gordon Leff, *The Dissolution of the Medieval Outlook: An Essay on Intellectual and Spiritual Change in the Fourteenth Century* (New York: Harper and Row, Harper Trochbooks, 1976), p. 96.

5. Copleston, *History of Philosophy*, vol. 3, *Late Mediaeval and Renaissance Philosophy, Part 2: The Revival of Platonism to Suarez*, p. 183.

6. Zhou Da-tong, *Zhu Xi*, pp. 79, 81–82.

7. Tang Jun-yi, *Zhongguo Zhexue Yuanlun: Yuan jiao Pian*, p. 72.

8. Zhang Zai, *Zhangzi Zhengmen Zhu* 4.103.

9. Tang Jun-yi, *Zhongguo Zhexue Yuanlun: Daolun Pian*, p. 308; Lu Kun, *Shenyin Yu* 2.119.

10. Wang Ting-xiang, *Yashu*, p. 85.

11. Shigeru Nakayama, "Japanese Scientific Thought," p. 746.

12. Huang Zong-xi, "Da Wan Zhen-yi Lun *Mingshi Lizhi* Shu" (A Letter to Wang Zhen-yi Discussing the *Ming History, Treatise on Astronomy*), in *Nanlei Wending, Houzhi* 1.14.

13. Wang Xi-shan, *Xiao-an Xinfa*, Zixu ([Wang] Xiao-an's New System, Author's Preface), in *Xiao-an Yishu* 1.1a. The famous eighth-century astronomer Yi Xing lamented a similar disjunction in the science of his own time. However, the two studies which Yi Xing believed had to be reconciled in order to make possible a proper understanding of the heavens were mathematical astronomy and astrology, not astronomy and Confucian cosmology. For Yi Xing's comments on this issue, see *Xin Tangshu* 27B, *Lizhi* 3B (New Tang History, Treatise on Astronomy), in *Lidai Tianwen Luli deng zhi Huibian*, 7:2215.

14. Lu Shi-yi, *Sibian Lu zhi Yao* 3.31, 34.

15. Ibid. 3.34.

16. Diao Bao, *Qianxing Zhaoji*, p. 17. The quotations are from the *Xiang-cu's* appendix to the *qian* and *kun* hexagrams in the *Classic of Change*, and may be found in *Zhouyi Zhushu* 1.5a, 14a.

17. Mou Zong-san, *Caixing yu Xuanli*, p. 101.

18. A more extended argument along this line may be found in Yu Ying-shi, "Qingdai Sixiang Shi de Yige Xin Jieshi," pp. 23–24.

19. Gu Yan-wu, "Yu Shi Yu-shan Shu" (Letter to Shi Yu-shan), in *Tinglin Wenji* (Prose

Collections of [Gu] Ting-lin) (SBBY ed.) 3.16a.

20. Hu Wei, *Yitu Mingbian* 3.179 ff.

21. Wang Ting-xiang, *Shen Yan*, p. 6.

22. Wang Ting-xiang, *Jiacang Ji*, pp. 192, 195.

23. Huang Zong-xi, *Poxie Lun*, p. 2b.

24. Hu Wei, *Yitu Mingbian*, quoted in Pi Xi-rui, *Jingxue Tonglun* 1.30.

25. Wang Fu-zhi, *Zhengmeng Zhu* 1.40.

26. H.D. Harootunian, "The Conscousness of Archaic Forms in the New Religion of Kokugaku," p. 82.

27. Wang Ting-xiang, *Yashu*, p. 102.

28. *Laozi* B.5a (chap. 42); *Zhouyi Zhushu* 7.2a (chap. 1 of *shang zhuan*).

29. *Huainanzi* 3.1a.

30. Yamada Keiji, "Shushi no uchūron josetsu," pp. 499, 506.

31. Nathan Sivin, "Shen Kua," p. 380; Zhu Xi, "Yuyao" 48.12b.

32. Gu Zu-yu, "*Fangyu Jiyao Chuandu Yitong Xu*" (Preface to [the Section on] Rivers and Streams in the *Whole Earth Catalogue*), in *Chingwen Hui* (Collection of Qing Writings) (Taipei: Chung-hua ts'ung-shu pien-shen wei-yuan hui, 1960), p. 508.

33. On the latter development, see Jiang Yong, *Shuxue* 1.52–53; and *Siku Quanshu Zongmu* 106:2093.

34. Lu Shi-yi, *Sibian Lu* 14.141.

35. Ruan Yuan, *Chouren Zhuan* 45.589.

36. Lu Shi-yi, *Sibian Lu* 22:228–29.

37. For an account of some of the criticisms which late-Ming and Qing scholars directed at the *houqi* arrangement, see Derk Bodde, "The Chinese Cosmic Magic Known as Watching for the Ethers," pp. 31 ff.

38. Wu Yu-xing, *Wenyi Lun* (A Discussion of Febrile Epidemics), translated in Helen Dunstan, "The Late Ming Epidemics," pp. 41, 42. Dunstan comments that "the *Wen-yi Lun* was written in 1642, provoked by the experience of the previous year's epidemic, in which the inadequacy of traditional theories and remedies became woefully obvious." (p. 35).

39. Wang Ting-xiang, *Yashu*, p. 144.

40. Lu Kun, *Shenyin Yu* 1.64.

41. Liu Xian-ting, *Guangyang Zaji* 4.203.

42. Gu Yan-wu, "Junxian Lun" (Discussion of the Prefectural System), in *Gu Yan-wu Wen*, p. 1.

43. See, for example, Lu Shi-yi, *Sibian Lu* 14.143; Wang Xi-shan, *Xiao-an Xinfa* zixu, p. 5b; Gu Yan-wu, *Yuanchaoben Rizhi Lu* 30.855; Lu Long-qi, *Sanyu Tang Riji* A.22; Yan Ruo-ju, *Shangshu Guwen Shuzheng* 6A.48a.

44. *Xin Tangshu* 31, *Tianwen Zhi* 1 (New Tang History, Treatise on Astrology), in *Lidai Tianwen*, 3:707; Shen Gua, *Mengqi Bitan Jiaozheng* 7.294; Zhu Xi, *Zhuzi Yulei* 1.8.

45. The origins of the latter idea may be traced to *Hanshu* 21, *Luli Zhi* 1 (Han History, Treatise on Astronomy and Harmonics), in *Litai Tianwen*, 5:1399.

46. The astronomical systems traditionally attributed to the Yellow Sovereign, his grandson, Zhuan Xu, and the sovereigns of the Xia, Yin, and Western Zhou dynasties were almost certainly fabrications of late Warring States or early Han times. See Xu Fu-guan, *Liang Han Sixiang Shi*, 2:352.

47. Mei Wen-ding, *Lifa Tongkao*, zixu 60.3a-3b.

48. Mei Wen-ding, *Lixue Pianzhi* (Superfluous Studies on Astronomy), part 1, in *Meishi Zongshu Jiyao* (The Best of Mr. Mei's Collected Works) (Taipei:Yiwen yinshuguan, 1971) 41.8a-8b. The advantages of the Shou-shi's use of this more recent "epoch" are related in

Yuanshi 53, *Lizhi* 2 (Yuan History, Treatise on Astronomy), in *Lidai Tianwen*, 9:3357–58.

49. Several of the innovations and improvements ascribed by such seventeenth-century commentators as Mei Wen-ding, Fang Yi-zhi, and Mei Gu-cheng to Guo Shou-jing and the Shoushi were actually anticipated in earlier astronomical systems. According to the *Xin Wudai Shi* (New Five Dynasties History), the tenth-century astronomical official Ma Chong-zhi officially abandoned the method of calculation from the astronomical zero point or superior epoch (liyuan), supposedly one of the key innovations of the Shoushi. Further, this improvement was incorporated into an earlier unofficial system devised in the Tang by Cao Shi-wei. For an account of these early anticipations of Shoushi reforms, see *Xin Wudai Shi* 58, *Sitian Kao* 1 (New Five Dynasties History, Investigation of Official Astronomy) in *Lidai Tianwen*, 7:2405–6.

50. Ruan Yuan argued on similar grounds that the Ptolemaic system devised in Western Antiquity could not possibly have been so advanced as the Jesuits claimed it was; *Chouren Zhuan* 43:553.

51. Mei Wen-ding, *Lifa Tongkao, zixu*, p. 3b, and *Lixue Yiwen*, part 2, p. 18b.

52. Yan Ruo-ju, *Shangshu Guwen Shuzheng* 6A.21b–24a. An exact duplication of these pages on the theory of lunar motion appears in a work by Lu Shi-yi, which was almost certainly written earlier, Lu's "Yuedao Shu" (Explication of the Lunar Path), pp. 2b–4a, in *Lu Fu-ting Xiansheng Yishu*, ce 18. In neither work is there any mention of the other. Of course, the idea that the "nine road" theory of lunar motion was imprecise and arbitrary was hardly new. A similar opinion was expressed by Wang Pu in the tenth century (*Jiu Wutai Shi 104, Lizhi* [Old Five Dynasties History, Treatise on Astronomy], in *Litai Tianwen*, 7:2389); Shen Gua in the eleventh century (*Mengqi Bitan* 8.333); and Li Qian in the Yuan era (*Chouren Zhuan* 27.323).

53. Dai Zhen, "Zai yu Ding Sheng-qu Shu" (Another Letter to Ding Sheng-qu), in *Dai Zhen Wenji* 5.108–9.

54. Johan Huizinga, *The Waning of the Middle Ages*, pp. 207–8, 213. Francis Bacon argued that Renaissance natural philosophies were also guilty of having overextended correlative schema to the point of discrediting the cosmological premises on which they were based, for "the ancient opinion that man was *microcosmus*, an abstract or model of the world," Bacon wrote, "hath become fantastically strained by Paracelsus and the alchemists." For Bacon's brief discussion on this issue, see his *Advancement of Learning*, pp. 133–34.

55. E.M.W. Tillyard, *The Elizabethan World Picture*, pp. 7, 99.

56. Ibid., p. 8.

57. Edwin Honig, *Dark Conceit: The Making of Allegory* (Evanston: Northwestern University Press, 1959), p. 10. Honig's reference is to *Coriolanus*, act 1, scene 1.

58. Charles H. Hinnant, *Thomas Hobbes*, Twayne's English Authors Series, no. 215 (Boston: Twayne, 1977), p. 97.

59. Cao Xue-qin, *The Story of Stone*, vol. 2, *The Crab Flower Club*, trans. David Hawkes (New York: Penguin, 1977), pp. 122–23. My interpretation of this passage is based on a note by C.T. Hsia in his review of Andrew H. Plak's *Archetype and Allegory in the Dream of the Red Chamber*, p. 197.

60. On this point, Nathan Sivin has commented that "Yin and Yang were without exception relational conceptions. As a recent textbook of traditional medicine puts it, 'When speaking of the relation of chest and back, the chest corresponds to yin and the back to yang; but when associating the chest and abdomen, the chest, being above, corresponds to yang and the abdomen, being below, to yin.'" See Sivin, "Science in China's Past," p. 15.

61. Benjamin Elman, "From Value to Fact: The Emergence of Phonology as a Precise Discipline in Late Imperial China," *Journal of the American Oriental Society* (July–October

1982), 102:493. Evidence that such seventeenth-century critics of traditional cosmology as Yan Ruo-ju and Hu Wei benefited from community support for their scholarly effors may be found in several sources, among them Arthur W. Hummel, ed., *Eminent Chinese of the Qing Period (1644–1912)* (Washington D.C.: Government Printing Office, 1943; reprint ed., Taipei: Ch'eng-wen, 1972).

62. According to Ho Ping-ti, "really large-scale printing [in China] had to await the mid-Ming period." for Ho's discussion on printing, see *The Ladder of Success in Imperial China: Aspects of Social Mobility, 1368–1911* (New York: Columbia University Press, 1962; reprint ed., New York: Wiley, 1964), pp. 212–15.

63. Elizabeth L. Eisenstein, *The Printing Press as an Agent of Change: Communications and Cultural Transformations in Early Modern Europe* (Cambridge: Cambridge University Press, 1979), p. 457.

64. Frances A. Yates, *The Art of Memory*, p. 321.

65. Hsia, Review of *Archetype and Allegory*, pp. 197–98.

7. Criticism of Correlative Cosmology in Late-Traditional China

1. Xenophanes, trans. in Kathleen Freeman, *Ancilla to the Pre-Socratic Philosophers*, p. 22.

2. Francis Bacon, *The New Organon*, bk. 1, p. 50.

3. Francis Bacon, *De Augmentis Scientarum* (The Advancement of Learning), bk. 5, chap. 4, in James Spedding et al., eds., *The Works of Francis Bacon* (Boston: Houghton, Mifflin, n.d.), 2:401–2. Thanks are due to Professor Gary Crump for his help in translating this passage from the Latin.

4. John Donne, "An Anatomy of the World: The First Anniversary," 11. 275–83, in Hiram Hayden, ed., *The Portable Elizabethan Reader* (New York: Viking Press, 1946; reprint ed., Harmondsworth, Eng.: Penguin, 1980), p. 132.

5. Johan Huizinga, *The Waning of the Middle Ages*, p. 213.

6. Savonarola, quoted in Wayne Shumaker, *The Occult Sciences in the Renaissance*, p. 44.

7. G. Pico della Mirandola, *Disputationes Adversus Astrologiam Divinatricem*, vol. 2, quoted and translated in Shumaker, *Occult Sciences*, p. 22.

8. Pascal's wager appears in *Pensées*, no. 233. See *Pascal's Pensées*, trans. W.F. Trotter (New York: E.P. Dutton, 1958), pp. 65–69.

9. Wang Fu-zhi, *Siwen Lu, Waipian*, p. 43.

10. Wang Fu-zhi, *Shangshu Yinyi* 1.30.

11. Andō Shōeki, quoted in Maruyama Masao, *Studies in the Intellectual History of Tokugawa Japan*, p. 158.

12. Wang Ting-xiang, *Jiacang Ji*, p. 196. On the same subject, see ibid., p. 172, where Wang comments that "From the [time when the] government of the sage kings declined and heterodox arts arose, there were instances of the five phases being paired with the twelve branches with respect to the four seasons, of the five phases being paired with the five viscera and six entrails, of the five phases being used to name stars and planets, and of the five phases being used to discuss birth and transformations of men and things.

13. Wang Fu-zhi, *Zhangzi Zhengmeng Zhu* 8.247. On this subject, see also Wang's *Zhouyi Baishu* 8.24b–25a.

14. Li Gong, "Bian Hetu LuoShu Taiji" 13.9a.

15. Ibid., 13.8a.

16. Wang Fu-zhi, *Zhouyi Baishu* 8.25a.

17. Wang Fu-zhi, *Siwen Lu, Waipian*, p. 50.

18. Wang Ting-xiang, *Jiacang Ji*, p. 173.

19. Ibid., p. 184.

20. *Siku Quanshu Zongmu* 111.2208.

21. Wang Ting-xiang, in He Tang, "Yinyang Guanjian Bian" 9B.92 (*zhuan* 49).

22. Wang Ting-xiang, *Shenyan*, p. 59.

23. Jiao Hong, *Jiaoshi Bicheng* 1.10.

24. Huang Zong-xi, *Yixue Xiangshu Lun* 1.21.

25. Gong Zi-zhen, "Fei *Wuxing Zhuan*" (A Refutation of [Liu Xiang's] *Treatise on the Five Phases*), in *Gong Zi-zhen Quanji* 1.130–31.

26. Pi Xi-rui, *Jingxue Tonglun* 1.18–19.

27. Itō Tōgai, Introduction to *Kokon gakuhen*, trans. in Ryusaku Tsunoda, Wm. Theodore de Bary and Donald Keene, comps., *Sources of Japanese Tradition* (New York: Columbia University Press, 1964), 1:404–5.

28. Gu Yan-wu, "Guayao Wai, Wubie Xiang" (There are No images Apart from the Hexagrams and Their Lines), in *Yuanchao Rizhi Lu* 1.4–5.

29. Pi Xi-rui, *Jingxue Tonglun* 1.19.

30. Huang Zong-xi, *Yixue Xiangshu Lun* 1.46–47.

31. Chen Li, *Tongshu Dushu Ji* 4.53–54.

32. Wang Ting-xiang, *Yashu*, p. 82.

33. Wang Ting-xiang, in He Tang, "Yinyang Guanjian Bian" 9B.95 (*zhuan* 49). Later commentators have proposed at least three different interpretations of the *sixiang* (four images). These include: (1) the metal, mood, water, and the fire phases; (2) yin, yang, hardness, softness; (3) the greater and lesser yang and the greater and lesser yin.

34. Wang Xi-shan, "Li Ce" (Astronomical Schemata), in *Xiao'an Yishu* 5.1a.

35. Mei Wen-ding, *Lixue Dawen*, p. 16a.

36. *Siku Quanshu Zongmu* 106.2096. See also Xi Ze-zong, "Shilun Wang Xishan de Tianwen Gongzuo," p. 56. Xi Ze-zong has suggested that Wang's proposal had more rational mathematical advantages as well, pointing out that 384 is conveniently divisible by a large number of integers.

37. Jiang Yong, *Lülü Xinlun* A.4–5, 14–15.

38. Ibid., B.86.

39. Wang Fu-zhi, *Shangshu Yinyi* 4.92.

40. Wang Fu-zhi, *Siwen Lu, Waipian*, p. 44, and *Zhouyi Waizhuan* 5.9b.

41. Huang Zhen, *Dongfa Richao* 86.8a–8b.

42. Wang Ting-xiang, *Shenyan*, p. 56 and *Yashu*, p. 117.

43. Huang Zong-xi, *Yixue Xiangshu Lun* 5.263.

44. *Chouren Zhuan Sibian* (Fourth Compilation of *Biographies of Mathematicians and Astronomers*) 5.54, in *Chouren Zhuan Huibian* (Collected Editions of *Biographies of Mathematicians and Astronomers*) (Taipei: Shijie shuju, 1962).

45. Zhang Hui-yan, *Yitu Tiaobian*, pp. 25b–28a.

46. Ruan Yuan, *Chouren Zhuan* 41.516; Wang Fu-zhi, *Sibian Lu, Waipian*, p. 72.

47. Fang Yi-zhi, *Wuli Xiaozhi*, zonglun, p. 3; Fang Yi-zhi, *Dongxi Jun*.

48. Wang Ting-xiang, *Yashu*, pp. 115–16.

49. Wang Fu-zhi, *Liji Zhangju* 6.329–30.

50. Wang Fu-zhi, *Zhouyi Waizhuan* 5.16a.

51. Wang Fu-zhi, *Liji Zhangju* 6.338. Wang's interpretation of the origin, nature, and value of the *Yueling* is quite reminiscent of Ouyang Xiu's account of the "Great Commentary" to the *Change*, as described above in chapter 3.

52. Derk Bodde and Clarence Morris, *Law in Imperial China*, pp. 47–48.

53. Ian McMorran, "Wang Fu-chih's Involvement in the Politics of the Yung-li Court," in Jonathan D. Spence and John E. Wills, eds., *From Ming to Ch'ing: Conquest, Region, and Continuity in Seventeenth-Century China* (New Haven: Yale University Press, 1979), p. 156. McMorran's reference is probably to the last few lines of the "Yuanchen" chapter of the *Mingyi Daifang Lu* (p. 4b in SBBY ed.).

54. Lu Shi-yi, *Sibian Lu Zhiyao* 14.142.

55. Ibid., 22.230.

56. According to Joesph Needham, the thirteenth-century scholastic Ristoro d'Arezeo similarly proposed "that the configuration of the earth's surface corresponded to the positions of the fixed stars in the eighth sphere (whether nearer to or farther from the earth), an idea which received the support of Dante Alighieri." See Needham, *Science and Civilisation*, 3:603.

57. Lu Shi-yi, "Fenye Shuo" (A Discourse on the Field Allocation), pp. 1b–2a, in *Lu Fu-ting Xiansheng Yishu, ce* 18.

58. Fang Yi-zhi, *Dongxi Jun*, pp. 139–140.

59. Ibid., p. 85.

60. Paul S. Ropp, *Dissent in Early Modern China*, pp. 173, 184.

61. Hui-chen Wang Liu, *The Traditional Chinese Clan Rules* (Locust Valley, NY: J.J. Augustin for the Association for Asian Studies, 1959), p. 169.

62. Sidney D. Gamble, *North China Villages: Social, Political, and Economic Activities Before 1933* (Berkeley: University of California Press, 1963), pp. 261–62.

63. C.T. Hsia, Review of *Archetype and Allegory in the Dream of the Red Chamber*, by Andrew H. Plaks, p. 197.

64. Zhao Yi, *Ershier Shi Zhaji*, p. 30.

65. *Siku Quanshu Zongmu* 108.2131.

66. Hui Dong, *Yili* A.4.

67. According to Benjamin Elman, there is little evidence that new-text scholars before the late nineteenth century articulated such a comprehensive vision. See Elman, "The Hsueh-hai T'ang and the Rise of New Text Scholarship in Canton," pp. 70, 79.

68. Wu Ze, "Kang Yu-wei Gongyang Sanshi Shuo de Lishi Jinhua Guantian Yanjiu," p. 544; Lu Bao-qian, *Qingdai Sixiang Shi*, p. 243.

69. Lu Bao-qian, *Qingdai*, pp. 246–47.

70. Wu Ze, "Kang You-wei," pp. 560, 565.

71. Lu Bao-qian, *Qingdai*, pp. 244–45.

72. Donald W. Treadgold, *The West in Russia and China: Religious and Secular Thought in Modern Times, vol. 2, China, 1582–1949* (Cambridge: Cambridge University Press, 1973), p. 107.

73. Lu Bao-qian, *Qingdai*, p. 269.

74. See, for example, Junichiro Ide, "China's Great Cultural Revolution Has Opened a New Era in World History," *Peking Review* (May 19, 1967), 10(21): 25–26.

75. Paul Reiff, *Die Asthetik der Deutschen Frühuromantik*, Illinois Studies in Language and Literature, vol. 31, nos. 1–2 (Urbana: University of Illinois Press, 1946), p. 61.

76. M.H. Abrams, *Natural Supernaturalism*, pp. 169–70.

77. Novalis (Friedrich Philipp von Hardenberg), "Selected Aphorisms," in Charles E. Passage, trans., *Hymns to the Night and Other Selected Writings*, The Library of Liberal Arts (Indianapolis: Bobbs-Merrill, 1960), p. 71.

78. Abrams, *Natural Supernaturalism*, pp. 170–71.

79. "Extract from Report of the Meeting of the Chemical Society, March 1, 1866," from the *Chemical News* (March 9, 1866), 13:113, in John Alexander Reina Newlands, *On the Discovery of the Periodic Law*, p. 18. This volume is available in microprint form in Sir

Harold Hartley and Duane H.D. Roller, eds., *Landmarks of Science* (New York: Readex, Microprint, 1967–75). Thanks are due to my colleague Stephen Farmer for calling Newlands' work to my attention.

80. "On the Law of Octaves," from the *Chemical News* (August 18, 1865), 13:83, in ibid., p. 14.

81. Mendeleyev, quoted in Daniel Q. Posin, *Mendeleyev: The Story of a Great Scientist* (New York: McGraw Hill, 1948), p. 167.

82. Michel Foucault, *Madness and Civilization: A History of Insanity in the Age of Reason*, trans. Richard Howard (New York: New American Library, Mentor, 1967). See especially the first two chapters.

83. Karl Jaspers, *Strindberg and Van Gogh: An Attempt at a Pathographic Analysis with Reference to Parallel Cases of Swedenborg and Holderlin*, trans. Oskar Woloshin (Tuscon: University of Arizona Press, 1977), pp. 115–26, esp. p. 121.

84. Baudelaire's famous poem "Correspondences" may be read as a manifesto of the Symbolists' aesthetic rehabilitation of correlative thought. Arthur Rimbaud's "Voyelles" is another well-known example of the drawing out of correspondences by a Symbolist poet. See, for example, Arthur Symons, *The Symbolist Movement in Literature* (New York: E.P. Dutton, 1958), pp. 38–39.

85. James F. Anderson, *Reflections on the Analogy of Being* (The Hague: Martinus Nijhoff, 1967), p. 30.

86. George Lakoff and Mark Johnson, however, have argued that metaphors are used so systematically in everyday speech as to "allow us to understand one domain of experience in terms of another. This suggests that understanding takes place in terms of entire domains of experience and not in terms of isolated concepts." For example, "in the ARGUMENT IS WAR metaphor, the gestalt for conversation is structure . . . by means of correspondences with selected elements of the gestalt for war. Thus one activity, talking, is understood in terms of another, physical fighting." See Lakoff and Johnson, *Metaphors We Live By* (Chicago: University of Chicago Press, 1980), pp. 81 and 117.

87. Howard Baker and Harry Elmer Barnes, *Social Thought From Lore to Science*, 3rd ed. (New York: Dover, 1961), 2:678. On Comte and Spencer, see pp. 679–81. Thanks are due to my colleague David Lindenfeld for calling these passages to my attention.

88. Sigmund Freud, *Totem and Taboo: Resemblances Between the Psychic Lives of Savages and Neurotics*, trans. A.A. Brill (New York: Random House, Vintage, 1946), p. 117.

89. A similar interpretation of binary forms in Lévi Strauss may be found in G.S. Kirk, *The Nature of Greek Myths* (Harmondworth, Eng.: Penguin, 1974), pp. 81–82.

90. Friedrich Engels, *Dialectics of Nature*, trans. Clemens Dutt (New York: International Publishers, 1940), p. 153.

91. James A. Boon, *From Symbolism to Structuralism: Lévi Strauss in a Literary Tradition* (New York: Harper and Row, 1972), p. 6.

92. E.H. Gombrich notes that Freud as well "derived many of his ideas about symbolism and the unconscious from Romanticism," and thus ultimately from Neoplatonic sources. For a brief discussion by Gombrich on modern revivals of Neoplatonism, see his *Symbolic Images*, pp. 187–90.

93. Bacon, *New Organon*, p. 50.

94. Alexis Tostoy, quoted in Igor Stravinsky, *Poetics of Music in the Form of Six Lessons*, trans. Ingolf Dahl (Cambridge: Harvard University Press, 1947), pp. 114–15.

8. Criticism of Geometrical Cosmography in Late-Traditional China

1. Francis Bacon, *The New Organon*, bk. 1, p. 50.

2. Galileo, *The Starry Messenger*, in Stillman Drake, trans., *Discoveries and Opinions of Galileo* (Garden City, NY: Doubleday, Anchor, 1957), p. 31.

3. Lynn White, Jr., "The Context of Science," in White, *Machina ex Deo: Essays in the Dynamism of Western Culture* (Cambridge: MIT Press, 1968), p. 103. Another authority, Amos Funkenstein, also sees "some correspondence between the foundation of universal harmony in elliptical orbits and the predilection for elliptical forms in Baroque architecture." See Funkenstein, "The Dialectical Preparation for Scientific Revolutions," in Robert S. Westman, ed., *The Copernican Acheivement* (Berkeley: University of California Press, 1975), p. 201.

4. S.K. Heninger, Jr., *The Cosmographical Glass*, p. 95.

5. Peter J. French, *John Dee: The World of an Elizabethan Magus* (London: Routledge and Kegan Paul, 1972), pp. 70, 80.

6. Ma Duan-lin, "Introduction to the Survey on the Land Tax" (from *Wenxian Tongkao*, Author's Introduction), in Wm. Theodore de Bary et al., comps., *Sources of Chinese Tradition*, 1:448.

7. Zhang Zai, "Zhouli" ([Notes on the] *Rites of Zhou*), in *Zhangzi Quanshu* 4.2a, 3a.

8. Lu Long-qi, *San Yutang Riji* B.113.

9. Lu Long-qi, *San Yutang Wenji, zazhu* 3.1b–2a.

10. Huang Zong-xi, *Mengzi Shishuo* 3.3a.

11. Gu Yan-wu, "Chang-cheng" (The Great Wall), in *Yuanchaoben Rizhi Lu* 31.908.

12. Lu Shi-yi, *Sibian Lu Jiyao* 19.191–96.

13. Yan Ruo-ju, *Shangshu Guwen Shuzheng* 6B.79b.

14. Chen Li, *Dong-shu Dushu Ji* 5.70.

15. For Zheng Qiao's comment on the ancient nine provinces, see the "Dili Lue" (Outline of Geography) chapter in Zheng's *Tongzhi* A.218, 224.

16. Zhu Xi, quoted in *Rijiang Liji Jieyi* (Daily Talks Which Explain the Meaning of the *Record of Rites*) 13.9a, in *Yingyin Siku Quanshu Zhenben, Jiuzhi* (Reprints of Rare Editions from the *Complete Library in Four Treasuries*, series 9) (Taipei: Shangwu yinshugan, 1979), vol. 45.

17. Mao Qi-ling, *Shangshu Guangting Lu* 2.13a–13b.

18. Gu Yan-wu, "Jiuzhou" (The Nine Provinces), in *Rizhi Lu* 23.626–27.

19. Liu Xian-ting, *Guangyang Zazhi* 4.198.

20. Gu Jie-gang, *Handai Xueshu Shilue*, pp. 117–118; Tan Si-tong, *Renxue* (A Study of Humanity), excerpted in Qian Mu, *Zhongguo Jin Sanbainian Xueshu Shi* (History of Chinese Learning of the Past Three Hundred Years) (Taipei: Shangwu yinshuguan, 1968), 2:668.

21. Giulio Aleni, *Xifang Dawen* (Questions and Answers on the West), trans. in John L. Mish, "Creating an Image of Europe for China," p. 73.

22. Wang Ting-xiang, *Shenyan*, p. 55.

23. Fang Yi-zhi, *Tongya* 11.23a. Fang also included a brief note on *fenye* in his *Wuli Xiaozhi* 1.32.

24. Yan Ruo-ju, *Shangshu Guwen Shuzheng* 6A.6b, 10a–10b.

25. Huang Zong-xi, *Poxie Lun*, p. 5a.

26. Lu Long-qi, *Sanyu Tang Riji* B.46–47.

27. *Siku Quanshu Zongmu* 110.2186.

28. Fang Yi-zhi, *Tongya* 11.12b; Dai Zhen, *Chu Yuan Fuzhu* 3.27. Nathan Sivin notes that before the introduction of Western science in the seventeenth century, the Chinese had never used degrees (du) to mark terrestrial locations (personal communication).

29. Mao Qi-ling, "Hetu Luoshu Yuanshu Bian" (A Treatise on the Original Distinctions of the Yellow River Chart and Luo River Writing), pp. 7b, 15a–15b, in *Xihe Heji*, Ce 10.

30. Wang Fu-zhi, *Liji Zhangju* 14.696.
31. Lu Shi-yi, *Sibian Lu* 21.218.
32. Jiang Fan, *Li Jingwen* 1.1–2.
33. Pi Xi-rui, *Jingxue Lishi*, p. 291; Pi Xi-rui, *Jingxue Tonglun* 1.28; Song Lian, "Hetue Luoshu Shuo" 36.3a; Mao Qi-ling, "Hetu Luoshu Yuanshu Bian," p. 16b.
34. Gui You-guang, "Yitu Lun" (A Discussion of the Diagrams Associated with the *Change*), in *Zhenchuan Xiansheng Ji* 1.1b, 3a–3b.
35. Gui You-guang, "Hongfan Zhuan" (Commentary on the "Great Plan"), in *Zhenchuan Xiansheng Ji* 1.4b–5a.
36. Mao Qi-ling, *Shangshu Guangting Lu* 3.8b–10b.
37. Joseph Needham, *Science and Civilisation in China*, 2:442.
38. Hu Wei, *Yitu Mingbian* 2.104, 121; 5.306.
39. Huang Zong-xi, *Yixue Xiangshu Lun* 114–15.
40. Mao Ji-ling, "Hetu Luoshu Yuanshu Bian," p. 1a; Huang Zong-yan, *Yixue Bianhuo*, p. 5a.
41. Hu Wei, *Yitu Mingbian* 1.46.
42. *Lunyu*, bk. 9, chap. 8. Cheng Yi, citing this passage in the *Analects*, declared that such auspicious signs as the Hetu appeared when the fortunes of a state were on the rise. Cheng, however, went on to remark that the sage does not put much stock in such omens and portents. See *Er Cheng Yulu* 11.179.
43. Yan Ruo-ju, *Sishu Shidi Xu*, p. 35.
44. Hu Wei, *Yitu Mingbian* 1.41, 65.
45. Lu Shi-yi, *Sibian Lu* 3.34.
46. Lu Long-qi, *Lu Jia-shu Xiansheng Wenxue Lu* 3.35.
47. Li Guang-di, *Zhujie Zhengmeng* A.43b.
48. Wang Mao-hong, *Zhuzi Nianpu, Kaoyi* (Chronological Account of Master Zhu, Investigation of Divergences) (Taipei: Shangwu yinshuguan, 1971) 2.281–82.
49. Pi Xi-rui, *Jingxue Tonglun* 1.33.
50. George N. Kates, *The Years that Were Fat*, p. 72. Kates comments that "This gate ... is more than two miles as the crow flies from where the Emperor hypothetically would have sat enthroned. So sensitive is the Chinese feeling for symmetry."
51. Ibid., p. 255.

9. Qing Scholar's Anticosmological World View
1. Wang Ting-xiang, *Shenyan*, p. 56; Huang Zong-xi, *Yixue Xiangshu Lun* 5.263; Zhang Hui-yan, *Yitu Tiaobian*, p. 28a.
2. Michael Sullivan, *A Short History of Chinese Art* (Berkeley: University of California Press, 1967), p. 226; James Cahill, "Style as Idea in Ming-Qing Painting," in Maurice Meisner and Rhoads Murphy, eds., *The Mozartian Historian: Essays on the Works of Joseph R. Levenson* (Berkeley: University of California Press, 1976), p. 149. Cahill is here summarizing a thesis advanced in Werner Speiser's *Chinese Art*.
3. James Cahill, *Chinese Painting*, p. 32.
4. Michael D. Freeman, "From Adept to Worthy," p. 484.
5. Su Shih, trans. in Susan Bush, *The Chinese Literati on Painting Su Shih (1037–1101) to Tung Ch'i-ch'ang (1555–1636)*, Harvard-Yenching Institute Studies, no. 27 (Cambridge: Harvard University Press, 1971), p. 42. The Chinese text of the relevant passage from Su Shih's *Collected Prose* appears on p. 191 of Bush.
6. Cahill, *Chinese Painting*, p. 167.
7. Wang Fu-zhi, *Siwen Lu, Waipian*, p. 50.

8. Zong Bing, "Introducation to Landscape Painting" (from *Lidai Minghua Ji* 6.36b–4b), trans. in Wm. Theodore de Bary et al., comps., *Sources of Chinese Tradition*, 1:254. On directional orientation in early Chinese landscapes, see Sherman E. Lee, *Chinese Landscape Painting*, p. 3.

9. Lee, *Chinese Landscape Painting*, pp. 22–23.

10. Arthur Waley, *An Introduction to the Study of Chinese Painting* (New York: Scribner's, 1923), p. 251; Laurence Sickman and Alexander Soper, *The Art and Architecture of China*, p. 196. These quotations from Waley and Sickman and Soper are juxtaposed in Chu-tsing Li, *A Thousand Peaks and Myriad Ravines: Chinese Paintings in the Charles A. Drenowatz Collection* (Ascona, Switzerland: Artibus Asiae, 1974), 1:206.

11. Chu-tsing Li, *Thousand Peaks*, 1:209. James Cahill, however, has suggested that Western artistic influence may account for some of the peculiarities in Gong's landscape art; see *The Compelling Image: Nature and Style in Seventeenth-Century Chinese Painting* (Cambridge: Harvard University Press, 1982), pp. 176, 178.

12. William Theodore de Bary, "Introduction," in de Bary and Irene Bloom, eds., *Principle and Practicality: Essays in Neo-Confucianism and Practical Learning* (New York: Columbia University Press, 1979), p. 22.

13. Cahill, *Chinese Painting*, pp. 180–81.

14. Louis Pasteur, *Researches on the Molecular Asymmetry of Natural Organic Products*, Alembic Club Reprints, no. 14 (Edinburgh: The Alembic Club, 1905), pp. 29, 43.

15. Martin Gardner, *The Ambidextrous Universe: Mirror Asymmetry and Time Reversed Worlds*, 2d ed. (New York: Scribner's, 1979), p. 138.

16. M.H. Abrams, *Natural Supernaturalism*, pp. 216–17, 431–32.

17. Lu Xiang-shan, "Sanwu Yibian Cuozong Qishu" (The Numbers 3 and 5 are Irregular by Virtue of Being Associated with Change), in *Xiang-shan Quanji* 21.3b.

18. Zhang Zai, *Zhangzi Zhengmeng Zhu* 3.92–93. This translation is modified from Wing-tsit Chan, *A Source Book in Chinese Philosophy*, p. 512.

19. Cheng Hao, *Henan Chengshi Yishu* (Surviving Works of the Chengs of Henan) 2A.1b, in *Er Cheng Quanshu* (Complete Works of Two Chengs) (SBBY ed.), vol. 1. Translation modified from Chan, *Source Book*, p. 529.

20. Yan Yuan, *Cunxing Bian* 2.29–30.

21. Lu Shi-yi, *Sibian Lu Zhiyao* 14.142–43.

22. Wang Fu-zhi, *Siwen Lu, Waipian*, p. 63. Wang goes on to argue that the various "proofs" adduced by the Westerners for the sphericity of the earth are actually based on optical errors and illusions.

23. See, for example, Jiang Yong, *Shuxue* 1.10–11.

24. Wang Fu-zhi, *Liji Zhangju* 5.323.

25. Wang Fu-zhi, *Du Tongjian Lun* 3.6b.

26. Ibid., 3.15a.

27. Wang Fu-zhi, *Zhouyi Waizhuan* 6.8a.

28. Wang Xi-shan, *Xiao-an Xinfa*, zixu ([Wang] Xiao-an's New System, Author's Preface), in *Xiao-an Yishu* 1.2b.

29. For Fang's comments on this issue, see his *Wuli Xiaozhi* 1.30. Willard Peterson notes Fang's criticism of the Western division of the great circle into 360 degrees in his "Fang Yi-zhi," p. 395.

30. Wang Fu-zhi, *Siwen Lu, Waipian*, p. 53. Even though the idea of evening off historical epochs in this fashion might well appear ridiculous to us, as it apparently did to Wang Fu-zhi, Chinese chronologists actually did follow a somewhat similar practice in their division of reign eras. As Derk Bodde explains, "If an Emperor died during the fifth month of a certain

year, for example, his reign was officially recorded as extending to the end of that year even though his successor had ascended the throne immediately following his death. Here again may perhaps be seen the Chinese preference for formal regularity as against realistic irregularity." See Derk Bodde, *Festivals in Classical China*, p. 34.

31. Mei Wen-ding, *Lixue Yiwen*, part 2, p. 1b. Wang Xi-shan, *Xiao-an Xinfa*, zixu, pp. 2a–3a. For a simple and concise explanation of the problem of intercalation in traditional Chinese astronomy, see Nathan Sivin, "Shen Kua [Gua]," p. 378.

32. For a fuller explanation of Shen's proposed solar calendar, see Sivin, "Shen Kua," p. 379.

33. Ruan Yuan, *Zhouren Zhuan* 20.242.

34. Zhang Wen-hu's commentary to Shen Gua's *Mengqi Bitan* 7.305.

35. Henri Maspero, "L'Astronomie Chinoise avant les Han," p. 278.

36. Shen Gua, *Mengqi Bitan* 7.308.

37. Mei Wen-ding, *Lixue Yiwen*, part 2, p. 17b.

38. See, for example, chapter 10 of the "Great Commentary" to the *Change* (*Zhouyi Zhushu* 7.14b–15a).

39. Wang Ting-xiang, *Yashu*, pp. 84, 95, 145.

40. Wang Ting-xiang, *Jiacang Ji*, p. 167. Although earlier cosmologists also recognized the existence of such botanical and meteorological anomalies as those noted by Wang Ting-xiang, they generally regarded them not as part of the natural order of things, as did Wang, but as monstrosities or evil portents. See Michael Loewe, *Ways to Paradise*, p. 7. According to Zhu Xi, such anomalous meteorological phenomena as cold in summer and heat in winter belong to the category of "weird" (guai) things "of which Confucious did not speak" and hence "the scholar also need not understand" ("Yuyao" 48.15b).

41. Wang Ting-xiang, *Jiacang Ji*, p. 167.

42. Ibid., pp. 177–78.

43. Wang Ting-xiang, *Shenyan*, p. 58. The cosmogonic theory which Wang attempted to refute was apparently quite popular in sixteenth-century China, as illustrated by its appearance in chapter 1 of Wu Cheng-en's *Journey to the West*. For an English translation of this passage, see Anthony C. Yu, trans., ed., *The Journey to the West*, 1:66.

44. Lu Kun, *Shenyin Yu* 4.175, 2.115.

45. Jiang Yong, *Shuxue* 1.6–8.

46. Ibid. 1.9. The mode of calculation from a "superior epoch" that supposedly stood at the beginning of time had been abandoned long before Jiang posed these comological arguments against the possibility that such a point could be determined. For a brief account of the more practical reasons for astronomers' having eschewed this cosmic zero point, see *Yuanshi* 53, *Lizhi 2* (Yuan History, Treatise on Astronomy), in *Lidai Tianwen Luli Tengzhi Huipian*, 9:3357. Jiang's argument concerning east-west time differences is apparently based on his knowledge of Western astronomy, as Nathan Sivin has pointed out (personal communication); for no such idea existed in traditional China.

47. Wang Fu-zhi, *Zhouyi Waizhuan* 5.25b.

48. Wang Fu-zhi, *Siwen Lu, Neipian* (Record of Intellectual Inquiry, Inner Chapters), p. 29, in *Lizhou Chuanshan Wushu* (Five Books by [Huang] Li-zhou and [Wang] Chuan-shan) (Taipei: Shijie shuju, 1974).

49. Lu Kun, *Shenyin Yu* 1.53.

50. Fang Yi-zhi, *Dongxi Jun*, pp. 95–6.

51. Wang Fu-zhi, *Shangshu Yinyi* 4.96.

52. Fang Yi-zhi, *Wuli Xiaozhi* 1.4; Wang Xi-shan, *Xiao-an Xinfa*, zixu, pp. 4a–4b; Gu Yan-wu, "Yueshi" (Lunar Eclipses), in *Yuanchaoben Rizhi Lu* 30.856–57.

53. Wang Xi-shan, "Ceri Xiao zhi Xu" (A Short Account of Astronomical Measurement, in *Xiao-an Yishu* 4.47b.

54. Wang Fu-zhi, *Du Tongjian Lun* 19.2a.

55. Li Guang-po, excerpted in Ruan Yuan, *Zhouren Zhuan* 40.501.

56. Lu Shi-yi, *Sibian Lu* 14.143.

57. Fang Yi-zhi, *Wuli Xiaozhi* 1.25.

58. Ibid., "Zong Lun" (General Introduction), p. 3.

59. Jiang Yong, *Shuxue* 1.52–53.

60. *Siku Quanshu Zongmu* 106.2093.

61. *Yuanshi* 52, *Lizhi* 1, in *Lidai Tianwen*, 9:3311.

62. Wang Xi-shan, "Li Ce" (Astronomical Schemata), in *Xiao-an Yishu* 4.1a.

63. Wang Xi-shan, "Lishuo" (Astronomical Theories), in *Xian-an Yishu* 4.5a.

64. Wang Xi-shan, "Ceri Xiao zhi Xu," in *Xiao-an Yi-shu* 4.48a.

65. Mei Wen-ding, *Lifa Tongkao*, zixu pp. 2b–3a.

66. Huang Dao-zhou, "Zhuli Zonglun" (General Discussion of All Aspects of Astronomy), in *Zhongting Baiwu Tianhui* 1.32a, 33a–33b.

67. Huang Dao-zhou, excerpted in Fang Yi-zhi, *Tongxi Jun*, p. 104. Hou Wai-lu, the modern editor of this work by Fang, comments that the probable source for this excerpt, Huang Dao-zhou's *Dadi Wenyi* (Lessons Learned on Dadi Mountain), does not seem to have survived (ibid., p. 105).

68. Wang Ting-xiang, *Shenyan*, p. 56.

69. Jiang Yong, *Shuxue* 1.28–29. Jiang advanced other cosmological explanations for the differentiation of equator and ecliptic, and even for the divergence of the paths of the moon and five planets from the ecliptic. Thus he compared the sun with the sovereign (jun) and the moon and the five planets with vassals (chen), who "do not dare [to proceed] right along the sun's path, but also do not dare [to stray] far from it."

70. Ibid., 1.26.

71. Zhang Xue-cheng, "Tianyu" (Analogy of Heaven), in *Wenshi Tongyi* 3.42.

72. Ibid., 3.41–42.

73. Marshall Clagett, "Nicole Oresme," in Charles Coulston Gillispie, ed. in chief, *Dictionary of Scientific Biography* (New York: Scribner's, 1974), 10:224.

74. Dudley Shapere, *Galileo*, p. 137.

75. Plato, *Republic* 7, in Francis M. Cornford, trans., *The Republic of Plato*, p. 248. On this point see also Shapere, *Galileo*, p. 134.

76. Shapere, *Galileo*, p. 88.

77. H. Zaiser, *Kepler als Philosoph*, quoted and trans. in Gerald Holton, "Johannes Kepler's Universe," p. 212.

78. Ernst Cassirer, *The Philosophy of Symbolic Forms*, 2:88.

79. Kepler, "Letter to Mästlin, April 19, 1597," quoted and trans. in Holton, "Johannes Kepler's Universe," p. 213.

80. Shapere, *Galileo*, p. 134.

81. Curt J. Ducasse, "John F. W. Herschel's Method's of Experimental Inquiry," in Edward W. Madden, ed., *Theories of Scientific Method: The Renaissance Through the Nineteenth Century* (Seattle: University of Washington Press, 1966), p. 159.

82. Leibniz, "Excerpts from a Letter to Remond de Montmort, 1715," in Phillip P. Wiener, ed., *Leibniz Selections* (New York: Scribner's, 1951), p. 189. The idea that apparent anomalies, irregularities, and deformities were only such with respect to a "partial system," and that all disorders were reconciled and subsumed within the larger harmony was, of course, stated by Stoic philosophers. See Samuel Sambursky, "Harmony and Wholeness in Greek Scientific

Thought," pp. 450–451.

83. Alexander Pope, *An Essay on Man*, in Maynard Mack, ed., *The Poems of Alexander Pope*, vol. 3, *An Essay on Man* (London: Methuen, 1950; New Haven: Yale University Press, 1951), pp. 50–51 (epistle 1, lines 289–94).

84. Ruan Yuan, *Chouren Zhuan* 46.610.

85. Wang Fu-zhi, *Siwen Lu, Waipian* pp. 63–64.

86. J.Z. Young makes such a suggestion in his *Programs of the Brain* (Oxford: Oxford University Press, 1978), p. 148.

87. An example of a speculation along this line is E.H. Gombrich's suggestion that "Indo-European languages tend to this particular figure we call personification, because many of them endow nouns with gender which makes them indistinguishable from names for living species." See Gombrich, *Symbolic Images*, p. 125.

88. Jean Piaget devotes a brief discussion to this issue in his *Play, Dreams, and Imitation in Childhood*, trans. G. Gattegno and F.M. Hodgson (New York: Norton, 1962), pp. 287–89.

89. Some material for the study of this topic may be found in G.E. von Grunbaum and Roger Caillois, eds., *The Dream and Human Societies* (Berkeley: University of California Press, 1966).

Glossary of Chinese
Book and Chapter Titles

Baiwen Pian 百問篇

Baihu Tongyi 白虎通議

Chouren Zhuan 疇人傳

Chuci 楚辭

Chunqiu 春秋

Chunqiu Fanlu 春秋繁露

Cunzhi Bian 存治編

Cunxing Bian 存性編

Dongxi Jun 東西均

Dongya 東雅

Du Tongjian Lun 讀通鑑論

Dadai Liji 大戴禮記

"Dayu Mo" 大禹謨

Fawei Lun 發微論

"Gaoyao Mo" 皋陶謨

Gongyang zhuan 公羊傳

Gujin Renbiao 古今人表

Guliang Zhuan 穀梁傳

Guanzi 管子

Guoyu 國語

Hanshu 漢書

"Hongfan" 洪範

Hongfan Zhenglun 洪範正論

Hongfan Huangji 洪範皇極

Huannanzi 淮南子

Huangji Jingshi Shu 皇極經世書

Huangdi Zhaijing 黃帝宅經

Huangdi Neijing Suwen 黃帝內經素問

Jiaoshi Yilin 焦氏易林

Kaogong Ji 考工記

Laozi 老子

Liji 禮記

"Lizhi" 曆志

"Lüli zhi" 律曆志

"Lüxing" 呂刑

Lunheng 論衡

Lunyu 論語

Lülü Xinlun 律呂新論

Lüshi Chunqiu 呂氏春秋

Mengqi Bitan 夢溪筆談

Mingyi Daifang Lu 明夷待訪錄

Qianxu 潛虛

Rizhi Lu 日知錄

Rulin Waishi 儒林外史

Shanhai Jing 山海經

Shangshu Guwen Shuzheng 尚書古文疏証

Shangshu Guangting Lu 尚書廣聽
錄
Shangshu Yinyi 尚書引義
"Shengde" 盛德
Shiji (Record of the Historian) 史
記
Shiji (Monthly Record) 時紀
Shijing 詩經
"Shize Xun" 時則訓
Shujing 書經
"Shuogua" 說卦
Siku Quanshu 四庫全書
Siku Quanshu Zongmu 四庫全書
總目
Sibian Lu 思辨錄
Sicun Bian 四存編
Songshi 宋史
Songyuan Xue'an 宋元學案
Taiji Tushuo 太極圖說
Taiping Jing 太平經
Taixuan Jing 太玄經
Tiandui 天對
Tianwen 天問
"Tianyu" 天喻
"Tianguan Shu" 天官書
"Wangzhi" 王制
Weishu, "Lüli Zhi" 魏書, 律歷志
Wenxin Diaolong 文心雕龍
Wuxing Kao 五行考
Wuli Xiaozhi 物理小識

Xifang Dawen 西方答問
"Xia Xiaozheng" 夏小正
Xin Tang Shu 新唐書
Xunzi 荀子
Yaodian 堯典
Yijing 易經
Yijing Tujie 易經圖解
Yi Tongzi Wen 易僮子問
Yiwei Qianzuo Du 易緯乾鑿度
Yitu Mingbian 易圖明辨
Yitu Tiaobian 易圖條辨
Yixue Qimeng 易學啟蒙
Yixue Xiangshu Lun 易學象數論
"Youguan" 幼官
"Yugong" 禹貢
Yugong Zhuizhi 禹貢錐指
Yuanshi 元史
Yueling 月令
Yunqi Lun 運氣論
Zhengmeng 正夢
Zhongyong 中庸
Zhouyi 周易
Zhouyi Benyi 周易本義
Zhouyi Caitu 周易採圖
Zhouyi Can Tongqi 周易參同契
Zhouyi Waizhuan 周易外傳
Zhouli 周禮
Zhuangzi 莊子
Zuozhuan 左傳

Glossary of Chinese Names and Mythical Figures

Ban Gu 班固

Cai Chen 蔡沈

Cai Yong 蔡邕

Cai Yuan-ding 蔡元定

Cao Xue-qin 曹雪芹

Chen Li 陳澧

Chen Rong-jie 陳榮捷

Chen Ying-run 陳應潤

Chen Zhuo 陳卓

Cheng Hao 程顥

Cheng Yi 程頤

Dai Fa-xing 戴法興

Dai Zhen 戴震

Dao Ji 道濟

Diao Bao 刁包

Dong Ba 董巴

Dong Zhong-shu 董仲舒

Du Yu 杜預

Fan Kuan 范寬

Fang Dong-shu 方東樹

Fang Yi-zhi 方以智

Feng You-lan 馮友蘭

Fu Xi 伏羲

Gao Pan-long 高攀龍

Gong Xian 龔賢

Gong Zi-zhen 龔自珍

Gu Jie-gang 顧頡剛

Gu Xian-cheng 顧憲成

Gu Yan-wu 顧炎武

Gu Zu-yu 顧祖禹

Gui You-guang 歸有光

Guo Mo-ruo 郭沫若

Guo Shou-jing 郭守敬

Han Kang-bo 韓康伯

Han Yu 韓愈

He Cheng-tian 何承天

He Xiu 何休

Hu Ju-ren 胡居仁

Hu Shi 胡適

Hu Wei 胡渭

Huan Tan 桓譚

Huang Dao-zhou 黃道周

Huang Zhen 黃震

Huang Zong-xi 黃宗義

Huang Zong-yan 黃宗炎

Hui Dong 惠棟

Hui Neng 惠能

Hui Zi 惠子

Jia Kui 賈逵

Jiang Chong 江充

Jiang Fan 江藩

Jiang Wei-qiao 蔣維喬

Jiang Yong 江永

Jiao Hong 焦竑

Jiao Xun 焦循

Jiao Yan-shou 焦延壽

Jie 桀

Jing Fang 京房

Kang You-wei 康有為

Kong Ying-da 孔穎達

Lai Qu-tang 來瞿唐

Li Ao 李翱

Li Cheng 李成

Li Chun-feng 李淳風

Li Ding-zuo 李鼎祚

Li Gong 李塨

Li Guang-di 李光地

Li Guang-po 李光坡

Li Yan 李儼

Li Zhi-zao 李之藻

Liang Qi-chao 梁啟超

Liao Ping 廖平

Lin Zhao-en 林兆恩

Liu Ji 劉基

Liu Xian-ting 劉獻廷

Liu Xiang 劉向

Liu Xin 劉歆

Liu Xie 劉勰

Liu Zhi-ji 劉知幾

Liu Zong-zhou 劉宗周

Liu Zong-yuan 柳宗元

Lu Bao-qian 陸寶千

Lu Long-qi 陸龍其

Lu Shi-yi 陸世儀

Lü Cai 呂才

Lü Kun 呂坤

Lü Liu-liang 呂留良

Lu Xiang-shan 陸象山

Luo Guang 羅光

Ma Duan-lin 馬端臨

Ma Rong 馬融

Mao Qi-ling 毛奇齡

Mei Wen-ding 梅文鼎

Mei Zu 梅鷟

Meng Xi 孟喜

Mou Zong-san 牟宗三

Ni Zan 倪瓚

Niu Seng-ru 牛僧儒

Ouyang Xiu 歐陽修

Peng Zu 彭祖

Pi Xi-rui 皮錫瑞

Qian Da-xin 錢大昕

Qian Mu 錢穆

Ruan Yuan 阮元

Sang Hong-yang 桑弘羊

Shao Yong 邵雍

Shen Gua 沈栝

Shen Xiu 神秀

Shi Xiang-yun 史湘雲

Shun 舜

Sima Guang 司馬光

Sima Qian 司馬遷

Song Lian 宋濂

Su Shi 蘇軾

Su Xun 蘇洵

Sun Qi-feng 孫奇逢

Sun Si-miao 孫思邈

Tan Si-tong 譚嗣同

Tang 湯

Tang Jian 唐鑑

Tang Jun-yi 唐君毅

Wang An-shi 王安石

Wang Bi 王弼

Wang Chong 王充

Wang Fu 王符

Wang Fu-zhi 王夫之

Wang Mang 王莽

Wang Mao-hong 王懋竑

Wang Ting-xiang 王廷相

Wang Xi-shan 王錫闡

Wang Yang-ming 王陽明

Wang Yi 王禕

Wang Ying-lin 王應麟

Wang Yuan-qi 王原祁

Wei Bo-yang 魏伯陽

Wen Wang 文王

Wu 武

Wu Cheng-en 吳承恩

Wu Qi-chang 吳其昌

Wu You-xing 吳有性

Wu Zhi-hui 吳稚輝

Xi He 羲和

Xing Yun-lu 邢雲路

Xu Dao-lin 徐道鄰

Xu Fu-guan 許復觀

Xu Guang-qi 徐光啟

Xu Heng 許衡

Xu Zhong-shu 徐中舒

Xun Shuang 荀爽

Xun Yue 荀悅

Xun Zi 荀子

Yan Ruo-ju 閻若璩

Yan Yuan 顏元

Yang Shen 楊慎

Yang Xiong 揚雄

Yao 堯

Ye Shi 葉適

Yi Xing 一行

Yu 禹

Yu Fan 虞翻

Yu Xi 虞喜

Yu Ying-shi 余英時

Zhang Heng 張衡

Zhang Hui-yan 張惠言

Zhang Li-xiang 張履祥

Zhang Qian 張騫

Zhang Wen-hu 張文虎

Zhang Xue-cheng 張學誠

Zhang Zai 張載

Zhao Yi 趙翼

Zheng Qiao 鄭樵

Zhou 紂

Zhou Dun-yi 周敦頤

Zhu Da 朱耷

Zhu Xi 朱熹

Zou Yan 騶衍

Glossary of Chinese Terms

bai dao 白道

bao zhang 保章

bi yong 壁廱

bu qi 不齊

cai 才

cha 差

chang li 常理

chen 臣

Cheng Huang 城隍

da pi 大辟

da si dian 大祀殿

da tong 大同

da yan 大衍

Dao 道

dao wen xue 導問學

de 德

De Sheng Men 德勝門

di 地

di pi 地闢

di zhi 地支

du 度

dui 兌

fen ye 分野

gai tian 蓋天

gan ying 感應

ge wu 格物

gong 宮

gong tian 公田

gua qi 卦氣

guai 怪

Han xue 漢學

He tu 河圖

hou qi 候氣

hun tian 渾天

ji 幾

Jia ping 嘉平

jia zi 甲子

jiao 角

jin wen 今文

jing 井

jing tian 井田

jiu chou 九疇

jiu dao 九道

jiu fu 九服

jiu gong 九宮

jiu zhou 九州

ju luan 據亂

jue 角

jun 君

kan 坎

kun 坤

la 腊

li (measure of distance) 里

li (propriety) 禮

li (trigram) 離

li (ultimate principle) 理

li shu 曆書

li yuan 曆元

li xue 理學

ling tai 靈臺

ling tai lang 靈臺郎

liu fu 六府

liu yi 六藝

liu qi 六氣

Luoshu 洛書

mao 卯

min zhu 民主

ming tang 明堂

mou 畝

na jia 納甲

neisheng zhi xue 內聖之學

ni 逆

qi 氣

qian 乾

Qian long 乾隆

qiang pei 強配

Qing si 清祀

ren 仁

ren zhi tian 人之天

ren sheng 人生

ren yu 人欲

san da ru 三大儒

san jiao he yi 三教合一

san shi 三時

sheng ping 升平

sheng sheng 生生

shi xue 實學

shou 首

shou shi 授時

shu (document) 書

shu (number/ regularity) 數

shu shu 術數

shui 水

shun 順

si cha 四差

si duan 四端

si qi 四氣

si tian 四田

si xiang 四象

song xue 宋學

sui cha 歲差

tai chu 太初

tai cu 太簇

tai hu 太湖

tai ji 太極

tai ji tu 太極圖

tai miao 太廟

tai ping 太平

tai xu 太虛

tian 天

tian gan 天干

tian kai 天開

tian li 天理

tian zhi wei tian 天之為天

tong 通

tu (drawing) 圖

tu (earth) 土

tu chen 圖讖

wai wang zhi xue 外王之學

wu 午

wu chang 五常

wu ji 無極

wu xing 五行

wu yun 五運

Xi he 羲和

Xi he zhi guan 羲和之官

xiang 象

xiang ying 相應

xiao kang 小康

xin 信

xin xue 心學

xing (human nature) 性

xing (physical forms) 形

xing (punishments) 刑

xing er xia 形而下

xing shan 性善

xing tu 性圖

xiu 宿

xuan tang 玄堂

ya men 衙門

yang 陽

ye ma 野馬

yi li 義理

yin 陰

yin yang jia 陰陽家

Yong le 永樂

you 酉

yuan 元

Yuan feng 元封

zan 贊

Zha 蜡

zhang 丈

zhao mu 昭穆

zhao yu qi 昭餘祁

Zhen (name of marsh) 震

zhen (trigram) 震

zheng tong 政統

zhou 州

zi 子

zun de xing 遵德性

Selected Bibliography

This is not a comprehensive bibliography, but does include all the sources cited at least twice in the notes. Of the sources which appear only once in the notes, I have included only those which are particularly relevant to the study of the development of Chinese cosmology.

The bibliographical entries for primary sources in Chinese listed below generally cite only the larger works or collections of particular authors rather than individual essays or notes. However, in cases where I have consulted only one particular essay included within the larger work by a single author, I have cited both in the bibliographical entry.

Complete source citations for works not included here appear in the notes.

The following abbreviations are used in both the bibliography and the notes:

QRXA *Qingru Xue'an*
SBBY *Sibu Beiyao*
SYXA *Songyuan Xue'an*

Primary Sources in Chinese

Baihu Tongde Lun 白虎通德論 (Discussions of Comprehensive Virtue in White Tiger Hall). Sibu congkan ed.

Cai Chen 蔡沈. *Hongfan Huangji Neipian* 洪範皇極內篇 (Supreme Ultimate of the *Great Plan*, Inner Chapters). In SYXA, 67.6a–16a.

Cai Yong 蔡邕. "Mingtang Yueling Lun" 明堂月令論 (A Discussion of the Luminous Hall [in Connection with the] "Monthly Ordinances"). In *Cai Zhong-lang Ji* 蔡中朗集 (Collected Writings of Cai Zhong-lang), 10.1a–8b. SBBY ed.

Cai Yuan-ding 蔡元定. *Fawei Lun* 發微論 (A Discourse on Disclosing Subtleties). In *Yingyin Siku Quanshu Zhenben Jiuji* 影印四庫全書珍本九集 (Reprints of Rare Editions from the *Complete Library in Four Treasuries*, series 9), vol. 208. Taipei: Shangwu yinshuguan, 1979.

—— "Yixiang Yiyan" 易象意言 (On the Meaning of the Images Associated with the *Change*). In SYXA, 62.12a–19b.

Chen Li 陳澧. *Dongshu Dushu Ji* 東塾讀書記 (Reading Notes of [Chen] Dong-shu). Taipei: Shangwu yinshuguan, 1967.

Cheng Yi 程頤 and Cheng Hao 程顥. *Henan Chengshi Yishu* 河南程氏遺書 (Surviving Works of the Chengs of Henan). In *Er Cheng Quanshu* 二程全書 (Complete Works of the Two Chengs), *juan* 1–25. SBBY ed.

Chunqiu Fanlu 春秋繁露 (Luxuriant Gems of the *Spring and Autumn Annals*). Attributed to Dong Zhong-shu 董仲舒. Taipei: Shangwu yinshuguan, 1966.

Dai Zhen 戴震. *Dai Zhen Wenji* 戴震文集 (Prose Collections of Dai Zhen). Taipei:

Huazhen shuju, 1974.

—— *Qu Yuan Fuzhu* 屈原賦注 (Annotations on the Rhapsody of Qu Yuan). Taipei: Shangwu yinshuguan, 1968.

Diao Bao 刁包. *Qian-shi Zhaji* 潛室劄記 (Notebook of [Diao] Qian-shi). Shanghai: Shangwu yinshuguan, 1936.

Dong Zhong-shu, see *Chunqiu Fanlu*.

Er Cheng Yulu 二程語錄 (Recorded Conversations of the Two Chengs). Compiled by Zhu Xi 朱熹. Taipei: Shangwu yinshuguan, 1966.

Fang Yi-zhi 方以智. *Dongxi Jun* 東西均. Peking: Zhonghua shuju, 1962.

—— *Tongya* 通雅 (Comprehensive Refinement). 1666 ed.

—— *Wuli Xiaozhi* 物理小識 (Small Notes on the Principles of Things). Taipei: Shangwu yinshuguan, 1968.

Gong Zi-zhen 龔自震. *Gong Zi-zhen Quanji* 龔自震全集 (Complete Collected Writings of Gong Zi-zhen). Taipei: Hele tushu chubanshe, 1975.

Gu Yan-wu 顧炎武. *Gu Yan-wu Wen* 顧炎武文 (Writings of Gu Yan-wu). Annotated by Tang Jing-gao 唐敬杲. Taipei: Shangwu yinshuguan, 1969.

—— *Yuanchaoben Rizhi Lu* 原抄本日知錄 (The Original Manuscript Version of the *Record of Daily Knowledge*). Taipei: Minglun chubanshe, 1970.

Gui You-guang 歸有光. *Zhen-chuan Xiansheng Ji* 震川先生集 (Collected Writings of Mr. [Gui] Zhen-chuan). SBBY ed.

Hanshu, see *Xinjiao Hanshu JiZhu*.

Han Yu 韓愈. *Han Chang-li Quanji* 韓昌黎全集 (Complete Collected Writings of Han Chang-li). SBBY ed.

He Tang 何塘. "Yinyang Guanjian Bian" 陰陽官見辯 (A Debate [with Wang Ting-xiang] Concerning my Views on Yin and Yang). In *Mingru Xue'an* 明儒學案 (Anthology of Ming Confucians), 48.89–99. Compiled by Huang Zong-xi. Taipei: Hele tushu chubanshe, 1974.

Hu Ju-ren 胡居仁. *Juye Lu* 居業錄 (Records of [Hu] Ju-ye). Taipei: Shangwu yinshuguan, 1971.

Hu Wei 胡渭. *Yitu Mingbian* 易圖明辨 (A Clarifiying Critique of the Diagrams Associated with the *Change*). Taipei: Guangwen shuju, 1971.

—— *Yugong Zhuizhi* 禹貢錐指 (Boring the *Tribute of Yu*). Taipei: Guangxue She Yinshuguan, 1975.

Huainanzi 淮南子. SBBY ed.

Huang Dao-zhou 黃道周. *Zhongding Bowu Dianhui* 重訂博物典彙 (A Series of Articles on a Wide Range of Things, Reedited). 1663 ed.

Huangdi Neijing Suwen Wang Bing Zhu 黃帝內經素問王冰注 (Plain Questions of the *Yellow Sovereign's Inner Classic* with Wang Bing's Commentary). SBBY ed.

Huang Zhen 黃震. *Dongfa Richao* 東發日鈔 (Daily Notes of [Huang] Dong-fa). Excerpted in SYXA, 86.6a–11b.

Huang Zong-xi 黃宗羲. *Mengzi Shishuo* 孟子師說 (My Master's [Liu Zong-zhou's] Teachings on the *Mencius*) In *Li-zhou Yizhu Huikan* 黎洲遺著彙刊 (A Collection of [Huang] Li-zhou's Extant Works), vol. 2. Taipei: Longyan chubanshe, 1969.

——, comp. *Mingru Xue'an* 明儒學案 (Anthology of Ming Confucians). Taipei: Hele tushu chubanshe, 1974.

—— *Nan-lei Wending, Houji* 南雷文定後集 (Prose Works of [Huang] Nan-lei, Latter Collection). Taipei: Shangwu yinshuguan, 1970.

—— *Poxie Lun* 破邪論 (A Discussion Confuting Heterodoxy). In *Lizhou Yizhu Huikan*, vol. 2.

—— *Yixue Xiangshu Lun* 易學象數論 (A Discussion of the Images and Numerologies Associated with the Study of the *Change*). Taipei: Guangwen shuju, 1974.

—— and Quan Zu-wang 全祖望, comps. *Zengbu Song Yuan Xue'an* 增補宋元學案 (Anthology Song and Yuan Scholars with Supplements). SBBY ed.

Huang Zong-yan 黃宗炎. *Yixue Bianhuo* 易學辨惑 (An Exposé of Delusions Regarding the Study of the *Change*). In *Zhaodai Congshu* 昭代叢書, Ce 30.

Hui Dong 慧棟. *Yili* 易例 (Exempla from the *Change*). Taipei: Shangwu yinshuguan, 1965.

Jiang Fan 江藩. *Hanxue Shicheng Ji* 漢學師承記 (A Record of the Succession of Masters of the Han Learning). Taipei: Shangwu yinshuguan, 1970.

—— *Li Jingwen* 隸經文 (A Supplement to the Classics). Taipei: Shangwu yinshuguan, 1966.

Jiang Yong 江永. *Lülü Xinlun* 律呂新論 (New Discussion on Harmonics and the Pitchpipes). Taipei: Shangwu yinshuguan, 1966.

—— *Shuxue* 數學 (Mathematical Studies). Shanghai: Shangwu yinshuguan, 1936.

Jiao Hong 焦竑. *Jiaoshi Bicheng* 焦氏筆程 (Mr. Jiao's Notebook). Taipei: Shangwu yinshuguan, 1971.

Kang You-wei 康有為. *Da Dai Liji Buzhu* 大戴禮記補注 (Supplementary Commentary on the *Elder Dai's Record of Rites*). In *Kang Nan-hai Xiansheng Weikan Yigao* 康南海先生未刊遺稿 (Unpublished Manuscripts of Mr. Kang Nan-hai), pp. 99–173. Taipei: Wenshi zhe chubanshe, 1979.

Lai Qu-tang 來瞿唐. *Yijing Tujie* 易經圖解 (Explanations of the Diagrams Associated with the *Classic of Change*). Taipei: Guangtian chubanshe, 1975.

Laozi 老子. SBBY ed.

Lidai Tianwen Lüli Dengzhi Huibian 歷代天文律曆等志彙編 (Collected Treatises on Astrology, Astronomy, and Harmonics in the Standard Histories). 9 vols. Peking: Zhonghua Shuju, 1976.

Li Ding-zuo 李鼎祚, comp. *Zhouyi Jijie Zuanshu* 周易集解纂疏 (Collected Explications and Annotations of the *Zhou Change*). Taipei: Guangwen shuju, 1971.

Li Guang-di 李光地. *Zhujie Zhengmeng* 注解正夢 (An Annotations and Explication of [Zhang Zai's] Correcting Youthful Ignorance). In *Yingyin Siku Quanshu Zhenben, Jiuji* 影印四庫全書珍本九集 (Reprints of Rare Editions from the *Complete Library in Four Treasuries*, series 9), vol. 176. Taipei: Shangwu yinshuguan, 1979.

Liji Zhengzhu 禮記鄭注 (*Record of Rites* with Zheng [Xuan's] Commentary). SBBY ed.

Liu Xian-ting 劉獻廷. *Guang-yang Zaji* 廣陽雜記 (Miscellaneus Notes of [Liu] Guang-yang). Taipei: Hele tushu chubanshe, 1976.

Liu Zong-yuan 柳宗元. *Liu He-dong Quanji* 柳河東全集 (Complete Works of Liu He-dong). SBBY ed.

Liu Zong-zhou 劉宗周. *Liuzi Quanshu* 劉子全書 (Complete Works of Master Liu). In *Zhonghua Wenshi Congshu* 中華文史叢書, collection 7, no. 57. Taipei: Huawen shuju, n.d.

Lu Long-qi 陸隴其. *Lu Jia-shu Xiansheng Wenxue Lu* 陸稼書先生問學錄 (Record of Mr. Lu Jia-shu's Interrogations on Learning). Taipei: Shangwu yinshuguan, 1966.

—— *Sanyutang Riji* 三魚堂日記 (Diary from Three-Fish Hall). Taipei: Shangwu yinshuguan, 1965.

—— *Sanyutang Wenji* 三魚堂文集 (Prose Collections from Three-Fish Hall). In *Luzi Quanshu* (Complete Works of Master Lu). 1891 ed.

Lu Shi-yi 陸世儀. *Lu Fu-ting Xiansheng Yishu* 陸桴亭先生遺書 (Surviving Works of Mr. Lu Fu-ting). Peking, 1900.

—— *Sibian Lu Jiyao* 思辨錄輯要 (The Best of the *Record of Thinking and Sifting*). In *Kunzhi Jideng Sanzhong* 困知記等三種 (The *Record of Hard Study* with Two Other Works of the Same Sort). Taipei: Guangxue she yinshuguan,, 1975.

Lü Kun 呂坤. *Shenyin Yu* 呻吟語 (Groaning Words). Taipei: Hele tushu chubanshe, 1975.

Lüshi Chunqiu 呂氏春秋 (Master Lü's Spring and Autumn Annals). SBBY ed.

Lu Xiang-shan 陸象山. *Xiangshan Quanji* 象山全集 (Complete Collected Writings of Lu Xiang-shan). SBBY ed.

Mao Qi-ling 毛奇齡. *Shangshu Guangting Lu* 尚書廣廳錄 (Record of a Broad Understanding of the *Documents of Antiquity*). In *Yingyin Siku Quanshu Zhenben, Jiuji*, vol. 34. Taipei: Shangwu yinshuguan, 1979.

—— *Xi-he Heji* 西河合集 (Collected Writings of [Mao] Xi-he). 1770 ed.

Mei Wen-ding 梅文鼎. *Lifa Tongkao* 歷法通考 (Comprehensive Investigations of Astronimical Systems). In *Meishi Congshu Jiyao* 梅氏叢書輯要 (The Best of Mr. Mei's Collected Works), juan 60. Taipei: Yiwen yinshuguan, 1971.

—— *Lixue Dawen* 歷學答問 (Answers to Queries on the Study of Astronomy). In *Meishi Congshu Jiyao*, juan 59.

—— *Lixue Yiwen* 歷學疑問 (Queries on the Study of Astronomy). In *Meishi Congshu Jiyao*, juan 46–48.

Ouyang Xiu 歐陽修. *Ouyang Wen-zhong Ji* 歐陽文忠集 (Collected Commentaries of Ouyang Wen-zhong). SBBY ed.

Pi Xi-rui 皮錫瑞. *Jingxue Lishi* 經學歷史 (History of Classical Studies). Annotated by Zhou Da-tong 周大同. Taipei: Yiwen yinshuguan, 1966.

—— *Jingxue Tonglun* 經學通論 (Comprehensive Discussions of Classical Studies). Taipei: Hele tushu chubanshe, 1974.

Qingru Xue'an, see Xu Shi-chang.

Ruan Yuan 阮元. *Chouren Zhuan* 疇人傳 (Biographies of Mathematicians and Astronomers). In *Chouren Zhuan Huibian* 疇人傳彙編 (Collected Editions of *Biographies of Mathematicians and Astronomers*). Taipei: Shijie shuju, 1962.

Shangshu Kongzhuan 尚書孔傳 (*Documents of Antiquity* with Kong [An-guo's] Commentary). SBBY ed.

Shao Yong 邵雍. *Huangji Jingshi Shu* 皇極經世書 (Book of the Supreme Rules Governing the World). SBBY ed.

Shen Gua 沈括. *Mengqi Bitan Jiaozheng* 夢溪筆談校正 (Dream Brook Essays Collated and Corrected). Taipei: Shijie shuju, 1965.

Shiji, see *Xianjiao Shiji Sanjia Zhu*.

Siku Quanshu Zongmu 四庫全書總目 (General Catalogue to the *Complete Library in Four Treasuries*). Taipei: Yiwen yinshuguan, 1974.

Sima Guang 司馬光. "Zang Lun" 葬論 (A Discussion of Burials). In *Sima Wen-zheng Ji* 司馬文正集 (Collected Writings of Sima Wen-zheng), 13.7a–7b. SBBY ed.

Sima Qian, see *Xinjiao Shiji Sanjia Zhu*.

Su Xun 蘇洵. *Su Xun Ji* 蘇洵集 (Collected Writings of Su Xun). Taipei: Hele tushu chubanshe, 1975.

Sun Qi-feng 孫奇逢. *Sun Xia-feng Xiansheng Yulu* 孫夏峰先生語錄 (Recorded Conversations of Mr. Sun Xia-feng). Taipei: Guangwen shuju, 1970.

Sun Xing-yan 孫星衍. "Hetu Luoshu Kao" 河圖洛書考 (An Investigation of the Yellow River Chart and Luo River Writing). In QRXA, 110.17a–20a.

Song Lian 宋濂. "Hetu Luoshu Shuo" 河圖洛書說 (A Discourse on the Yellow River Chart and Luo River Writing). In *Song Wen-xian Gongquan Ji* 宋文憲公全集 (Complete Collected Writings of Song Wen-xian), 36.2b–4a. SBBY ed.

Tang Jian 唐鑑. *Qing Xue'an Xiaozhi* 清學案小識 (Small Anthology of Qing Scholars). Taipei: Shang-wu yinshuguan, 1969.

Tianwen Tiandui Zhu 天文天對註 (The *Queries on the Heavens* with [Liu Zong-yuan's] *Replies to the Queries on the Heavens* with Annotations). Edited by the Study Group on Classical Literature of the Futan University Department of Chinese Literature). Shanghai: Renmin chubanshe, 1973.

Wang Fu-zhi 王夫之. *Du Tongjian Lun* 讀通鑑論 (Discussion of the *Comprehensive Mirror* [of Sima Guang]). SBBY ed.

—— *Liji Zhangju* 禮記章句 (*Record of Rites* [with Commentary] by Paragraphs and Sentences). Taipei: Guangwen shuju, 1977.

—— *Shangshu Yinyi* 尚書引義 (An Interpretation of the *Documents of Antiquity*). Taipei: Hele tushu chubanshe, 1975.

—— *Siwen Lu, Waipian* 思問錄外篇 (Record of Intellectual Inquiry, Outer Chapters). In *Li-zhou Chuan-shan Wushu* 黎洲船山五書 (Five Books by [Huang] Li-zhou and [Wang] Chuan-shan). Taipei: Shijie shuju, 1974.

—— *Zhangzi Zhengmeng Zhu* 張子正夢注 (Master Zhang's *Correcting Youthful Ignorance* with [Wang Fu-zhi's] Commentary). Taipei: Shijie shuju, 1974.

—— *Zhouyi Baishu* 周易稗疏 (Minor Annotations on the Zhou Change). Excepted in QRXA, 8.21a–28a.

—— *Zhouyi Waizhuan* 周易外傳 (Outer Commentary on the Zhou Change). In *Chuan-shan Yixue* 船山易學 ([Wang] Chuan-shan's Studies on the *Change*), pp. 749–1056. Taipei: Guangwen shuju, 1971.

Wang Ting-xiang 王廷相. *Jiacang Ji* 家藏集 (Collections for the Family Repository). In *Wang Ting-xiang Zhexue Xuanji* 王廷相哲學選集 (Selected Philosophical Works of Wang Ting-xiang), pp. 147–219. Taipei: Hele tushu chubanshe, 1974.

—— *Shenyan* 慎言 (Prudent Words). In *Wang Ting-xiang Zhexue Xuanji* 王廷相哲學選集 (Selected Philosophical Works of Wang Ting-xiang), pp. 1–79.

—— *Yashu* 雅述 (Refined Explications). In *Wang Ting-xiang Zhexue Xuanji* 王廷相哲學選集 (Selected Philosophical Works of Wang Ting-xiang), pp. 80–146.

Wang Xi-shan 王錫闡. *Xiao-an Yishu* 曉菴遺書 (Surviving Works of [Wang] Xiao-an). In *Mu Xixuan Congshu* 木犀軒叢書, ce 30–34. Compiled by Li Sheng-duo 李盛鐸.

Wang Ying-lin 王應麟. *Kunxue Jiwen* 困學紀聞 (Record of Learning Gained Through Hard Study). SBBY ed.

—— *Liujing Tianwen Bian* 六經天文編 (Anthology of the Astronomy in the Six Classics). Taipei: Shangwu yinshuguan, 1965.

Xinjiao Hanshu Jizhu 新校漢書集注 (Newly Collated *Han History* with Collected Commentaries). Taipei: Shijie shuju, 1973.

Xinjiao Shiji Sanjia Zhu 新校史記三家注 (Newly Collated *Records of the Historian* with Commentaries by Three Scholars). Taipei: Shijie shuju, 1972.

Xu Shi-chang 徐世昌, comp. *Qingru Xue'an* 清儒學案 (Anthology of Qing Confucians). Taipei: Shijie shuju, 1979.

Yan Ruo-qu 閻若璩. *Shangshu Guwen Shuzheng* 尚書古文疏証 (Inquiry into the Authenticity of the Old Text Version of the *Documents of Antiquity*). Tientsin: Wushi kanben, 1796.

—— *Sishu Shidi* 四書釋地 (Explanations of the Place Names in the *Four Books*). Taipei: Shangwu yinshuguan, 1968.

Yan Yuan 顏元. *Cunxing Bian* 存性編 (Treatise on Preserving the Nature). In *Sicun Bian* (Treatises on the Four Preservations), pp. 3–38. Taipei: Shijie shuju, 1966.

Yijing, see *Zhouyi Zhushu*.

Zhang Zai 張載. *Zhangzi Zhengmeng Zhu* 張子正夢注 (Master Zhang's *Correcting Youthful Ignorance* with [Wang Fu-zhi's] Commentary). Taipei: Shijie shuju, 1967.

—— *Zhangzi Quanshu* 張子全書 (Complete Works of Master Zhang). SBBY ed.

Zhang Hui-yan 張惠言. *Yitu Tiaobian* 易圖條辨 (Systematic Critique of the Diagrams Associated with the *Change*). In *Zhang Hui-yan Yixue Shishu* 張惠言易學十書 (Ten Books by Zhang Hui-yan on the Study of the *Change*), vol. 2. Taipei: Guangwen shuju, 1970.

Zhang Li-xiang 張禮祥. *Zhongding Yang-yuan Xiansheng Quanji* 重訂楊園先生全集 (Complete Collected Writings of Mr. [Zhang] Yang-yuan, Reedited). Jiangsu shuju edition, 1871.

Zhang Xue-cheng 章學誠. *Wenshi Tongyi* 文史通義 (The Comprehensive Meaning of Culture and History). Taipei: Guangwen shuju, 1967.

Zhao Yi 趙翼. *Ershier Shi Zhaji* 二十二史劄記 (Notes on the Twenty-two Standard Histories). Taipei: Guangwen shuju, 1972.

Zheng Qiao 鄭樵. *Tongzhi, Ershi Lue* 通志二十略 (Comprehensive Treatises, Twenty Monographs). Taipei: Shijie shuju, 1970.

Zhong Yong 中庸 (Doctrine of the Mean). In *Sishu Jizhu* 四書集注 (The Four Books with Collected Commentaries). SBBY ed.

Zhouli Zhengzhu 周禮鄭注 (Rites of *Zhou* with Zheng [Xuan's] Commentary). SBBY ed.

Zhouyi Zhushu 周易注書 (*Zhou Change* with Commentaries). SBBY ed.

Zhouyi WangHan Zhu 周易王韓注 (*Zhou Change* with Commentaries by Wang [Bi] and Han [Kang-bo]). Taipei: Xinxing shuju, 1972.

Zhu Xi 朱熹. *Yixue Qimeng* 易學啟蒙 (A Primer on the *Change*). Taipei: Guangxue she yinshuguan, 1973.

—— Yuyao 語要 (Words of Importance). In SYXA, 48.11b–39b.

—— *Zhuzi Daquan* 朱子大全 (Great Collected Writings of Master Zhu). Compiled by Zhu Zai 朱在. SBBY ed.

—— *Zhuzi Yulei* 朱子語類 ([Abridged] Classified Conversations of Master Zhu). Compiled by Zhang Bo-xing 張伯行. Taipei: Shangwu yinshuguan, 1973.

Zhuangzi 莊子. SBBY ed.

Secondary Sources in Chinese and Japanese

Feng You-lan 馮友蘭. *Zhongguo Zhexue Shi* 中國哲學史 (History of Chinese Philosophy). Hong Kong: Taipingyang tushu gongsi, 1975.

Gu Jie-gang 顧頡剛. *Handai Xueshu Shilue* 漢代學術史略 (An Outline of the Intellectual History of the Han Era). Taipei: Qimeng shuju, 1972.

Guo Mo-ruo 郭沫若 et. al. *Guanzi Jijiao* 管子集校 (Guanzi with Collected Collations). Peking: Kexue chubanshe, 1956.

Hashimoto Masukichi 橋本增吉. *Shina kōdai rekiho shi kenkyū* 支那古代曆法史研究 (Studies on the History of Ancient Chinese Calendrical Astronomy). Tokyo: Tōyō bunko, 1943.

Luo Guang 羅光. *Zhongguo Zhexue Sixiang Shi* 中國哲學思想史兩漢南北朝片 (History of Chinese Philosophical Thought of the Han and Period of Disunion). Taipei: Xuesheng shuju, 1978.

Lu Bao-qian 陸寶千. *Qingdai Sixiang Shi* 清代思想史 (History of Qing Thought). Taipei: Guangwen shuju, 1978.

Mou Zong-san 牟宗三. *Caixing yu Xuanli* 才性與玄理 (The Innate Nature and the Mysterious Pattern). Taipei: Xuesheng shuju, 1974.

Qian Bao-cong 錢寶琮. "Cong Chunqiu dao Ming de Lifa Yanke" 從春秋到明末的曆法沿革 (The Vicissitudes of Mathematical Astronomy from the Spring and Autumn Era to the End of the Ming). *Lishi Yanjiu* 歷史研究 (Historical Studies) (1960), 3:35–67.

Qian Mu 錢穆. *Song Ming Lixue Gaishu* 宋明理學概書 (A General Survey of Song-Ming Neo- Confucianism). Taipei: Xuesheng shuju, 1977.

Su Qing-bin 蘇慶彬. "Yan Ruo-qu, Hu Wei, Cui Shu Sanjia Bianwei Fangfa zhi Yanjiu" 閻若璩胡渭崔述三家辨偽方法研究 (A Study for the Methods Used by Yan Ruo-qu, Hu Wei, and Cui Shu for Exposing Forgeries). *Xinya Shuyuan Xueshu Niankan* 新亞書院學術年刊 (New Asia College Academic Journal) (1961), 3:1–35.

Tang Jun-yi 唐君毅. *Zhongguo Zhexue Yuanlun: Taolun Pian* 中國哲學原論導論篇 (A Fundamental Exposition of Chinese Philosophy: Introductory Discussion). Hong Kong: Dongfang Renwen Xuehui, 1974.

—— *Zhongguo Zhexue Yuanlun: Yuanjiao Pian* 中國哲學原論原教篇 (A Fundamental Exposition of Chinese Philosophy: On Teaching). Hong Kong: Xinya yanjiusuo 新亞研究所, 1975.

Wu Ze 吳澤. "Kang You-wei Gongyang Sanshi Shuo de Lishi Jinhua Guandian Yanjiu" 康有為公羊三世說的歷史進化觀點研究 (A Study of the Progressive Theory of Hisory in Kang You-wei's Conception of the Three Ages of the *Gongyang* Commentary). In 中國近三百年學術思想論集 (A Collection of Articles on Chinese Thought and Scholarship of the Past Three Hundred Years), pp. 533–78. Hong Kong: Bowen shuju, 1978.

Xi Ze-zong 席澤宗. "Shilun Wang Xi-shan de Tianwen Gongzuo" 試論王錫闡的天文工作 (A Preliminary Discussion of Wang Xi-shan's Astronomical Works). *Kexueshi Jikan* 科學史集刊 (History of Science) (1963), 6:53–65.

Xu Di-shan 許地山. "Daojia Sixiang yu Daojiao" 道家思想與道教 (The Thought of the [Classical] Daoist School and Religious Daoism). In *Zhongguo Zhexue Sixiang Lunji,*

Liang Han, Wei Jin Sui Tang Pian 中國哲學思想論集兩漢魏晉隋唐篇 (Readings in Chinese Philosophy and Thought of the Han, Wei-Jin, and Sui-Tang Eras), pp. 179–215. Taipei: Mutong chubanshe, 1976.

Xu Fu-guan 徐復觀. *Liang Han Sixiang Shi* 兩漢思想史 (Intellectual History of the Han). Vol. 2. Hong Kong: Zhongwen Daxue, 1975.

Yabuuti Kiyosi 藪內清. "Astronomical Tables in China, from the Han to the Tang Dynasties." In *Chūgoku chūsei kagaku gijutsu shi no kenkyū* 中國中世科學技術史 的の研究 (Studies on the History of Medieval Chinese Science and Technology), pp. 445–92. Edited by Yabüti Kiyosi. Kyoto: Kyoto University Research Institute of Humanistic Studies, 1963.

—— *Chūgoku no tenmon rekihō* 中國の天文曆法 (Chinese Astronomy and Calendrical Science). Tokyo: Heibonsha, 1969.

Yamada Keiji 山田慶兒. "Shushi no uchuron josetsu" 朱子の宇宙論序說 (The Antecedents of Zhu Xi's Cosmology). *Tohō gakuhō* 東方學報 (Journal of Asian Studies) (1964), 36: 481–511.

Yu Ying-shi. 余英時. "Cong Song-Ming Ruxue de Fazhan Lun Qingdai Sixiang Shi" 從宋 明儒學的發展論清代思想史 (Qing Intellectual History from the Perspective of Song-Ming Neo- Confucianism). *Zhongguo Xueren* 中國學人 (Chinese Scholars) (September 1970), 2:19–42.

—— "Qingdai Sixiang Shi de Yige Xin Jieshi" 清代思想史的一個新解釋 (A New Interpretation of Qing Intellectual History). In *Zhongguo Zhexue Sixiang Lunji, Qingdai Pian* 中國哲學思想論集清代篇 (Readings in Chinese Philosophy and Thought of the Qing Era), pp. 11–48. Taipei: Mutong chubanshe, 1977.

Zhou Da-tong 周大同. *Chu Hsi* (Zhu Xi) 朱熹. Taipei: Shangwu yinshuguan, 1971.

Sources in Western Languages

Abrams, M.H. *Natural Supernaturalism: Tradition and Revolution in Romantic Literature.* New York: Norton, 1973.

Allan, Sarah. "Sons of Suns: Myth and Totemism in Early China." *Bulletin of the School of Oriental and African Studies* (1981), 44:290–326.

Bacon, Francis. *The Advancement of Learning.* Edited by William Aldis Wright. Oxford: Oxford University Press, 1926.

—— *The New Organon.* In *The New Organon and Related Writings.* Edited by Fulton H. Anderson. The Library of Liberal Arts. Indianapolis: Bobbs-Merrill, 1960.

Bennett, Steven J. "Patterns of the Sky and Earth: A Chinese Science of Applied Cosmology." *Chinese Science* (March 1978), 3:1–26.

Berling, Judith A. *The Syncretic Religion of Lin Chao-en.* New York: Columbia University Press, 1980.

Birnbaum, Raoul. "Introduction to the Study of T'ang Buddhist Astrology: Research Notes on Primary Sources and Basic Principles." *Society for the Study of Chinese Religions Bulletin* (Fall 1980), 8:5–19.

Bodde, Derk. "The Chinese Cosmic Magic Known as Watching for the Ethers." In *Studia Serica Bernhard Karlgren Dedicata: Sinological Studies Dedicated to Bernhard Karlgren on His Seventieth Birthday, October Fifth, 1959,* pp. 14–35. Edited by Soren Egerod and Else Glahn. Copenhagen: Ejnar Munksgaard, 1959.

—— *Festivals in Classical China: New Year and Other Annual Observances during the*

Han Dynasty 206 B.C. – A.D. 220. Princeton: Princeton University Press, 1975.

—— "Types of Chinese Categorical Thinking." *Journal of the American Oriental Society* (1939), 59:200–19.

—— and Clarence Morris. *Law in Imperial China, Exemplified by 190 Ch'ing Cases with Historical, Social, and Juridical Commentaries.* Philadelphia: University of Pennsylvania Press, 1973.

Boltz, William G. "Kung kung and the Flood: Reverse Euhemerism in the *Yao tien.*" *T'oung Pao* n.s. (1981), 67:141–53.

—— "Philological Footnotes to the Han New Year Rites." *Journal of the American Oriental Society* (1979), 99:423–39.

Broman, Sven. "Studies on the Chou Li." *Bulletin of the Museum of Far Eastern Antiquities* (1961), 33:1–89.

Cahill, James. *Chinese Painting.* Geneva: Editions d'Art Albert Skira, 1960; reprint ed., New York: Rizzoli, 1977.

Cammann, Schuyler. "The Magic Square of Three in Old Chinese Philosophy and Religion." *History of Religions* (Summer 1961), 1:37–80.

Cassirer, Ernst. *The Philosophy of Symbolic Forms.* Vol. 2. *Mythical Thought.* Translated by Ralph Manheim. New Haven: Yale University Press, 1955.

Chan, Wing-tsit. "The *Hsing-li ching-I* and the Ch'eng Chu School of the Seventeenth Century." In William Theodore de Bary and the Conference on Seventeenth-Century Chinese Thought, *The Unfolding of Neo-Confucianism,* pp. 543–79. New York: Columbia University Press, 1975.

——, trans. *Reflections on Things at Hand: The Neo-Confucian Anthology Compiled by Chu Hsi and Lü Tsu-chien.* New York: Columbia University Press, 1967.

——, trans. and comp. *A Source Book in Chinese Philosophy.* Princeton: Princeton University Press, 1963.

Chang, Kwang-chih. *The Archeology of Ancient China.* Rev. ed. New Haven: Yale University Press, 1972.

—— *Shang Civilization.* New Haven: Yale University Press, 1980.

—— et al. *Food in Chinese Culture: Anthropological and Historical Perspectives.* New Haven: Yale University Press, 1977.

Ch'ien, Edward T. "Chiao Hung and the Revolt Against the Ch'eng-Chu Orthodoxy." In William Theodore de Bary and the Conference on Seventeenth-Century Chinese Thought, *The Unfolding of Neo-Confucianism,* pp. 271–303. New York: Columbia University Press, 1975.

Dardess, John W. *Confucianism and Autocracy: Professional Elites in the Founding of the Ming Dynasty.* Berkeley: University of California Press, 1983.

De Bary, William Theodore, Wing-tsit Chan and Burton Watson, comps., *Sources of Chinese Tradition.* Vol. I. New York: Columbia University Press, 1964.

De Francis, John, and E-tu Zen Sun, eds. and trans., *Chinese Social History: Translations of Selected Studies.* American Council of Learned Societies Studies in Chinese and Related Civilizations, no. 7. New York: Octagon, 1966.

Dunstan, Helen. "The Late Ming Epidemics: A Preliminary Survey." *Ch'ing-shih wen-t'i* (November 1975), 3(3): 1–59.

Durkheim, Emile and Marcel Mauss. *Primitive Classification.* Translated and edited by Rodney Needham. Chicago: University of Chicago Press, 1963.

Eberhard, Wolfram. "Beiträge zur kosmologischen Spekulation in Chinas in der Han Zeit." *Baessler- Archiv* (1933), 16(1):1–100.

Elman, Benjamin. "Ch'ing Dynasty 'Schools' of Scholarship." *Qingshi wenti* (December 1981), 4(6): 1–44.

—— "The Hsüeh-hai T'ang and the Rise of New Text Scholarship in Canton." *Qingshi wenti* (December 1979), 4(2) 51–82.

Frankel, Hans H. *The Flowering Plum and the Palace Lady.* New Haven: Yale University Press, 1976.

Freeman, Kathleen. *Ancilla to the Pre-Socratic Philosophers: A Complete Translation of the Fragments in Diels, "Fragmente der Vorosokratiker."* Oxford: Basil Blackwell, 1948.

Freeman, Michael D. "From Adept to Worthy: The Philosophical Career of Shao Yung." *Journal of the American Oriental Society* (1982), 102: 477–91.

Ghyka, Matila. *The Geometry of Art and Life.* New York: Sheed and Ward, 1946; reprint edition, New York: Dover, 1977.

Glacken, Clarence J. *Traces on the Rhodian Shore: Nature and Culture in Western Thought from Ancient Times to the End of the Eighteenth Century.* Berkeley: U. of California Press, 1967.

Gombrich, E.H. *Symbolic Images: Studies in the Art of the Renaissance.* London: Phaidon Press, 1972.

Goody, Jack. *The Domestication of the Savage Mind.* Cambridge: Cambridge University Press, 1977.

—— , ed. *Literacy in Traditional Societies.* Cambridge: Cambridge University Press, 1968.

Graham, A.C. *Two Chinese Philosophers: Ch'eng Ming-tao and Ch'eng Yi-ch'uan.* London: Lund Humphries, 1958.

Granet, Marcel. *La Pensée Chinoise.* Paris: Editions Albin Michel, 1950.

Harootunian, H.D. "The Consciousness of Arcaic Form in the New Religion of Kokugaku." In *Japanese Thought in the Tokugawa Period: Methods and Metaphors,* pp. 63–104. Edited by Tetsuo Najita and Irwin Scheiner. Chicago: University of Chicago Press, 1978.

Heninger, S.K., Jr. *The Cosmographical Glass: Renaissance Diagrams of the Universe.* San Marino, CA: Hunington Library, 1977.

Ho, Peng-yoke. "The Astronomical Bureau in Ming China." *Journal of Asian History* (1969), 3: 137–57.

—— *The Astronomical Chapters of the Chin-shu.* Paris and the Hague: Mouton, 1966.

Holton, Gerald. "Johannes Kepler's Universe: Its Physics and Metaphysics." In *Toward Modern Science,* vol. 2, *Studies in Renaissance Science,* pp. 192–216. Edited by Robert M. Palter. New York: Noonday Press, 1961.

Hsia, C.T. Review of *Archetype and Allegory in the Dream of the Red Chamber,* by Andrew H. Plaks. *Harvard Journal of Asiatic Studies* (1979), 39: 190–210.

Hsü, Dau-lin. "Crime and Cosmic Order." *Harvard Journal of Asiatic Studies* (1970), 30: 111–25.

Huizinga, Johan. *The Waning of the Middle Ages: A Study of the Forms of Life, Thought, and Art in France and the Netherlands in the XIVth and XVth Centuries.* Garden City, NY: Doubleday, Anchor, 1954.

Kaltenmark, Max. "The Ideology of the T'ai-p'ing ching." In *Facets of Taoism: Essays in*

Chinese Religion, pp. 19–45. New Haven: Yale University Press, 1979.

Karlgren, Bernhard. "Glosses on the Book of Documents." *Bulletin of the Museum of Far Eastern Antiquities* (1948), 20: 163–205.

—— "Legends and Cults in Ancient China." *Bulletin of the Museum of Far Eastern Antiquities* (1946), 18: 199–365.

—— "Some Sacrifices in Chou China." *Bulletin of the Museum of Far Eastern Antiquities* (1968), 40: 1–32.

——, trans. *The Book of Documents.* Göteborg: Elanders Boktryckeri Artiebolog, 1950; reprinted from *Bulletin of the Museum of Far Eastern Antiquities*, no. 22.

Kates, George N. *The Years That Were Fat: The Last of Old China.* Cambridge: MIT Press, 1967.

Keightley, David N. "The Religious Commitment: Shang Theology and the Genesis of Chinese Political Culture." *History of Religions* (February–May 1978), 17: 211–25.

Kroll, J.L. "Toward a Study of the Economic Views of Sang Hung-yang." *Early China* (1978–79), 4: 11–18.

Lamont, H.G. "An Early Ninth Century Debate on Heaven: Liu Tsung-yuan's *Tien Shuo* and Liu Yu-his's *Tien Lun*; An Annotated Translation and Introduction, Parts 1 and 2." *Asia Major* (1973), 18: 181–208; (1974), 19: 37–85.

Lau, D.C. *The Analects* (Lunyu). Harmondsworth, Eng.: Penguin, 1979.

——, trans. *Mencius.* Penguin, 1970.

Le Blanc, Charles Yvon. "The Idea of Resonance (kan-ying) in the *Huananzi* with a Translation and Analyisis of *Huananzi* Chapter Six." Ph.D. dissertation, University of Pennsylvania, 1978.

Lee, Sherman E. *Chinese Landscape Painting.* New York: Harper and Row, Icon Editions, n.d.

Lévi Strauss, Claude. *Introduction to a Science of Mythology.* Vol. 1. *The Raw and the Cooked.* Translated by John and Doreen Weightman. New York: Harper and Row, 1970.

Li, Chu-tsing. *A Thousand Peaks and Myriad Ravines: Chinese Paintings in the Charles A. Drenowatz Collection.* Ascona, Switzerland: Artibus Asiae, 1974.

Liu, James T.C. "The Sung Emperors and the *Ming-t'ang* or Hall of Enlightenment." In *Etudes Song*, (1973), ser. 2.1, pp. 45–58. Edited by Francoise Aubin.

Liu, Shu-xian. "The Use of Analogy and Symbolism in Traditional Chinese Philosophy." *Journal of Chinese Philosophy* (June–September 1974), 1: 313–38.

Liu, Ts'un-yan. "The Penetration of Taoism into the Ming Neo-Confucianist Elite." *T'oung Pao* n.s. (1971), 57: 31–102.

—— "Taoist Self-Cultivation in Ming Thought." In William Theodore de Bary and the Conference on Ming Thought, *Self and Society in Ming Thought*, pp. 291–330. New York: Columbia University Press, 1970.

Lloyd, G.E.R. *Greek Science After Aristotle.* New York: Norton, 1973.

Loewe, Michael. *Ways to Paradise: The Chinese Quest for Immortality.* London: Allen & Unwin, 1979.

Major, John S. "Astrology in the *Huai-nan-tzu* and Some Related Texts." *Society for the Study of Chinese Religions Bulletin* (fall 1980), 8: 20–31.

—— "Myth, Cosmology, and the Origins of Chinese Science." *Journal of Chinese Philosophy* (March 1978), 5: 1–20.

—— "Notes on the Nomenclature of Winds and Directions in the Early Han." *T'oung Pao* n.s. (1979), 65: 66–80.

—— "Research Priorities in the Study of Ch'u Religion." History of Religions (February–May 1978), 17: 226–43.

Maruyama, Masao. *Studies in the Intellectual History of Tokugawa Japan.* Translated by Mikiso Hane. Tokyo: University of Tokyo Press, 1974; Princeton University Press, 1974.

Maspero, Henri. "L'Astronomie Chinoise avant les Han." *T'oung Pao* (1929), 26: 267–356.

—— "Le *Ming-t'ang* et la crise religieuse Chinoise avant les Han." *Mélanges Chinois et Bouddhiques* (1951), 9: 1–70.

—— *Taoism and Chinese Religion.* Translated by Frank A. Kierman, Jr. Amherst: University of Massachusetts Press, 1981.

Metzger, Thomas. *Escape From Predicament: Neo-Confucianism and China's Evolving Political Culture.* New York: Columbia University Press, 1977.

Meyer, Jeffrey F. "*Feng-shui* of the Chinese City." *History of Religions* (November 1978), 18: 138–55.

—— *Peking as a Sacred City.* Asian Folklore and Social Life Monographs, vol. 81. Taipei: Orient Culture Service, 1976.

Mish, John L. "Creating an Image of Europe for China: Aleni's *Hsi-fang ta-wen*; Introduction, Translation, and Notes." *Monumenta Serica* (1964), 23: 1–87.

Nakayama, Shigeru. "Characteristics of Chinese Astrology." *Isis* (Winter 1966), 57: 442–54.

—— "Japanese Scientific Thought." In *Dictionary of Scientific Biography*, vol. 15 (Supp. 1), pp. 728–58. Edited by Charles Coulston Gillispie et al. New York: Scribner's, 1978.

Needham, Joseph. *Science and Civilisation in China.* Vol. 2. *History of Scientific Thought.* Vol. 3. *Mathematics and the Sciences of the Heavens and the Earth.* Cambridge: Cambridge University Press, 1956, 1959.

Newlands, John Alexander Reina. *On the Discovery of the Periodic Law, and on Relations Among the Atomic Weights.* London: E. and F.N. Spon, 1884.

Perterson, Willard. "Fang I-chih: Western Learning and the 'Investigation of the Things'." In William Theodore de Bary and the Conference on Seventeenth-Century Chinese Thought, *The Unfolding of Neo-Confucianism*, pp. 369–411. New York: Columbia University Press, 1975.

—— "Making Connections: 'Commentary on the Attached Verbalizations' of the *Book of Change*." *Harvard Journal of Asiatic Studies* (June 1982), 42: 67–116.

Piaget, Jean. *The Child's Conception of Physical Causality.* Translated by Marjorie Gabain. Totowa, NJ: Littlefield, Adams, 1972.

Pico della Mirandola. *Heptaplus.* Translated by Douglas Carmichael. The Library of Liberal Arts. Indianapolis: Bobbs-Merrill, 1965.

Plaks, Andrew H. *Archetype and Allegory in the Dream of the Red Chamber.* Princeton: Princeton University Press, 1976.

Plato. *Laws.* In Benjamin Jowett, trans. *The Dialogues of Plato.* Vol. 2. New York: Random House, 1937.

—— *Republic.* In Francis M. Cornford, trans. *The Republic of Plato.* Oxford University Press, 1941.

Porkert, Manfred. *The Theoretical Foundations of Chinese Medicine: Systems of Correspondence.* East Asian Science Series, vol. 3. Cambridge: MIT Press, 1974.

Pulleyblank, E.G. "The Chinese Cyclical Signs as Phonograms." *Journal of the American Oriental Society* (1979), 99: 24–38.

Rickett, W. Allyn. *Kuan-tzu: A Repository of Early Chinese Thought.* Hong Kong: Hong Kong University Press, 1965.

Ropp, Paul S. *Dissent in Early Modern China: Ju-lin wai-shih and Ch'ing Social Criticism.* Ann Arbor: University of Michigan Press, 1981.

Rubin, Vitaly A. "The Concepts of Wu-Hsing and Yin-Yang." *Journal of Chinese Philosophy* (June 1982), 9: 131–57.

Sambursky, Samuel. "Harmony and Wholeness in Greek Scientific Thought." In *Mélanges Alexandre Koyre.* Vol. 2. *L'Aventure de l'esprit,* pp. 442–57. Paris: Hermann, 1964.

Saso, Michael. "What is the *Ho-t'u*?" *History of Religions* (February–May 1978), 17: 399–416.

Schafer, Edaward H. *Pacing the Void: T'ang Approaches to the Stars.* Berkeley: University of California Press, 1977.

Schipper, Kristofer. "The Taoist Body." *History of Religions* (February–May 1978), 17: 355–86.

Schwartz, Benjamin I. "On the Absence of Reductionism in Chinese Thought." *Journal of Chinese Philosophy* (December 1973), 1:27–44.

Shapere, Dudley. *Galileo: A Philosophical Study.* Chicago: University of Chicago Press, 1974.

Shumaker, Wayne. *The Occult Sciences in the Renaissance.* Berkeley: University of California Press, 1979.

Sickman, Laurence and Alexander Soper. *The Art and Architecture of China.* Harmondsworth, Eng.: Penguin, 1956.

Sivin, Nathan. "Chinese Alchemy and the Manipulation of Time." In *Science and Technology in East Asia,* pp. 108–22. New York: Science History Publications, 1977.

—— "Copernicus in China." *Studia Copernicana* (1973), 6:63–122.

—— "Cosmos and Computation in Early Chinese Mathematical Astronomy." *T'oung Pao* n.s. (1969), 55: 1–73.

—— "Discovery of Spagyrical Invention" *Harvard Journal of Asiatic Studies* (June 1981), 41: 219–35.

—— "Science in China's Past." In *Science in Contemporary China,* pp. 1–29. Edited by Leo A. Orleans. Stanford: Stanford University Press, 1980.

—— "Shen Kua." In *Dictionary of Scientific Biography,* 12: 369–93. Edited by Charles Coulston Gillispie et al. New York: Scribner's, 1975.

Soothill, William Edward. *The Hall of Light: A Study of Early Chinese Kingship.* London: Luttersworth Press, 1951.

T'ang, Yung-t'ung. "Wang Pi's New Interpretation of the *I ching* and *Lun-yu.*" Translated by Walter Liebenthal. *Harvard Journal of Asiatic Studies* (1947), 10: 124–61.

Tillyard, E.M.W. *The Elizabethan World Picture.* New York: Random House, Vintage, n.d.

Tjan, Tjoe Som, trans. *Po Hu T'ung: The Comprehensive Discussions in the White Tiger Hall.* Sinica Leidensia, vol. 6. Leiden: E.J. Brill, 1949; reprint ed., Westport, Conn.: Hyperion Press, 1973.

Unschuld, Ulrike. "Traditional Chinese Pharmacology: An Analysis of its Development in the Thirteenth Century." *ISIS* (June 1977), 68: 224–48.

Wheatley, Paul. *The Pivot of the Four Quarters: A Preliminary Enquiry into the Origins* and *Character of the Ancient Chinese City*. Chicago, Aldine, 1971.

Wright, Arthur F. "The Cosmology of the Chinese City." In *The City in Late Imperial China*, pp. 33–73. Edited by G. William Skinner. Stanford: Stanford University Press, 1977.

Yabuuti, Kiyosi. "Chinese Astronomy: Development and Limiting Factors." In *Chinese Science: Explorations of an Ancient Tradition*, pp. 91–103. Edited by Shigeru Nakayama and Nathan Sivin. East Asian Science Series, vol. 2. Cambridge: MIT Press, 1973.

Yampolsky, Philip B, trans. *The Platform Sutra of the Sixth Patriarch: The Text of the Tun-huang Manuscript with Translation, Introduction, and Notes.* New York: Columbia University Press, 1967.

Yang, C.K. *Religion in Chinese Society: A Study of Contemporary Social Functions of Religion and Some of Their Historical Factors.* Berkeley: University of California, 1967.

Yang, Lien-sheng. "The Concept of 'Pao' as a Basis for Social Relations in China." In *Chinese Thought and Institutions*, pp. 291–309. Edited by John K. Fairbank. Chicago: University of Chicago Press, Phoenix Books, 1967.

Yates, Frances A. *The Art of Memory.* Chicago: University of Chicago Press, 1966.

Yu, Anthony C., trans. and ed. *The Journey to the West.* Vol. 1. Chicago: University of Chicago Press, 1977.

Yu, Pauline. *The Poetry of Wang Wei: New Translations and Commentary.* Bloomington: Indiana University Press, 1980

Lightning Source UK Ltd.
Milton Keynes UK

178572UK00001B/197/P